For:

My friend Thomas

with best wishes

Andrew David

23rd March 1995

D1094419

THE ADMIRALTY CHART

*British Naval Hydrography
in the Nineteenth Century*

LAND GATE of the FORT of MOMBAS

ISLAND and PORTS

of

MOMBAS

Surveyed by

Lien.ᵗ Will.ᵐ Mudge and Rich.ᵈ Owen.

assisted by

Lien.ᵗ Nash and Mess.ʳˢ Barrelle and Tudor Mids.

by order of

Cap.ᵗ W.F.W. Owen of H.M. Ship Leven.

Title on Captain Owen's Chart of Mombasa, 1826. Drawn by J. G. Galley, Assistant Purser in H.M. Surveying Ship *Barracouta*. (Permission of the Hydrographer of the Navy.)

The Admiralty Chart

*British Naval Hydrography
in the Nineteenth Century*

A New Edition

Rear Admiral G. S. Ritchie, C.B., D.S.C.
Hydrographer of the Navy, 1966–1971

with an Introductory Essay by
Lieutenant Commander Andrew David, R.N.

The Pentland Press
Edinburgh – Cambridge – Durham – USA

By the same author:
Challenger—The Life of a Survey Ship (1957)
No Day too Long—An Hydrographer's Tale (1992)

© G. S. Ritchie 1967, 1995

First published in 1967
by Hollis & Carter Ltd.

This edition published in 1995
by The Pentland Press Ltd
1 Hutton Close
South Church
Bishop Auckland
Durham

British Library
Cataloguing-in-Publication Data

A catalogue record for this book
is available from the British Library

ISBN 1-85821-234-0

Typeset by Carnegie Publishing Ltd., 18 Maynard St., Preston
Printed and bound by Antony Rowe Ltd., Chippenham

CONTENTS

ILLUSTRATIONS

MAPS

The maps are drawn by K. J. Cattley, who has also designed the calligraphy for the jacket, reflecting the style employed on Admiralty Charts in the nineteenth century.

AUTHOR'S FOREWORD TO THE FIRST EDITION

When one has been writing a book of history for six years there have been so many whom one has called upon for help that it is impossible to mention them all.

Early encouragement came from Mr. G. B. Stigant, O.B.E., and Mr. L. A. Luff, M.B.E., both of whom, after retiring from responsible posts in the Hydrographic Department, were employed compiling an index of the thousands of Hydrographers' and Surveyors' letters in the Department, and which has simplified greatly the task of those who have to carry out research into British Hydrography.

I have read many of these letters, often in the course of my duties in the Hydrographic Department, and these have provided my background in a way that prevents my listing them in the bibliography, but the index referred to is available to the public enquirer at the Department.

Mr. R. A. Skelton, Superintendent of the Map Room, British Museum,* at my request read my earliest chapters when I was beginning to think the task beyond me; his remarks gave me courage to carry on.

Memoirs of Hydrography by Commander L. S. Dawson, R.N., and published by Henry W. Keay of Eastbourne in 1885, gives, in two volumes, a biography of every British Surveyor up to that date and without this book, long since out of print, the writing of my history would have been virtually impossible.† Vice Admiral Sir Archibald Day, K.B.E., C.B., D.S.O., was working in 1963 on a third volume of *Memoirs of Hydrography* to bring it up to the present date, and in doing so he reviewed the work of the Hydrographic Department in the nineteenth century.‡ It was of great assistance

---

* Now British Library.
† A facsimile edition was published by Cornmarket Press (London, 1969).
‡ Admiral Day's book has not been published.

to me when Admiral Day gave me a typescript copy of this part of his work.

The late Commander R. T. Gould, R.N., F.R.G.S., whose books on chronometers and on strange happenings at sea are well known, attempted in the early twenties to write a history of the Hydrographic Department. On reaching the Beaufort period he found the work of the many surveyors in such far-flung fields made the task so complex, if justice was to be done at all, that he gave up. I found the manuscript of his early chapters in the Hydrographic Department and these showed me the way and warned me of the difficulties.

A number of descendants of naval surveyors of the nineteenth century have been most generous in showing me relevant documents still in the family. Miss Ann Parry sent me copies of important letters written by Rear Admiral Sir William Parry, F.R.S., at the time of his appointment as Hydrographer; Captain H. M. Denham, C.M.G., R.N., allowed me to inspect in his home a delightful collection of pictures painted by Glen Wilson when sailing in H.M.S. *Herald* during the voyage of Captain H. M. Denham (later Admiral Sir Henry Denham, F.R.S.) in the years 1852–61; Mr. A. M. Channer has shown me much interesting material relating to Vice Admiral Sir George Richards, C.B., F.R.S., including his extensive diaries written during sledge journeys in the Arctic when searching for the *Erebus* and *Terror* in 1852–53; Professor J. P. M. Tizard has told me much about his grandfather, Captain T. H. Tizard, C.B., F.R.S., R.N., one of the great surveyors of the late nineteenth century, and invited me to browse through his papers which I found of great interest.

An invaluable aid to the hydrographic historian is a chronological list of all British surveying voyages from the earliest times down to 1900 compiled by Captain Tizard and published in that year by the Hydrographic Department.

In 1962, Professor R. S. Harris of the University of Toronto told me of various letters written by Captains W. F. W. Owen and Henry Bayfield to John Harris during the years 1817 to 1846. Professor Harris subsequently presented the Hydrographic

Department with copies of these letters which throw light on the early surveys of the Great Lakes of Canada.

Lieutenant Commander G. S. Ingleton, R.A.N., informed me of the work of King, Lort Stokes and others on the coasts of Australia, and Ingleton's book, *Charting a Continent*, has been extremely valuable to me concerning the needs for surveying in Australia and New Zealand in the nineteenth century, and also gives details of all the early colonial surveys in Australia.

Mr. A. S. Mountford sent me a copy of his paper on Captain H. M. Denham's work at Liverpool which resulted in the opening up of the Mersey to meet the demands of deep-draught vessels and this has greatly assisted me in trying to describe Denham's work.

The hydrographic papers of the late Sir John Edgell, K.B.E., C.B., F.R.S., which were passed to me for the Hydrographic Department by Dr. J. N. Carruthers, contain notes on the early life of Captain Hurd which I found most valuable.

I have to thank Mr. A. W. H. Pearsall, Custodian of Manuscripts at the National Maritime Museum at Greenwich for prompt replies to many queries sent to him.

Commander P. K. Kemp, O.B.E., Head of Naval Historical Branch, Ministry of Defence, has been most generous in arranging for me to obtain references, often under difficult circumstances for I was so often at sea whilst writing. To Commander Kemp's staff, Mr. A. P. Young and Miss V. S. Heath and to Mrs. C. S. Auckland of the Secretariat of the Hydrographic Department I am deeply indebted for their help in so many ways over such an extended period.

The maps have been drawn by Mr. K. J. Cattley who has been most patient throughout in his attempts to get a quart into a pint-pot, which I believe he has succeeded in doing.

Again, my wife has read and corrected my work at every stage and I should never contemplate the writing of a book without her assistance.

G. S. Ritchie

Wiveliscombe, Somerset,
June 1966

AUTHOR'S FOREWORD TO THE NEW EDITION

The Admiralty Chart, first published in 1967, has been out of print for a number of years. With the Bicentenary of the British Hydrographic Office falling in the year 1995 it seems fitting to publish a New Edition of this book which describes the work of the Royal Navy's sea surveyors, ashore and afloat, during the first hundred years.

My good friend and fellow surveyor Lieutenant Commander Andrew David, Royal Navy, spent a number of recent years in the Sailing Directions Division of the Hydrographic Office. Here he became acquainted with the ships' logs, journals, surveyors' letters and general documents held in the archives. In 1974 he prepared a provisional catalogue of these very numerous items.

I therefore asked Andrew to examine my original text of *The Admiralty Chart* with a view to correcting or amending any statements or assumptions I had made, unaware as I was at the time of writing of the wealth of historical information which he has now uncovered. This has resulted in a more exhaustive and reliable account of British naval hydrography in the nineteenth century.

At my request Andrew David also agreed to contribute an Introductory Essay to the New Edition of my work.

Whilst updating the text we have also been able to take into account a number of relevant books and papers which have been published since 1967. These titles have been added to the Bibliography where appropriate.

One of the many changes that have occurred since the book was first published is that the title of the shore establishment which was known as the Hydrographic Department at the time when the book was first published has now reverted to Hydrographic Office, which was its title during most of the nineteenth century. I have therefore decided to use Hydrographic Office throughout this book, except in my original foreword, which I feel should be retained in the manner in which it was originally published, and a few places in the Bibliography.

I wish to thank Captain Richard Campbell, O.B.E., Head of Sailing Directions in the Hydrographic Office, for his guidance concering geographical orthography.

G. S. Ritchie

Collieston, Aberdeenshire
August 1994

THE ADMIRALTY CHART

British Naval Hydrography
in the Nineteenth Century

The Hydrographers of the Navy
until 1900

Alexander Dalrymple, F.R.S., 1795–1808

Captain Thomas Hurd, R.N., 1808–1823

Captain Sir William E. Parry, Kt., F.R.S., 1823–1829

Rear Admiral Sir Francis Beaufort, K.C.B., D.C.L., F.R.S., 1829–1855

Rear Admiral John Washington, 1855–1863

Rear Admiral George H. Richards, C.B., F.R.S., 1863–1874

Captain Sir Frederick J. O. Evans, K.C.B., F.R.S., 1874–1884

Rear Admiral Sir William J. L. Wharton, K.C.B., F.R.S., 1884–1904

Introduction

England was a slow starter in gaining her rightful place in chart-making among the maritime nations of the world. True, her great explorers were making surveys in distant waters during the eighteenth century, but when they returned home their priceless charts were apt to lie unused upon the dusty shelves of the Admiralty. A commander of one of His Majesty's Ships had to find his own charts, for none were provided, purchasing them from the chart sellers of the City who catered for the merchantman.

England's rivals, the French, had founded a hydrographic office in 1720, whilst the Dutch traditionally had better charts of our coastal waters than we ourselves.

My story tells how the Admiralty belatedly appointed a civilian Hydrographer in 1795, and, after reviewing the people engaged in chart-making at the time and describing the instruments available to them, goes on to show how the continuing absence of good printed charts in the midst of the Napoleonic Wars led to a more vigorous policy for providing the Fleet.

Starting thus from behind, the Royal Navy made increasing progress in the making of charts during the long peace which followed the 'old wars', and by the middle of the nineteenth century, during the twenty-six year reign of Admiral Beaufort as Hydrographer, a position of ascendancy had been reached with officers of the naval Surveying Service at sea in every ocean and charting nearly every remote and distant shore. The Admiralty chart gained then a name for accuracy and a lead in world sales which have been maintained to this day.

For six years I toiled in my leisure hours upon this book. Much of it was written onboard Her Majesty's Surveying Ships *Dalrymple* and *Vidal*, on passage to and from the Persian Gulf and during oceanographic cruises in the Atlantic; a considerable portion was written in a 'bed-sitter' in Kilburn when I was employed in the Hydrographic Office, whilst the last four chapters were completed in Newlands at the Cape of Good Hope, only half a mile from the site of Liesbeek Cottage where John Barrow lived with his wife in the early years of the nineteenth century, and who later became, as Secretary to the Admiralty, the greatest supporter the Surveying Service ever had.

Only at Kilburn was it easy for me to consult the many references required in writing a book of this nature, and to inspect the thousands of charts and surveyors' letters in the Hydrographic Office.

The difficulty of carrying references to sea made more complex the task of writing the history, the magnitude of which I had seriously underrated.

The discerning reader will realise how much has been omitted in order to compress the long story between the covers of a single volume, and this introduction will serve as an apology for the omission of names and deeds of so many of Britain's sea surveyors of the nineteenth century.

Little mention has been made of the extensive surveys of Indian waters and in the Persian Gulf completed by British officers, many from the Royal Navy, who performed their work as servants of the East India Company, the Indian Navy, the Marine Survey of India and the Indian Marine, as each of these in succession assumed responsibility for the hydrographic surveys.

No mention has been made of the 'amateur' surveyors, of whom Admiral John Moresby is an outstanding example. When appointed in 1870 to command H.M.S. *Basilisk* for general service on the Australian Station he went to see the Hydrographer, Admiral Richards, to borrow a few surveying instruments. With these, but without the blessing of his Commander-in-Chief, he charted 600 miles of the north-east coast of New Guinea and the off-lying islands, discovering Port Moresby and many other anchorages.

By confining my history to the Royal Navy it may seem to readers that I have ignored the great work of other nations. I am fully aware from my reading of much that was achieved by foreign surveyors during the period, but apart from a few references to the activities of the United States surveyors, where these affected our own service, the temptation to mention the many meritorious voyages of other nations had to be resisted.

I hope I have presented a broad picture of the progress of British hydrography throughout the nineteenth century, accompanied by detailed sketches here and there to show something of the men, the ships in which they sailed, and the conditions under which they worked in the ever changing theatres of hydrographic interest dictated by politics, war and, above all, trade.

The true greatness of Captain Cook has become clear to me whilst writing this book, for his influence runs on through the nineteenth century. Whilst developing his impeccable running surveys which have stood the test of time, he formed a school of surveyors among the junior officers who sailed with him to the Pacific. Men like Vancouver and Bligh passed on their knowledge in turn to Mudge, Broughton, Flinders and others, and thus we can trace through many lines the handing down of knowledge to Richards, Evans and Wharton at the end of the century, the original techniques constantly improved upon, with the dedication to accuracy unimpaired. It is not surprising that Admiral Wharton, the last Hydrographer in our story, edited and published Captain Cook's *Endeavour* Journal.

I trust that I have shown that throughout the nineteenth century the naval surveyors were alert to every aspect of the physical properties of the sea and the floor beneath, and that these properties were observed, measured and recorded to limits imposed only by the instruments and equipment available to them.

With their navigational skill, their enquiring minds and their sense of discipline, the naval surveyors combined with the sea-going scientist to form a well-balanced team for the exploration of the oceans. Ever since the Forsters sailed with Cook, scientists have sailed as a matter of course in Her Majesty's Surveying Ships, to the lasting benefit of our nation.

The twentieth century has seen an intensification of the exploration of the seas, which is giving the naval surveyor a unique opportunity to add to the knowledge of the world's oceans. When the history of the Royal Naval Surveying Service in the twentieth century comes to be written I sincerely hope it will be seen that this opportunity was not cast away.

Introductory Essay
by Andrew David

During the nineteenth century the British Hydrographic Office expanded from a mere custodian of manuscript surveys held by the Admiralty, with no ships dedicated to carrying out surveys and no printing facilities, to the world's major chart producing country with often up to twelve ships carrying out surveys in almost all parts of the world. To do justice to all the 150 or so dedicated officers employed in the surveying service during this period would require a number of volumes. Thus a single volume work such as this one by Admiral Ritchie is of necessity a compromise. Some surveyors such as Matthew Flinders or Robert FitzRoy are well known because they published accounts of their voyages. The records of many others, such as George Thomas, who carried out extensive surveys along the east coast of England and Scotland over the course of thirty-five years, lie unpublished in the archives of the Hydrographic Office and the Public Record Office, apart from occasional articles which appeared from time to time in the *Nautical Magazine* and other journals.

Surveying ships were often absent from the United Kingdom during the nineteenth century for two or more years on voyages which merited published accounts on their return, but usually the commanding officer was immediately employed on other hydrographic duties and so the publication of such voyages was often undertaken by the naturalist appointed to accompany the voyage. John MacGillivray's account of Owen Stanley's voyage in the

Rattlesnake to the east coast of Australia and the south coast of New Guinea (1846–50), referred to in this book, is typical. Many equally important voyages remain unpublished because of the lack of a suitable author. The work of the dedicated officers, who surveyed the waters around the British Isles, merit an exhaustive account in their own right. The archives of the Hydrographic Office are a rich source for the work carried out by these officers, particularly during the period that Beaufort was Hydrographer. The published accounts of L. S. Dawson and Admiral Day give excellent resumes of where the surveying ships were operating from year to year, while Admiral Ritchie in the later chapters of this book goes into much greater depth for a selected number of the more important voyages.

Although Beaufort was able to call upon a substantial fleet of surveying ships to carry out the numerous surveys that were needed in many parts of the world, he realised that this could not be done by the Royal Navy alone. On the one hand it would be a waste of time to duplicate surveys carried out by other nations and on the other hand it was essential to obtain the co-operation of foreign governments to carry out surveys in the territorial waters of nations who did not have the facilities to carry out such surveys themselves. Thus Beaufort was in constant correspondence with the heads of foreign hydrographic offices, while the Foreign Office made the necessary approaches to foreign governments for British surveying ships to operate in their coastal waters.

Admiral Ritchie describes how Vancouver and the Spanish surveyors Cayetano Valdés and Dionisio Alcalá-Galiano worked together for a short time off the coast of British Columbia. It was, however, the work of Captain H. W. Smyth in the Mediterranean, between 1810 and 1824, which showed what could be achieved by co-operation with other hydrographic surveyors. Smyth carried out his first major survey in 1810 in Cadiz when he was appointed in command of the large Spanish gun-boat *Mors aut Gloria*. Here he was able to acquire a copy of Don Vicente Tofiño's *Atlas Maritimo de España* published in Madrid in 1789, through the courtesy of the same Cayetano Valdés, who had co-operated with Vancouver almost twenty years earlier. (Alcalá-Galiano had died a hero's death at Trafalgar in command of the 74-gun *Bahama*.) Although Smyth had the highest regard for Tofiño's work, he found that his survey of Cadiz contained various errors and omissions. During the next two years, when other naval duties permitted, Smyth was able to make a number of valuable amendments to Tofiño's charts in the Strait of Gibraltar and along the Mediterranean coast of Spain.

In 1813, after a brief visit to London to consult Captain Hurd, Smyth rejoined his old commander Sir Robert Hall in the Anglo-Sicilian flotilla defending Sicily, which enabled him to commence a detailed survey of this island. In Palermo Smyth met the amiable astronomer Abbaté Piazzi who taught Smyth some improvements in his surveying techniques and calculations and became a life-long friend. Their meeting also stimulated Smyth to take a great interest in astronomy and on his retirement he became an amateur astronomer of some distinction. When Smyth's son was born in Naples in 1819 he was named Charles Piazzi in honour of his father's friend. He too developed an interest in astronomy, eventually becoming Astronomer Royal for Scotland. Smyth was not only an able surveyor, he was also a talented artist. In addition he became a noted antiquarian and author. His *Sailor's Word-book* published posthumously in 1867, after being revised for the press by his friend Sir Edward Belcher, is still a very useful reference book. Smyth's antiquarian interests can clearly be seen in his charts of Sicily (published in 1823 in his atlas *Hydrography of Sicily, Malta and the Adjacent Islands*), which are decorated with Roman coins and often with views of archaeological interest as well as of navigational value.

In consequence of his Sicilian survey, Smyth was formally appointed to take charge of the survey of the Mediterranean in command of the *Aid*. One of his first tasks was to visit Tripoli where he supervised the embarkation of some relics from the ruins of Leptis Magna, which the Bashaw had presented to the Prince Regent. This enabled Smyth to obtain permission from the Bashaw for an expedition eastwards along the coast of North Africa towards Alexandria at some future date. Smyth's first priority was, however, to survey the Ionian Islands, where British ships were frequently running aground. Meanwhile he had been in correspondence with the Austrian authorities who were carrying out a land survey of their Adriatic coastline. On hearing that Smyth intended to extend his survey into the Adriatic the Austrians proposed that the two surveys should be combined, realising that the survey could then cover the whole of the Adriatic because of Turkish respect for the British flag. Accordingly, Smyth visited Naples early in 1818 to negotiate with the Neapolitan and Austrian authorities. Agreement was reached and it was arranged that a party of four Austrian and four Neapolitan officers should join the *Aid*. In addition, the Austrian sloop *Velox* was placed under Smyth's command with the promise of further assistance from Austrian gun-boats at the principal ports. By the end of 1819 the survey was complete and Smyth was able to discharge the Austrian sloop and the foreign officers, much to everyone's regret.

Smyth also co-operated with French surveyors. When he was in Malta in 1816, Captain Guattier of the French Navy arrived there to measure meridian distances so that various detached surveys that the French possessed could be linked up. Far from resenting what could have been construed as an intrusion into his domain, Smyth went out of his way to offer Guattier every assistance, even helping him place his astronomical circle on the very spot that Smyth himself had used. A comparison of their results was most satisfactory, not only did the French and British positions agree exactly, but a free interchange of methods and documents took place afterwards. Smyth and Guattier continued to meet each year to compare results. When the *Aid* was paid off, Smyth returned to London, where he was consulted on the Mediterranean survey by Lord Melville, who then sent him to Paris to draw up an agreement to avoid duplication between French and British surveys. As a result it was agreed that the French should continue surveying in the Greek Archipelago, while the British would concentrate on the western Mediterranean and the north coast of Africa. In Paris Smyth was supplied with copies of all the French surveys of the Black Sea, the Greek Archipelago and the Levant.

In 1821 Smyth returned to the Mediterranean in the *Adventure* to survey the north African coast from Tripoli to Alexandria. While

Smyth worked westward in the ship from Alexandria, Lieutenant Frederick William Beechey, who had just returned from a polar voyage with Parry, set off eastward from Tripoli dressed in Arab clothes to survey the coastline, accompanied by his brother, a well-known traveller in Egypt. Beechey and Smyth met at Derna on completion of the survey. For the remainder of his time in the Mediterranean, Smyth surveyed the African coast from Cape Bon to Tripoli, parts of Sardinia and the west coast of Italy. In Sardinia Smyth came across the French brig *Lloiret*, Captain Allégre, sheltering from a gale. Allégre, who had formerly served with Guattier, told Smyth that he had spent three years with Captain Hell carrying out a detailed survey of Corsica, where Smyth had also observed some geographical positions. A comparison between Smyth's and Captain Hell's positions showed good agreement and Smyth had no hesitation in telling Allégre that he would not carry out any further surveys of the French island.

On his return to England in 1824, Smyth began working up his charts for engraving, during which he continued to correspond with his many foreign friends and the British officers continuing his Mediterranean survey. He also befriended the exiled Spanish Hydrographer Don Felipe Bauzá. While he was working on a plan of the Spanish Columbretes Islands, Smyth found that few of the islands and off-lying dangers had been given names by the Spaniards. He therefore consulted Bauzá and, as a result, he named these features after 'the most scientific officers in the Spanish navy'. Shortly afterwards Smyth was ordered out of the Hydrographic Office by John Croker, the First Secretary. Taking offence at this apparent high-handed action, Smyth left the Admiralty at once taking all his charts with him, including his plan of the Columbretes. It was only when Beaufort took over as Hydrographer that Smyth was persuaded to start working on his charts again and so it was not until May 1835 that Smyth's completed plan of these islands finally reached the Hydrographic Office. Prior to this Smyth had read a paper on these islands in January 1831 at the newly formed Royal Geographical Society, published later that year in the Society's *Journal*, together with a plan of the islands. On this plan the principal harbour in the group is called Port

Tofiño, with other rocky islets and dangers named after Malaspina, Espinosa, Valdés, Navarette, Galiano and several other Spanish officers. It seems likely that Bauzá sent a copy of this article to Spain since the Spanish Hydrographic Office published a chart of the Columbretes in 1833, based on Smyth's survey, retaining all his names, which still feature on current Spanish and British charts.

One of the unsung heroes of the surveying service and someone who had a considerable influence on it during its fledgling years was Captain David Ewen Bartholomew, whose untimely death may well have robbed him of a well-merited entry in Dawson's *Memoirs of Hydrography*. Bartholomew first went to sea in Baltic traders and a Greenland whaler, before taking part in the seizure of Martinique in a West Indiaman in 1794. In January 1795, when leaving his ship at Wapping, Bartholomew was seized by a press gang and sent on board the *Scipio*. In 1799 he was at Den Helder in the *Experiment* where he was sent ashore to take part in combined operations under Captain Sir Home Riggs Popham. Popham had already carried out a number of surveys off Namibia and in 1808 became one of the members of the Chart Committee (referred to by Admiral Ritchie on page 108). Bartholomew was closely associated with Popham for some years as coxswain, master's mate, acting master, midshipman and acting lieutenant. In 1801–2 Popham carried out some important surveys in the Red Sea in the *Romney* during which Bartholomew looked after the ship's eight chronometers and became proficient in obtaining longitude by lunar distances. In 1808 Bartholomew, while first lieutenant of the *Sapphire*, Captain George Davies, carried out a number of surveys in the entrance to the Persian Gulf and along the southern and western coasts of Iran, while the *Sapphire* was transporting the baggage of Sir Harford Jones on a diplomatic mission to Persia. As a result, Aaron Arrowsmith published a chart of the Persian Gulf in 1810, based partly on Bartholomew's survey, while the Admiralty published his survey of Bushire in 1820.

In 1818 Bartholomew was appointed in command of the *Leven* to carry out surveys on the west coast of Africa. During this survey, four of his officers, Alexander Vidal, William Mudge, Alexander Becher and George Frazer, became accomplished hydrographic surveyors. On 27 December 1818 Bartholomew sailed from Plymouth, first stopping at Lisbon to obtain the necessary clearance from the Portuguese authorities. Here he was given every assistance and allowed to set up his instruments in the Royal Observatory to obtain rates for his chronometers. He next called at Funchal where his reception was not so friendly as warning shots were fired at him on his arrival and he was not allowed to anchor until the morning as he had arrived after dark! The purpose of Bartholomew's visit to Funchal and his subsequent visit to Santa Cruz in Tenerife was to obtain their longitudes by chronometer. During his visit to the latter port Mudge was able to make a partial survey of the anchorage. Here Becher noted that in one of the convents in the town two union jacks, captured during Nelson's abortive attempt to storm the town, were displayed over the entrance of the convent, well out of anyone's reach. He also noted that the natives took great pride in pointing out to visitors the gun which had shot off Nelson's arm. By March the *Leven* had reached the Cape Verde Islands, where Bartholomew remained for several months surveying the archipelago and the adjacent coast of Africa, during which he searched unsuccessfully for Porgas Bank and Bonetta Rock. The position of Leton Rock, situated to the westward of Bonavista, was, however, fixed by anchoring a boat with a flag at its masthead and measuring the angles to it from two high hills on Bonavista. In June Bartholomew was back in Funchal, where the Governor was at first reluctant to allow him to obtain the longitude of the town by observing the emersions and immersions of Jupiter's satellites and to allow the *Leven*'s officers to survey the coast of Madeira and sound round the island. However, when Bartholomew promised the Governor a sketch of the Desertas and Porto Santo he agreed. In reporting to Croker that he had duly presented the plans to the Governor, Bartholomew added that he had done so while 'withholding the principal soundings and Hydrographical information'. At Funchal the British Consul, Henry Veitch, was particularly helpful, allowing Bartholomew to set up his instruments in his garden and providing beds for the *Leven*'s officers. This proved to be a happy arrangement for Vidal as, after visiting Funchal several times subsequently, he returned in 1839 and married Sarah Veitch, the consul's daughter. In September Bartholomew visited the Azores where he carried out an unsuccessful search for Whale Rock, reported to lie to the north of the island of São Miguel. On 22nd November Midshipman George Bartholomew, presumably the captain's son, died on board of smallpox. Bartholomew anchored off Spithead on 22nd December and the following month moved to Woolwich where the *Leven* was taken in hand by the dockyard.

After the completion of an extensive refit, Bartholomew sailed from Spithead on 6th May 1820 and, after a brief stop at Santa Cruz, resumed his survey of the African coast in the vicinity of Cap Blanco, working his way south towards the Cape Verde Islands, which he reached on 9th June. On 26th August Bartholomew returned to the Azores as he had received an apparently correct position of Whale Rock and the tides were favourable for sighting it, if it existed. When the equinoctial gales set in on 12th September he was forced to abandon the search and make for Funchal, where he remained until 8th October. Bartholomew next carried out a sketch survey of the Salvages, a group of isolated rocky islets situated about midway between Madeira and the Canaries, in order to fix their position. He then resumed his survey of the coast of Africa to the east of the Canaries between Cap Rhir and Cabo Bajador, breaking off the survey on one occasion to return to Santa Cruz to fish his foremast which had sprung (i.e. to repair his mast by securing two pieces of specially shaped hardwood 'fishes' to either side of the damaged part). At the end of November he returned to the Cape Verde Islands to complete his survey. On 19th February 1821 Bartholomew died in Porto Praya of tuberculosis, after a short illness. He was buried the following day in one of the bastions of the fort, attended by all his officers and the Portuguese Governor and staff. Robert Baldey, the *Leven*'s first lieutenant, took command while Vidal and Mudge completed the survey of the islands and the coast of Africa. On 24th June Baldey paid a final visit to Santa Cruz and on 22nd July he anchored off Spithead on completion of the survey. Later that year, as told by Admiral Ritchie, Captain William FitzWilliam Owen took command of the *Leven* to continue the survey of Africa.

Owen, who may well have met Bartholomew in the East Indies, twice visited Bartholomew's grave, first in 1826 when burying Midshipman Edward Owen Tudor alongside the *Leven*'s former captain and again the following year when on his way to Fernando Po in command of the *Eden*.

The need to obtain the co-operation of foreign governments to carry out surveys in their waters has already been mentioned. One officer, however, who found it difficult on at least one occasion to co-operate with foreign officials was Captain Henry Craven St John, who was employed in the *Sylvia* between 1869 and 1877, surveying the coasts of Japan. In 1875 St John was ordered to examine the coast of Korea. In an attempt to contact the Korean authorities St John first anchored off Pusan. When no official came on board he landed on a nearby island to stretch his legs. After a few hours he returned on board with three pheasants, a hog-deer, one snipe and a small boar. (St John's *Notes and Sketches* reads more like a game book than an account of a surveying voyage. Shooting expeditions after snipe and mallard, wild geese and pheasants are much more in evidence than the dull routine of survey activities.) The following morning he weighed anchor and followed the coast to the south-west, entering a magnificent bay later that day which did not feature on any chart. Shortly after St John anchored the chief official of the district came on board to ask the reason for the visit, expressing repeated hopes that St John would go away. St John, however, ignored this request and the following day he sent several boats away in different directions to sound the bay. That evening one of the whalers, in charge of Lieutenant Pearce, failed to return and when it was still missing the following morning St John set off in the steam cutter to look for it. On approaching a narrow channel leading to the open sea, St John was surprised to find both shores and the adjoining hills lined with about a thousand soldiers armed with Japanese matchlocks, crossbows and swords, with a hundred or so boats arranged along both shores. St John was met by about fifteen of these boats, one of which came within about ten yards of the steam cutter when the soldiers in them presented their matchlocks and crossbows. Fearing that his boat's crew had been captured St John avoided taking any offensive action, which he otherwise would have done, and prudently returned to the ship. Shortly afterwards Pearce also reached the ship from the opposite direction and was able to recount his adventures. As he approached the narrow channel under sail, with a brisk breeze blowing, a man, evidently on watch, blew a bugle, at which several hundred soldiers sprang from concealment and manned six or seven boats and set off to intercept the whaler. Pearce dashed through the narrow channel, the only possible course of action open to him, and after about five miles the pursuers abandoned the chase. Shortly afterwards the whaler was intercepted by a single boat whose crew fired two shots in an attempt to bring the whaler to. Unable to return the way he had come, Pearce was forced to take a circuitous route of over eighty-four miles, forty of which were in the open sea. Fortunately it was a calm night, otherwise he would have stood the risk of being driven far out to sea or being captured. As a result of this incident it was clear to St John that he could only continue his survey if backed up by force and he prudently decided to abandon it.

But in Japan it was a different matter. One of St John's first encounters with the Japanese was in 1863 when he took part in an attack by a squadron of British warships on Kagoshima, at the southern end of the island of Kyushu. The cause of this unfortunate affair was, according to St John 'owing to a wilful lady, and an after-lunch expedition on horse-back – we being entirely in the wrong and the Japanese in the right'. As a result the British commodore found himself involved in a minor war with one of the chief Japanese princes. The engagement lasted about an hour and a half, during which the squadron, sailing in line ahead close to the shore, fired at a series of batteries fronting Kagoshima. In consequence the town was set alight, burning for at least four days and nights. Expecting the Japanese to be armed like the Chinese, the squadron was astonished to find seven-inch shells flying about their ears, resulting in heavy casualties. The day after the engagement the squadron captured three steamers in one of which St John found a Japanese official whom he befriended. This official was later appointed Ambassador to the United Kingdom and subsequently became Foreign Minister, during the time that St John was surveying the coast of Japan. On meeting again they resumed their former friendship, much to St John's advantage. In spite of his fondness for shooting, St John achieved much; his friendly assistance to an unknown Japanese official in 1863 paid handsome dividends some years later.

In this essay I have described the achievements of just three of the company of hydrographic surveyors employed by the British Admiralty during the nineteenth century. There are many lesser known surveyors of the period also deserving of attention. However, Admiral Ritchie and I are denied the space within a single volume to recount all their adventures or to assess the hydrographic harvests they brought home from many parts of the world. It is our hope that this new edition of *The Admiralty Chart* will cast sufficient light on the labours of these resolute seamen to encourage historians to investigate further the imperishable works to which they devoted and sometimes gave their lives.

CHAPTER ONE

Dalrymple Becomes the First
Hydrographer of the Navy

The globe was circumnavigated and the four continents discovered before the greatest discovery and the most elusive of all was made—the discovery of longitude. Longitude is a measurement east or west from the meridian of Greenwich, and today it is difficult to imagine a world where such a measurement was not possible at sea.

From the early sixteenth century navigators and theoretical writers, in their search for a means of finding their longitude at sea, considered and tried to use methods based on the variation of the compass needle. They realised that the value of variation of the magnetic needle from the north could be measured by taking bearings of the Pole Star, and that the variation changed with the ship's longitude. But the complex nature of the shifting pattern of variation over the surface of the globe and the annual changes to which this pattern is subject were not fully realised, and in fact, this method of finding longitude never proved satisfactory.

In the latter part of the seventeenth century, however, it still seemed a likely possibility in the all-important search, and so considerable nautical as well as scientific interest was attached to the first voyage of that delightfully-named vessel the *Paramore* pink. 'Pink' was a term originally used to describe small Mediterranean vessels with lateen sails, but in fact this craft was built in England specifically for the task. She was an extremely small vessel with a narrow stern. Her commander was Edmond Halley, who has been described as 'astronomer, mathematician, physicist, navigator, diplomat and scholar', but unfortunately he was not a seaman of long experience, and this command, for which he had been recommended by the Royal Society, was his first appointment in naval service. His object was to obtain a full knowledge of the nature of the variation of the compass over the whole earth and to experiment to discover how this information could aid the determination of longitude.

Halley confessed a general dislike for warrant officers, and asked that his mate be a lieutenant, even in so small a craft as a ninety-ton 'pink'; so the Navy Board appointed a certain Edward Harrison, a lieutenant of eight years' standing. Harrison was a self-styled practical seaman who had thought up a means of finding longitude at sea, and for this reason he may have been specially selected, but, as so often happens with such well-intentioned appointments, the choice could not have been more unfortunate. In 1694, his method of determining longitude had been submitted to the Royal Society, who chose Halley to read the paper to the Council in Harrison's absence. Two years later Harrison submitted a similar paper to the Admiralty, the Navy Board and the Royal Society, but received no favourable comment. Harrison, the practical seaman, blamed, in his own mind, Halley the philosopher for this lack of official enthusiasm for his scheme.

When Halley commissioned the *Paramore* in 1698, having just completed two years issuing new coinage as Deputy Controller of the Mint at Chester, he was quite unaware of Harrison's identity, never having met him, whilst Harrison nursed his grudge against the mathematician who had been placed in command.

Although the *Paramore* had been built for the task, she was cranky and a poor sailer to windward. The expedition got to sea two months later than planned, in October 1698, and encountered foul weather in the Atlantic, and here Harrison seized his opportunity to embarrass his inexperienced captain. Both he and the Boatswain steered deliberately off course at night, pretending that the candle had gone out in the binnacle, and that they could not light it. The First Lieutenant had on such an occasion justified himself to Halley 'not without reflecting language'. The Gunner and the Boatswain were not backward in supporting Harrison against their commander.

Despite all these difficulties Halley made a voyage via Madeira, the coast of Brazil, the West Indies, Newfoundland and back to Plymouth. Halley assumed that Harrison 'envied him his command and conveniences on board, and that he disdained to be under one that had not served so long in the Fleet as himself'. It was not until after he had court-martialled Harrison on arrival in England that he discovered the reason for the deep-seated grievance which Harrison held against him.

Halley was, however, undaunted, and the results of his voyage were well received at the Royal Society. With a completely new complement of officers he was soon off to sea again for a very successful eleven-month voyage, resulting, with the data from the first voyage, in a chart, dedicated to King William III, showing the variation of the magnetic needle over the entire Atlantic Ocean. The map was hung in the meeting room of the Royal Society; his ventures had been highly productive from the scientific viewpoint—but on the other hand the Navy never forgot that this man of science, who had been given command of one of His Majesty's Ships, had court-martialled his first lieutenant.

Halley made a third voyage in the *Paramore* in 1701, when he carried out a remarkable survey of the tidal currents on both sides of the English Channel. He next makes an impact on our story when he was appointed a member of the Board of Longitude in 1714. This was a select body set up by Act of Parliament to administer an award to anyone who could prove that he had developed a satisfactory method of finding longitude at sea.

In 1716, Halley, then Secretary to the Royal Society, contributed a paper to the *Philosophical Transactions* of that Society in which he pointed out the potential value of the two transits of Venus across the Sun due to take place in 1761 and 1769. This is the first hint of the famous voyage of H.M.S. *Endeavour* in 1769, and of two leading characters in hydrographic history—the one who commanded her so brilliantly and the one who had expected so confidently to have that command and so bitterly resented his rival's success. Halley pointed out that although much was known of the functions of the Universe, including the relative positions of Sun and planets, its vast scale was yet to be determined. With the diameter of the Earth roughly known, if the time of passage of Venus across the Sun during transit could be recorded at two or more widely separated points on the surface of the globe, then the Sun's diameter could first be calculated and then its true distance from the Earth determined.

From 1720 to 1742, when he died, Halley served as the second Astronomer Royal, in succession to Flamsteed, at the Royal Observatory, Greenwich, which had been established by Charles II for rectifying the tables of the motion of the heavens, and the places of the fixed stars, so as to find out the so-much-desired longitude of places for perfecting the art of navigation. But it was a later Astronomer Royal, Maskelyne, who instituted the Nautical Almanac, in which the angular distances between the Moon and ten selected stars were recorded for every three hours at Greenwich, and thus enabled navigators to find longitude by observing these angles with a quadrant and to compute their position with reference to Greenwich. Known as 'Lunars', these sights were the standard method of determining longitude at sea, being used well into the nineteenth century. It was an extremely laborious and not very accurate method. Finding latitude had posed no difficulties for centuries, the altitude of the Sun at its zenith being observed first with the astrolabe and later with the Davis backstave and, subsequent to 1731, increasingly with the Hadley quadrant, the forerunner of the modern sextant.

In 1752, a young Scot aged fifteen, Alexander Dalrymple, had been sent out as a writer to the Madras establishment of the East India Company. He was ambitious, well-educated and a voracious reader—he read the voyages of the Spaniards, Magellan, Mendana, Quiros and the Dutchmen Schouten, Le Maire, Tasman and Roggeveen. He longed to sail the eastern seas himself and to restore the trade of the eastern islands to the Company. To his delight, in 1759 he was appointed to the Secret Service of the Company, sailing in the schooner *Cuddalore* under Captain Baker to explore the eastern passages. They sailed to Macao for stores, and then to Taiwan and the Philippines, where Dalrymple took command for further explorations in the East. He made his way to Sooloo (Solo) where he entered into a trading agreement with the Sultan. He enjoyed contact with the natives, or 'Indians' as he termed them generally, and got on well with them, a fact upon which he always prided himself.

After a return to Madras he went again to Sooloo, this time in command of the *London* packet, and obtained the grant of the island of Balambangan as a trading post for his Company. He visited Manila, where he met Spanish sailors and gathered many tales of exploration, including the information that Torres had passed through a strait south of Papua New Guinea.

By 1765 he was in England to find the East India Company lukewarm about Balambangan and his enterprises in the eastern seas, nor would they send him out again in person to take over from the inefficient agents he claimed were now ruining his trading post. He had, however, another occupation to interest him now. Throughout his voyaging in the East he had made running surveys of the coasts—he did not claim them as surveys but rather as charts incorporating reports and information from other vessels sailing these seas, so that the maximum information was presented. He himself had sailed along the coasts, obtaining his latitude by the Sun's altitude at noon, his longitude by lunar distances, meanwhile fixing by intersecting compass-bearings the hilltops and headlands. The accuracy of his surveys of north-south coastlines was generally in excess of that of the east-west, denoting the superiority of latitude sights over lunars, but careful use of the log helped to control the scale of distance along the coastlines. He attached great importance to sketches of the coastline as seen from seaward, most of which he had to draw himself, for, as he wrote, 'My journal of the coast of Hainan is perhaps the most imperfect of any in my whole voyage; it was on my first setting out in command of *Cuddalore*; the Chief Mate was not an artist and had all the prejudice which constantly attends ignorance. He was besides very careless at keeping the log.'

Dalrymple thus had many charts of his own to draw—and to have engraved on copper—of the coasts of China, Hainan, Palawan, Borneo and the South China Sea. Once that work was well in hand he commenced the compilation of *An Account of the Discoveries made in the South Pacific Previous to 1764*, which was printed in 1767, enabling him to present a copy to Joseph Banks to take on Cook's first voyage. In this work he detailed the voyages that had been made in that ocean up to the year 1764; and, with the aid of beautifully engraved charts, set out the arguments for the existence of a Southern Continent. He assessed the amount of land and water in the explored portions of the globe and was satisfied that a continent was required on the south of the equator to counterpoise the land on the north and to maintain equilibrium necessary to the earth's motion. He believed that the Spanish and Dutch voyagers whose works he had translated confined the limits of the continent on all but its southern shores. Tasman had de-lineated a portion of the western coast when he sailed along the coast of New Zealand in 1642; Roggeveen had seen signs of a continent, so Dalrymple believed, in 30° S., 100° W., and both he and Quiros had limited its possible extent to the north by the very course of their east-to-west Pacific voyages; but his greatest belief in the continent stemmed from one of the strange tales he had heard from the Spanish sailors in Manila. In the year 1572, a pilot, Juan Fernandez, sailing from Peru to Chile, and wishing to avoid the north-going coastal current, had sailed westward, discovering the islands which bear his name; more than this, he had sailed further in latitude 40° S. and found a coast where he saw the mouths of large rivers, from which came boat-loads of natives so white, so well-clad, so much richer and in every way so different from those of Chile and Peru, that he knew it to be the shores of a continent. The old pilot had, however, died before ever returning to these populous shores, and Dalrymple earnestly hoped that he would be the next man to set foot on this vast continent, which he estimated to stretch from 90° W. to 170° E. and southward from 30° S.; in his opinion it would have a population of over fifty million inhabitants.

In writing *An Historical Collection of the Several Voyages and Discoveries in the South Pacific Ocean*, in two volumes which was published in 1770–1, Dalrymple was following the fashion for writers in the eighteenth century, which met an ever-growing demand for travel literature with the spread of literacy at home and voyaging abroad.

Campbell's Voyages, Astley's Voyages, Callander's Voyages, Dalrymple's Voyages: the writers' and publishers' names were attached to the voyages in the shortened popular titles as the series followed one another through the years. These massive works, often in two or three volumes, were purchased almost without question to augment the libraries of every stately home. Both British and foreign voyages were described, each series attempting to cover the widest fields of exploration, many of the works being but faintly disguised copies of their rivals' or predecessors'. Dalrymple admitted that he owed much to works of Charles de Brosses, President to the Parlement of Dijon, who in his *Histoire des Navigations aux Terres Australes* had used many of the arguments subsequently employed by Dalrymple in support of the existence of a Southern Continent, and had urged France to form a colony in New Britain as a base for further exploration in the South Seas.

A number of expeditions, both British and French, had set out to observe the transit of Venus in 1761, but for many reasons had been only partially successful. As a result of these failures the transit of 1769 had taken on an increased importance and the Royal Society was formulating plans for five expeditions, to be carried by the Royal Navy, including one to northern Norway and another to the South Pacific. The former would permit observations of the longest time of transit, the latter the shortest; good observations at both places would provide superb data for computing the true distance to the Sun—as Halley had proposed. It is needless to state that Dalrymple had his eye on the expedition to the South Pacific. He was on the friendliest of terms with Joseph Banks who was an enthusiast for the expedition, he was a surveyor to the East India Company and he was known to be compiling the work that would assemble all the existing evidence for a Great Southern Continent. In his own and many other eyes he was the one man who could command the vessel which was to carry the observers to the South Pacific.

But, unknown to Dalrymple, two men stood between him and his life's ambition: Lord Hawke, First Lord of the Admiralty, and a little-known surveyor working off the coasts of Newfoundland.

In 1755 bitter fighting was in progress between the British and

the French in North America, and in that year a fine body of
regular British troops was ambushed and severely defeated by a
combined force of French and Indians who had employed back-
woods methods of warfare. This defeat had so seriously alarmed
British military authorities that they had formed the Royal American Regiment of Foot; recruited in the Colonies, the regiment was
trained in what we now call 'commando' methods. About fifty of
the officers were of Swiss, Dutch or German origin, which was not
surprising for Britain had been sending emigrants from those
countries to North America. Two of these, Des Barres, a Swiss,
and Samuel Holland, a Dutchman, were military engineers, the
former trained at the Royal Military College, Woolwich, and the
latter in the Dutch Army. These two were destined to play important roles in the great surveying effort that was made in North
America by the British once peace was restored by the Treaty of
Paris in 1763.

Both these officers had outstanding merit, Des Barres energetic
and self-confident, Holland modest and painstaking. They both
excelled themselves at the fall of Louisbourg in 1758 where they
secured French plans and documents relating to the Gulf and River
of St. Lawrence. On the day after the surrender of Louisbourg,
Holland was surveying the harbour of Kennington Cove using the
plane table, a simple form of portable plotting board which could
be set up on a tripod at various stations and upon which conspicuous points could be fixed by plotting intersecting bearings. He
became aware, much as an artist at work becomes aware of an
observer, that he was overlooked and turning saw the Master of
H.M.S. *Pembroke*, a vessel lying in the bay. This was James Cook,
who, there and then, asked Holland to instruct him in the use of
the plane table, and an appointment was accordingly made for the
next day. This was a fortunate and historic meeting, the more so
as Cook's Captain, Simcoe, was a most scientifically inclined person and a navigator of considerable talent. Hearing of Cook's
lesson, he invited Cook to bring Holland on board to dine, bringing
his plane table with him.

During the long hard winter of 1758/59 which followed, *Pembroke* lay at Halifax. Captain Simcoe fitted a drawing table in his

great cabin: he provided what drawing instruments he had and his copies of Leadbetter's mathematical works lay to hand. Here he encouraged Holland and Cook to work and here the French documents were laid down to form the chart of the Gulf and River of St. Lawrence which played such a vital role in the campaign leading to the fall of Quebec. There was much discussion on surveying matters between these three and in this great cabin Cook first learned the trade of which he became the supreme master.

The year 1759 saw the mounting of the attack on Quebec but not even the captured charts gave sufficient details through that part of the St. Lawrence known as the 'Traverses' to permit the passage of Admiral Saunders' ships. In ships' boats Cook and other Masters from the Fleet performed this daring survey, and as a result, in the words of the French Governor, 'The enemy have passed 60 ships of war where we dare not risk a vessel of 100 tons by night or day.'

After the fall of Quebec, Cook, now master of H.M.S. *Northumberland*, was able to carry out a number of minor surveys, first in the St. Lawrence River, and then on the coast of Nova Scotia, where he came under the eye of Lord Colville, his captain and soon to become the Commander-in-Chief of the America Station, who granted him £50 for making himself proficient in the navigation of the St. Lawrence.

The *Northumberland* entered St. Johns, Newfoundland, in September 1762 after a military force under Lieutenant Colonel Amherst had re-captured the place from the French. Colville then sent Cook to accompany Des Barres, now on Amherst's staff, to survey Conception Bay. Whilst Des Barres surveyed the French fortifications Cook made plans of the anchorages. It would seem that Des Barres learnt as much about hydrography from the practical seaman as Cook learnt about survey control from the military engineers.

After the signing of the Treaty of Paris in 1763 the French evacuated Newfoundland and at the request of the newly appointed British Governor, Commodore Graves, the Admiralty appointed Cook as the 'King's Surveyor', providing him with a small schooner, the *Grenville*, and a crew of seven men. Cook spent four seasons on the coast of Newfoundland, where he completed and drew many beautiful surveys, embracing the whole western and southern coasts. Some of these are triangulated surveys extended from measured base lines by which he extended the shore base to fix the triangulated points. He certainly used a quadrant and it is almost certain that he had a theodolite with him; doubtless he was still guided by the advanced methods of Des Barres and Holland.

In August 1766 he observed an eclipse of the Sun on Eclipse Island in the Burgeo group off the south coast of Newfoundland. His position thus obtained for this point is marked by his cairn to this day and differs in longitude only a few hundred feet from modern determinations. The taking of these observations was a happy event for Cook, for in the following winter his paper on the subject was read before the Royal Society which brought him to the notice of those who were planning the 1769 expedition. Thus the first shadow was thrown across Dalrymple's bright hopes of being the discoverer of the Great Southern Continent. A further shadow appeared with the publication of Cook's charts of Newfoundland, for which Captain Palliser had obtained permission from Their Lords Commissioners. Private publication of charts was still the only way of having work produced for the Board of Admiralty had no engravers in their employ at this stage.

'He raised himself solely by his merit from a very obscure birth to the rank of Post Captain in the royal navy'—so reads the inscription on the Cook monument erected by Admiral Sir Hugh Palliser in the park of The Vache, Chalfont St. Giles. But it was necessary in those days to have 'interest', however great the merit, in order to advance through the ranks to Post Captain. That Cook was fully aware of his good fortune in being noticed by the right officers in the early days of his career is evident to those who study the charts of New Zealand, where three majestic capes are named respectively after Saunders, Colville and Palliser.

Dalrymple confidently prepared for command of the expedition to observe the transit of Venus, and has written that he was responsible for choosing and fitting out the bark *Endeavour*. A statement of his, written at this stage, rings so true to the ear of

·

a modern surveying officer in the Royal Navy, that one is inclined
to think that he must have had a considerable hand in the plans.
When he gave as his reason for preferring *Endeavour* to another
smaller vessel that the ability to carry another anchor and cable
might be of the utmost consequence, a 'navy oracle' told him that
he was 'much mistaken if he thought he should have just what
stores he pleased, that there was an Establishment, although he
might be allowed an anchor and cable extraordinary on such a
voyage.' Dalrymple answered that on such an expedition he
thought there was no Establishment but what the ship could carry.

At the Admiralty Their Lords Commissioners had been studying
the situation in the Pacific. Captain Wallis returned in *Dolphin* in
1768 having discovered Tahiti and, incidentally, an excellent spot
there for the observation of the transit.

Despite their defeat in the Seven Years' War France was were
leading the hunt for the Southern Continent. To Lord Hawke,
First Lord, the transit of Venus was but a convenient cover story,
for once the observations had been made *Endeavour's* Captain
would refer to his Secret Orders which would instruct him to
search south and west for the Southern Continent.

Remembering Halley and his misfortunes with his officers, senior officers at the Admiralty wanted no 'philosophers' in command
of such an enterprise. Lord Hawke entrusted his Secret Orders to
Lieutenant James Cook, King's Surveyor from Newfoundland.
Dalrymple was overcome with disappointment; he felt that his
failure to be selected was due to his not having been brought up
in the Royal Navy. He turned all his energy to writing—books,
treatises and tracts. He wrote copiously in the years ahead largely
on hydrographic and navigation matters but also on the affairs,
iniquitous or otherwise, of the East India Company; on the 'Roman Catholic' question; on the high price of corn; on the Indian
trade; on the humane treatment of Indians; on the relative merits
of the chronometers of Earnshaw and Arnold; on the inadvisability
of forming a 'thief colony' at Botany Bay and, after the publication
of Dr. Hawkesworth's account of the *Endeavour* voyage, upon the
shortcomings of Cook as an explorer. He wrote always vigorously
with explosive use of italics and capitals to bring out his points.

Whilst I was reading Dalrymple's works in preparation for the writing of this book I was in command of Her Majesty's Surveying Ship which bore his name, homeward bound from the Persian Gulf. The surveying captain has a lonely life in such circumstances, confined as he is alone in his cabin during the long evenings. The cuddy is situated well forward in the ship below the bridge and around it the wind buffets and sighs continually. A portrait of Dalrymple at the age of fifty-seven by George Dance hung above my chair—a portly man, bald with a fringe of hair hanging to his collar, a long nose and a sad determined expression. As I read nightly the querulous works, I got to know him; I felt the frustration that was his, sitting in the wings whilst a rival occupied the world's stage.

In 1769, the East India Company had paid Dalrymple £5,000 for past services, but although he continually pressed the Company to send him back to a post in the East, they were not to be persuaded except for a brief period as a Member of the Madras Council in 1776. They did, however, appoint him Hydrographer to the Company in 1779, his task being to prepare and have printed charts for the use of the Company's vessels.

Dalrymple worked at an amazing speed with the production of charts, which were compiled from the surveys of numerous ships' captains from almost every part of the world; well set out, modestly titled, engraved by Harrison, John Walker and others, they are beautiful examples of the cartographer's and engraver's art. They were compiled in folios covering geographical areas and often there are two or more charts of the same area on different scales and with different limits, as decided by the individuals who had made the surveys, so that all available knowledge was placed at the mariner's disposal.

In appointing themselves a Hydrographer the East India Company showed themselves considerably more enlightened than the Board of the Admiralty, who had been murmuring about such an appointment for over twenty years. Captain Anson had remarked during his voyage round the world in 1740 upon the absence of surveying officers in the Navy and the lack of a hydrographic office at the Admiralty. He had sailed his great voyage with surveying instruments on board but without the men trained to use them. He was aware that the French *Dépôt des Cartes et Plans* had been established as long ago as 1720. Material had accumulated at the Admiralty to such an extent that one of the Secretary's clerks was taking charge of it at a salary of £180 per annum to no useful purpose so far as the Fleet was concerned.

It seems likely that George III had decided to confer the title of Hydrographer of the Navy upon Cook on return from his third voyage, and it is sad to reflect that, but for the tragic incident on the beach at Kealakekua Bay, the Hydrographic Office would have held for ever the honour of having Cook's name at the head of its list of Hydrographers. Dalrymple, an eminent hydrographer experienced in charting Far Eastern waters and a distinguished Fellow of the Royal Society, was the obvious choice for the newly appointed Secretary to the Admiralty, Evan Nepean, to recommend to the Board as their Hydrographer. Dalrymple took up the post on 13th August 1795, the day after the Order in Council establishing a Hydrographer's Office was dated.

The Order in Council recommending that a proper person should be appointed Hydrographer charged him with the duty of selecting and compiling all existing information and making it available to the Commanders of His Majesty's Ships. The expenses of the establishment were limited to £650, which, when Dalrymple's salary had been paid, left only £100 per annum for Aaron Arrowsmith, his assistant, and £50 per annum for a draughtsman. But like many a good Civil Servant before and since, Dalrymple almost imperceptibly built up his establishment to meet the circumstances despite the overriding financial stricture, and by 1800 he had John Walker, who had worked with him before, as his assistant, Aaron Arrowsmith having left to set up his own well-known map making business. He had a draughtsman who compiled the new charts under Walker's direction and three copper engravers who made the copper printing plates. One copper plate printer was able to cope with the output of the three engravers, and all were housed in two rooms in the Old Building at the Admiralty. The annual wage bill had risen to £1,400.

The hours were from 10.00 a.m. to 4.00 p.m. daily which sounds fairly easy until we read that the only holiday in the whole year permitted by Dalrymple was Christmas Day. The staff were on daily pay, which was paid to them weekly by Dalrymple himself, a portion being invariably deducted for any absence, whether through illness or any other cause.

The country was fighting a desperate war with France; the ships of the Royal Navy numbered hundreds; the demand for charts was desperate. Dalrymple now had the potential for providing them, and for the moment we shall leave him with John Walker in the Old Building of the Admiralty arranging and cataloguing the piles of documents that lay upon the dusty shelves.

CHAPTER TWO

Men and Methods:
Hydrographic Surveying at the End of
the Eighteenth Century

In the reign of Charles II English seafarers finally became aware of the hopeless inadequacy of the charts of their own coasts and harbours. Those available were mainly the 'waggoners', being but anglicized versions of the Dutch charts which took the name from Waghenaer, the great Dutch exponent of hydrography.

There was a quickening of the tempo of harbour surveys by local pilots and by Trinity House, the latter established since 1514, and various maritime bodies persuaded the King to arrange for a systematic survey of our coasts to be put in hand, which resulted in the appointment of Captain Greenvile Collins to undertake this vast task in the yacht *Merlin*.

Collins was a man well suited to this work, having sailed as Sir John Narborough's Master in *Sweepstakes* in 1670, when together they had compiled a remarkable chart of the Magellan Strait which was in general use by all expeditions entering the Pacific for many years. Narborough was a great navigational enthusiast and this enthusiasm he had passed on in full measure to Collins, who had made a number of minor surveys on his own in the Mediterranean before he was offered the task of tackling his native shores.

With so little knowledge in England at the time of what survey-ing entailed, those who commissioned the work had no conception of the magnitude of the problem, for it must be remembered that there was no land survey worthy of the name which Collins could use as a basis for his work. Yet Collins made quite remarkable progress and after ten years the results of his work were published as *Great Britain's Coasting Pilot*, which ran into a number of editions and was in general use at sea for a hundred years. The *Pilot* must have been very widely published, for even today copies of this great work are not infrequently reported as coming to light in some seldom visited boxroom or attic, the charts often bearing copious notes in longhand, for it was the habit of the users of those days to compile their own sailing directions as they gained knowledge of the little-known coastal waters. Samuel Pepys and others were critical of Collins' results, but we today having some knowledge of the primitive methods available to him, and knowing that his instruments were probably confined to a five foot radius brass quadrant for use ashore, a Gunter's quadrant for hand-held use offshore, a measuring chain or wheel, a meridian compass and a lead-line, have to admire the clear drafts of the concise directions for entry into the many ports and harbours around our shores.

In the latter half of the eighteenth century there were a number of 'chart sellers', as they called themselves, in London—Robert Sayer 'At the Sign of the Golden Buck', William Heather 'At the Sign of the Little Midshipman' and many others. But the situation was not satisfactory for merchantmen as the chart sellers relied for new surveys upon the whims of sea captains, having no surveying service of their own. The Royal Navy was even worse off, relying entirely as they did upon what the chart sellers had to offer them, the sellers themselves being primarily employed in meeting the demands of the merchant trade.

The Admiralty made a start themselves with surveying in home waters in 1751 when they engaged a civilian surveyor, Murdoch Mackenzie, to make charts of the west coasts of Britain and Ireland. Mackenzie, who was a very enlightened man, had been employed on his own account for some years in the Orkneys and had published a folio of charts called *Orcades* in 1750.

Mackenzie wrote a *Treatise on Maritim Surveying* in 1774 and Dalrymple had published his *Essay on the Most Commodious Methods of Marine Surveying* three years earlier. By studying these two works we are able to discover the methods of survey and the instruments in use by a few of the more advanced surveyors towards the end of the eighteenth century.

Of the two works, Dalrymple's is the more theoretical and less practical; whereas Mackenzie's bears the stamp of a surveyor working in the field, Dalrymple's gives the impression that it was written by one who had given great consideration to the most modern methods of the time but had enjoyed few opportunities for putting them into practice. For instance, in Dalrymple's *Method of surveying with progressive flags*, published in a third edition of his *Essay* in 1806, he needs a party of Lascars onshore, with horses, to transport and erect nine massive flagstaffs, each with its individually numbered flag upon it. At any time there are to be three flags in a line along the shore, whilst the other six are erected at suitable points inland so that they may form equilateral triangles including the front three, observing the angles of which will enable the positions of the shoreline flags to be fixed relative to each other. Meanwhile the ship offshore fixes herself by means of angles taken between the three front flagstaffs. Steadily the whole calvalcade fleets along the shore as the survey proceeds. Even with portable radio sets I should shrink today from attempting such an operation on any but the most unencumbered shoreline. It is interesting, however, to note that in this description Dalrymple envisages the use of a theodolite ashore, and Hadley's sextant onboard, for observing the horizontal angles. He was aware also that a horizontal angle taken between two fixed points placed the observer's position somewhere on the circumference of a circle passing through these points, and that if two angles were taken simultaneously between three fixed points then the observer was situated at a point where the two circles intersected. In 1765 his friend the Reverend Mr. Mitchell, in a paper recommending the use of the Hadley for surveying, had set out a geometrical method whereby such fixes could be plotted: the line between two of the objects was bisected by a line running at right angles; the tangent of the angle obtained by subtracting the observed angle from ninety degrees laid off along the perpendicular from the point of bisection gave the position of the centre of a circle; this circle, when drawn through the two fixed objects, embraced the position of the observer on its circumference. As two of these geometrical problems had to be worked out for each fix the work was laborious when constantly fixing a ship sounding at sea. For thirty years or so the Hadley had been used for taking horizontal rounds of angles so that the observer's position might be set down graphically with reference to the stations observed, but in formulating a geometrical solution to the problem when only three points were observed, the Reverend Mitchell had solved the resection problem and devised a method of fixing which has endured as the mainstay of hydrographic survey down to the present day.

Out of sight of land, Dalrymple, in the 1806 edition of his essay, proposed another method, the '*Quincunx*', based on the pattern which four trees in an orchard make when a fifth is planted in the centre. The method required the same number of ships and I doubt if any surveyor ever enjoyed such munificence. In fact Dalrymple says that although five vessels will do, nine will be more convenient!

With the ships anchored in a quincunx, each three vessels forming an exact equilateral triangle between their flagged anchor buoys, and at two or three miles distant from each other, the skiffs and whaleboats were lowered. With a leadsman forward they quartered the ground, being propelled by Captain Blair's method of sculling. The boats were fixed by Hadley angles or hand compass-bearings of the ship's anchor buoys. He suggests that a trawl net be added to the ship's stores so that the area within the quincunx may be trawled for submerged rocks, and he adds happily that Admiral Pigot, when Captain of the *York*, caught enough fish to feed the whole ship's company with such a net. This last part of the evidence was certainly noted by surveying officers studying the essay in later years and it is only within the last thirty years that a seine net has been removed from the outfit of naval stores carried in a survey ship.

Dalrymple also usefully points out that a simple method of finding the distance of a sounding boat from the ship is to observe the vertical angle with the Hadley between the masthead and a horizontal line painted on the ship's hull at a known distance below the masthead; this too is a custom which has lingered on almost to the present day and every one of Her Majesty's snow white surveying ships should, by regulations, wear such a black band upon her hull. It is seldom, however, that recalcitrant First Lieutenants can be persuaded to let their sideparties spend the time on this ticklish task.

There are more practical methods in Dalrymple's essay, and it is clear that he realised the importance of extending angles or bearings from the terminals of a baseline to fix points on the survey by intersecting rays. He recommends sound as by far the best method of measuring a base. If a bullet be tied to the end of a silk thread 11·24 inches long, each swing will equal 612 feet or ⅒th of a geographic mile; by counting the number of swings between the flash and the report of a distant gun, a distance of between 2 to 6 miles may be accurately measured.

Murdoch Mackenzie had a firmer grasp of the essentials, and in setting them down in his Treatise he was laying the foundations of hydrographic surveying methods for a century to come. He realised that a well-measured, long baseline ashore was the first essential for any harbour or coastal survey. Its direction must be obtained by the compass needle, and then intersecting angles must be taken with a theodolite or Hadley, from either end of the base to what he termed stasimetric points, among them preferably being two on hill-tops at the extremities of the survey from which he could intersect further points. Once a number of such points had been intersected they were plotted on paper by protractor and, though only two rays were used to plot them, he checked the third angle of the triangle on his plotting sheet by observing the angle in the field.

He then plotted the coastline by taking angles to prominent features by compass needle bearings from two or more of his stasimetric points; but when he came to important headlands or out-jutting rocks he fixed them by resection with the Hadley or a theodolite. He set down geometrical and trigonometrical methods of finding the distance of the observer's station from the three stasimetric points in the three different cases when the points formed a straight line, or when the observer was either inside or outside the triangle formed by them. In this way, of course, he became aware of the danger of a 'circular fix'—when all three stasimetric points lie on or near the circumference of the same circle which also passes through the observer's position.

To fix his soundings taken from a boat he took bearings to two of his stasimetric points with a hand-held compass.

Murdoch Mackenzie measured his first base in the Orkneys on a frozen lake, using a thirty-foot accurately measured pole, to the foremost end of which was affixed a flat board which enabled the leading man to insert an iron pin squarely in the ice. The rear end of the pole was tipped with a metal loop which fitted over the rear pin until the next forward pin was driven, when the rear man then pocketed the rear pin, enabling the number of fleets to be surely counted at the end of the measurement. Later, along the coasts of Britain, Mackenzie used beaches or coastal plains for his base measurements. On extensive small scale coastal surveys he found it too laborious to extend from a measured base but observed for latitude at two points about ten miles apart and, allowing for the magnetically observed bearing between them, used their difference of latitude for the baseline. If the coast ran east and west, his inability to measure longitude with accuracy entailed one end of the baseline far inland.

In 1771 Murdoch Mackenzie was superseded as Admiralty Surveyor by his nephew of the same name, a Lieutenant in the Royal Navy who had learnt his trade as a Midshipman sailing round the world with Byron. The old man settled down to write his Treatise. Lieutenant Murdoch Mackenzie continued charting where his uncle left off in the Bristol Channel and worked his way round to Plymouth Sound. It was here, after completing his baseline and fixing his stasimetric points and when he was poised to commence his sounding that he was called away by the Admiralty in 1744 to search for a new channel off Margate. How many surveyors can recall similar frustrations! On this occasion it was probably a fear of the Dutch Fleet once again entering the Thames, for it is correct to say that the Dutch seamen still knew more about the Thames Estuary than the British did themselves.

Meanwhile, Murdoch Mackenzie senior, working on his Treatise, had conceived the idea of an instrument to solve the laborious problem of finding one's position from two horizontal angles observed between three stasimetric points. This was to become the station pointer, and little different in construction from the invaluable instrument still in use today. It consisted of a graduated circle of brass, six inches in diameter, to which three legs, the centre one fixed and the other two movable, were attached. By means of clamping screws the two movable legs could be fixed so as to measure the same angles as observed by the Hadley. When the instrument was moved so that the three legs passed through the plotted positions of the three observed points, the surveyor's position at the centre of the instrument could be marked upon the plotting sheet.

Joined by an able assistant, his cousin Graeme Spence, Lieutenant Mackenzie measured his base on the sands of Margate Beach, extended to his stasimetric points and went afloat with his station pointer. His chart of Margate Road is thickly carpeted with soundings, clear evidence of the great simplification of fixing afloat which this instrument had brought about. Within a few years the first commercial models of the station pointer were being made by Troughton, the instrument maker.

It is here convenient to glance at the history of the other two instruments, the theodolite and the Hadley which, together with the station pointer, had enabled the Mackenzies to bring hydrographic surveying to this advanced stage.

In 1730 there was in Philadelphia a Philosophical Club led by Mr. Tench Francis, whose father had been so great a lover of fish that he had baptised his children after the tench, the roach and the perch. Among the members of this club was a glazier named Godfrey who claimed that one day he was putting in a window on the first floor of a house when, having a pane of glass in each hand, he noticed the double reflection. He ran through the streets to the club shouting 'I've got it! I've got it!'; and later, constructing an instrument which he claimed was vastly superior to the 'Davis pig-yoke' for observing the Sun's altitude, he sent his son off to the West Indies to try it. There, Godfrey said, his son fell in with some naval officers and Hadley, then a lieutenant, who was among them, desired to see the instrument and patented it himself on return to England.

Research into this story does not disprove the discovery of the glazier, but it is certain that Hadley did not serve in the Navy or in the West Indies. He was a man of science, a Vice-President of the Royal Society, and had worked for many years on the improvement of optical instruments. He showed his quadrant for observing the altitude of heavenly bodies at sea to the Royal Society in May 1731 and generously stated that similar principles had been set before the Society by Sir Isaac Newton some long time earlier. But it is pleasing to read that both Hadley and Godfrey received a monetary award from the Society.

The history of the theodolite is much older and it is not intended to pursue it here. There is a picture of a theodolite in use on the cover of *The Surveyor* by Aaron Rathbone published in London in 1616. It appears to be capable of measuring both true horizontal and vertical angles on graduated circles. Also shown on this same cover is a plane table in use, which is little different from the instrument of today.

George Robertson, who was Wallis' master in the *Dolphin* on the voyage during which Tahiti was discovered, in 1767 speaks of his 'thurtolete' when reporting on his survey of Port Famine in the Strait of Magellan. He was assisted by the 'young gentlemen' so that it appears that sending the midshipmen away to do a little surveying has been the stand-by of a desperate 'snotties' nurse' for at least 200 years.

Early forms of theodolite were greatly handicapped by the difficulty of graduating a circle, for it is difficult to accomplish without finding the final division either too large or too small, and it was not only theodolites which suffered from poor division of the arc. 'Hadleys' were not sufficiently accurately divided for nautical astronomy and it was an offer of a reward by the Board of Longitude that resulted in Jesse Ramsden, a Yorkshireman, inventing his dividing engine in 1775, for which he was paid £615 on condition that he explained its use to ten mathematical instrument makers. John Troughton was one of these, and assisted by his brother Edward he made a superior model of the machine, which not only enabled them to graduate Hadleys and theodolites, but also the station pointer which the Mackenzies now set before them.

The greatest prize the Board of Longitude had to offer was, however, reserved for a timepiece which would operate successfully at sea, existing pendulum type clocks being, of course, useless. It had long been realised that if the time that the Sun passed its meridian could be read on a clock on which time had been carried faultlessly from Greenwich, then the observer's longitude with reference to the Greenwich meridian would be known. It was not only in England that progress was being made but, as the eventual winner of the £20,000 reward was another Yorkshireman, it is intended to follow his struggle to gain his full reward for the invention of a timepiece which revolutionised navigation and opened the door to the surveying of the whole world.

Son of a carpenter, John Harrison seems an unlikely candidate for the Fellowship of the Royal Society, which he was eventually offered but which he declined in favour of his son. The moving parts of his first clock were mostly made of wood. It was built in 1715, the year after the Board had first offered its reward and had claimed his boyish enthusiasm. Hadley was a member of the Board and he encouraged Harrison, who called upon him on his arrival in London where he had travelled in order to devote himself to the task of finding Longitude.

Harrison's first marine clock was a massive affair controlled by two large balances instead of a pendulum, connected together by wires so that their respective motions were opposed, thus overcoming the effect of the ship's motion upon them. There were many other innovations including a new form of escapement, two mainsprings, a device to ensure its speed was maintained when being wound, and compensation for the varying effects of hot and cold weather. Harrison succeeded in getting the Admiralty to give the clock a trial in a vessel sailing as far as Lisbon and back. Although successful, the small change in longitude entailed in this voyage did not make the trial impressive, and the inventor received only £500 as an encouragement to make a second timepiece for which in due course he received a similar reward. It took him seventeen more years to make the third. Numbers 2 and 3 were only slightly less cumbersome than Number 1, which weighed over 70 lbs. It is therefore astounding to find that his Number 4, in the construction of which he was assisted by his son, is a beautiful watch in a case whose diameter is but five inches and looks like one of those watches carried in a gentleman's waistcoat pocket only a generation ago. It required no special fittings or gimbals but was designed to lie flat in a wooden case aboard ship.

Harrison was now sixty-seven. His son accompanied Number 4 to the West Indies in H.M.S. *Deptford* on what appeared to be a highly successful trial, but the Board did not pay the full reward. Further trials were insisted upon: the fixing of Barbados and Portsmouth, terminals of the run, was to be carried out by competent observers using Jupiter's satellites. Dr. Maskelyne, later Astronomer Royal, and Green, who was destined to observe with Captain Cook at Tahiti, travelled to Barbados ahead of young Harrison, who followed with his father's Number 4 in H.M.S. *Tartar*. Harrison felt some objection to Maskelyne in the role of referee for he also was a contender for the prize with his recently computed lunar tables, but for the second time Number 4 was equal to the occasion and was estimated to have had an error of less than a tenth of a second a day on the passage out.

Still Harrison senior did not get his deserts for the Board made further stipulations, the chief of which was that he should now take Number 4 to pieces and explain its working to six nominated persons, three of whom were watchmakers, after which he had to surrender the watch to the Board. One of these watchmakers was Larcum Kendall whose first time-keeper, modelled on Harrison's Number 4, accompanied Captain Cook on his second and third voyages. Cook gave the timepiece unstinted praise for the facility it gave him to obtain accurate longitudes of his many discoveries.

Thomas Mudge was another of the six who witnessed the dismembering of Harrison's Number 4, and both he and Kendall introduced improvements when copying the watch. But the demand by seamen for this revolutionary aid to navigation far exceeded the modest output of these two men, and it was not until John Arnold and Thomas Earnshaw got to work that these timepieces began to be manufactured by craftsmen on a scale wide enough to meet commercial requirements. There was keen rivalry between these two clockmakers as their timepieces underwent the

increasingly severe trials imposed upon them by the Board of
Longitude, both at the Royal Observatory and at sea. In this
rivalry we find the new Hydrographer of the Navy throwing
himself into the fray in true Dalrymple fashion. His old friend Sir
Joseph Banks was a member of the Board and a keen advocate of
Arnold's timepieces. A paper published by Dalrymple reviewing
about a dozen tests of both Earnshaw's and Arnold's timepieces
finds fault with every one of the former's trials and some extenu-
ating circumstances for every shortcoming of the latter's. But
Earnshaw was a good match for Dalrymple in the field of public
abuse, and published his paper *Longitude* in which he said to
Dalrymple: 'In your late puffing publication, you appear to have
had two motives, one to puff off your darling boy, the present Mr.
Arnold, son of your old tutor and friend; and another to please
Sir Joseph. The first was, to be sure, an act of friendly generosity,
the other a tolerably good step to please a great man, who keeps
a great and good table; and everyone knows how necessary it is
to have a good table at every quarter of the town. It is so
convenient when you take your departure from Arnold's in the
east, and sail west, to know the exact longitude of a good table,
in order to step in and take a plate.'

And so the rivalry between the two clockmakers went on into
the new century, first one and then the other receiving some
portion of money from the Board to encourage him in his efforts
to provide the mariner with this much prized instrument.

The eighteenth century had witnessed a great stride forward in
the provision of the tools of the trade for the surveyor at sea. The
theodolite had been much improved as a result of the invention
of the dividing engine; the Hadley and the marine timekeeper,
shortly to be called a chronometer, had been invented, as had the
station-pointer; and from an earlier century had been handed
down the plane table, the chain and the hand compass. During
the nineteenth century there was to be no similar advance in
equipment available to the sea surveyor; it is the stupendous efforts
made by surveying officers of the Royal Navy, and the magnificent
and world-wide results that they obtained with the tools available,
that makes the hydrographic story of this century so remarkable.

Before moving on to the nineteenth century it is as well to go back to Dalrymple in his office, where we left him looking over the mass of accumulated surveys upon the already crowded shelves of the Hydrographic Office archives.

For a hundred years or so it had been the custom for captains of both naval vessels and merchant ships to make what surveys they could wherever they sought shelter or called to trade; many of these sketch surveys had found their way to the Admiralty; many of them were unreliable, being compiled with little knowledge of chart-making.

The great majority of the material stemmed from four main sources. First, there was the great collection of charts compiled over the last twenty years or so by Dalrymple from his own surveys and those of very many others, officers of the East India Company, such as Captain John Ritchie's surveys in the Bay of Bengal, Archibald Blair in the Indian Ocean islands and the ubiquitous Lieutenant John McLuer in the Persian Gulf, on the coasts of India, in the Philippine Islands and many other areas in the Eastern Seas. Dalrymple, as Hydrographer to the Company, had done his work well and all these surveys had been published, and to look at this collection today, all superbly engraved, shows that as a cartographer Dalrymple was without peer.

The constant search by 'John Company' to maintain trade in the East was the overriding factor in the building up of this great collection. In fact, it will be found over the years that the vast labour and considerable expense entailed in surveying at sea have never been lightly incurred; compelling reasons, provided by trade or warfare, will be found to lie behind every considerable series of charts.

The second collection of surveys and charts in the office were due to the Admiralty themselves who had commissioned both the Murdoch Mackenzies and Graeme Spence for work around the shores of Britain using hired boats. Such surveys were required for the safety of the Fleet in its own home waters. But surprisingly enough, by no means all these surveys had reached the office and Dalrymple was engaged for some while on a fruitless search for the missing plans.

The third source comprised charts compiled by numerous surveyors (including naval officers) published privately or by commercial map sellers. These were of uneven quality but many were good.

The fourth great category comprised the charts resulting from the many surveys carried out by army officers, naval officers and civilians in North America. As we have seen, surveying started in earnest both ashore and afloat in North America after the fall of Quebec and the Peace of Paris which followed. Both the Admiralty and the Board of Plantations commissioned work, and Governors appointed to the various parts of these colonies did what they could themselves to employ surveyors so that the harbours might be opened up for fishing and trade. The Admiralty were particularly keen to foster the fishing industry for they saw thriving communities of fishermen in Nova Scotia and Newfoundland as an inexhaustible supply of recruits for the Royal Navy.

It is as well that this great effort had been made, for in 1774 the Revolutionary War was imminent and Earl Howe recalled Des Barres, who had been surveying on the American coast since 1763, and set him to work to publish his own charts together with all the other surveys which had been achieved in these waters. The completed work, often known as *Des Barres' Atlantic Neptune*, is in fact a compilation of the works of many men—Cook, and his successor Michael Lane, in Newfoundland; Holland in the River St. Lawrence, Prince Edward Island and Cape Breton Island, the coasts of Maine and New Hampshire; Des Barres himself on the coasts of Nova Scotia and New Brunswick and the remote and dangerous sandy Sable Island, a haunt then of beachcombers and wreckers; Lieutenant Hurd, R.N., from Saint John to Passamaquoddy Bay; and a single chart by George Gauld of Pensacola in the Gulf of Mexico.

Des Barres gave too little credit to the many surveyors whose work he published. It is clear that *Atlantic Neptune* was available to all who could pay for it and it was even published abroad. It is likely therefore that, as was the custom of the day, Des Barres made good money privately from its sale, and that is perhaps why the Admiralty refused to pay his salary and a long and bitter struggle between them resulted. Des Barres claimed remuneration for all the expenses he had incurred during his eleven years' survey work on the American coast, and compensation too for having failed to gain promotion during this period in the Royal American Regiment owing to his preoccupation with this work. He received about £4,000 from the Admiralty, but never recovered a further £9,000 or so which he claimed. In addition he had been paid 35 guineas each for 247 plates of *Atlantic Neptune* and the Admiralty had bought from him the copies of this publication, but Des Barres retained a grievance against Their Lords' Commissioners past his hundredth birthday, on which day he danced upon a table to amuse his friends. He had retired to Halifax after a stormy career as Governor of Cape Breton Island; one senses that it was the idea of some harassed official in Whitehall to offer him this Governorship whence his daily visits to demand remuneration for his work would at last be impossible.

In addition to the great collections, there were a considerable number of track charts and running coastal surveys from earlier English expeditions, among which was Dampier's voyage to New Guinea of 1700, beautifully illuminated and drawn upon sheepskin. The most famous was probably Cook's running survey of the whole coasts of New Zealand which bears comparison with the coastline delineation of modern maps.

Other expeditions which had similarly contributed to the Admiralty collection of charts were the two voyages of H.M.S. *Dolphin* around the world, the first commanded by John Byron and the second by Samuel Wallis between the years 1764 and 1767.

Larger scale surveys of the islands discovered by these expeditions and of the anchorages they had occupied had also been made, amongst the more notable being those drawn by Cook's officers, such as the anchorages in New Zealand drawn by Pickersgill, who sailed on the first two voyages; the chart of Van Diemen's Land by William Bligh, master of the *Resolution* at the time of Cook's death; and various plans by George Vancouver.

Cook had learnt his hydrography in the North American school and, he in turn having become the master, developed his own school while sailing the Pacific. Of his pupils Pickersgill met an unfortunate end in the waters of the Thames, having imbibed too freely after returning from an unsuccessful search for the North

West Passage in command of H.M.S. *Lion* with Michael Lane as his master; but Bligh and Vancouver carried with them after Cook's death his methods, his standards of accuracy and above all his dedication, which in turn they passed on to those who served under them. Here is the first small nucleus of a band of naval officers who devoted themselves to the making of charts, and it will be seen how this team developed and grew in strength with each generation, and how directly the doings of the nineteenth century were influenced by the teaching and direction of Captain Cook.

CHAPTER THREE

Vancouver in the Northeast Pacific

Two months after Dalrymple's appointment there were laid before the new Hydrographer two magnificent series of surveys by their author, Captain Vancouver, on his return from a four-year voyage round the world, about three years of which had been spent in surveying in the North Pacific. The larger series completed the charting of the North American coastline from 30° N. in Mexico to Cook Inlet in 60° N., together with a number of plans of anchorages and passages along this intricate shoreline; the other series completed a survey of the whole of the Sandwich Island group, as Cook had named the Hawaiian Isles.

These surveys had been carried out at the direct instructions of the Admiralty, although the reason for the voyage in the first instance had in fact been more political than exploratory.

When Captain Cook, on his last voyage, had reached the Northwest coast of America he entered a deep, fjord-like inlet, where he found the Indians friendly, fresh water abundant, game plentiful, and where giant hemlock, spruce and fir trees growing on every hand supplied timber for all his repair needs. The natives indicated in their language that a great mass of land in the centre of the inlet was in fact an island—'nootka' they said, a term indicating that one could sail round it in a canoe. Cook took this to be the name of the place and named it Nootka Sound.

Sea otters swam in abundance off the North American shores in those distant days and many members of Cook's ships' companies in *Resolution* and *Discovery* purchased the smooth thick pelts in barter with the Indians.

Much later in the voyage, after Captain Cook had been tragically

The
NORTH PACIFIC
OCEAN IN 1797
Showing Coastline Surveyed by
Captains Cook, Vancouver and Broughton

A S I A

Kamchatka

Petropavlovsk

Aleutian

Sakhalin

Kuril Is.

—— Capt. Broughton

G. of Tartary

La Perouse Strait

Jefo (Hokkaidō)

Korea

Volcano Bay

40°

Chusan (Pusan)

Nipon (Honshū)

C H I N A

JAPAN IS.

N O R T H   P A C

Nanking River

Quelpart

Fuji-Yama

N

Typinsan (Miyako Shima)

Macao

Formosa

Canton R.

Typa

0°

Semarang

Torres St.

Endeavour Strait

140°

Fiji Is.

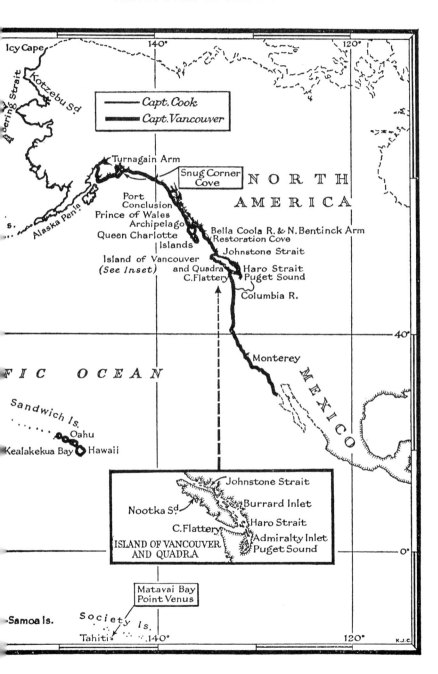

Icy Cape

Bering Strait

Kotzebu Sd.

140°   120°

NORTH
AMERICA

Turnagain Arm

Snug Corner
Cove

Port
Conclusion
Prince of Wales
Archipelago
Queen Charlotte
Islands

Alaska Penta.

Bella Coola R. & N. Bentinck Arm
Restoration Cove
Johnstone Strait

Island of Vancouver
(See Inset)   and Quadra   Haro Strait
C. Flattery   Puget Sound
Columbia R.

———— Capt. Cook
▬▬▬ Capt. Vancouver

40°

FIC   OCEAN

Monterey

MEXICO

Sandwich Is.
Oahu
Kealakekua Bay   Hawaii

Johnstone Strait
Burrard Inlet
Nootka Sd.
Haro Strait
C. Flattery   Admiralty Inlet
ISLAND OF VANCOUVER   Puget Sound
AND QUADRA

0°

Matavai Bay
Point Venus

Samoa Is.   Society Is.
Tahiti   140°   120°

K.J.C.

murdered in the Sandwich Islands and his successor, Captain Clerke, had died and been buried in Kamchatka, the ships reached Macao on their homeward voyage, much in need of provisions and refitting. Here the Chinese offered fantastic sums for the sea otter skins which the sailors showed them; so high were the prices the men were able to demand that, despite their years of hardship, the ships' companies tried desperately to persuade their Captains, now Lieutenants Gore and King, to return to Nootka for a cargo of otter skins.

Their pleadings were in vain, but once home in England the news of the fabulous trade awaiting exploitation between the Northwest coast and China spread through the seaport towns, and a number of officers and men who had served in the Navy, including some who had so recently returned from Cook's last voyage, found backers for such enterprises.

About eight different expeditions entered the field between 1785 and 1789, each comprising one or two ships. The most notorious was that of Captain John Meares, a former naval lieutenant, in his vessel *Nootka*, and the most successful was probably that of Captains Dixon and Portlock, both of whom had sailed with Cook, in their ships *King George* and *Queen Charlotte*. The latter expedition had a decided advantage over Meares in holding both South Sea and East India Company licences which were required by law to be held on board English ships trading on the American and Asian coasts respectively at this time.

Meares made the mistake of wintering in Snug Corner Cove in 57° N. where he lay frozen up from November to May, when more prudent seamen were already falling into the habit of returning to the Sandwich Islands during the winter months. Meares had decided upon this unwise course in fear of losing his already mutinous seamen by desertion in those happy isles. When Portlock and Dixon, encountering Meares in the spring of the year, had rescued him and his now scurvy crew from his unhappy predicament, they ordered him off the coast as he held no South Sea licence.

Meares, after reaching Macao and recovering from his winter experiences, decided that he was not to be kept out of the fur trade and sailed again from Asia with two ships, *Iphigenia* and

Felice, without licences, and flying the Portuguese flag. He brought with him a number of Chinese artisans to Nootka and built there a warehouse and a schooner, the first European vessel, he claimed, to be launched on this coast. He proudly named her the *North West America*, and whether she wore a Portuguese flag or a red ensign on that day we shall probably never know, despite the fact that we can see a print of her entering the water flying an outsize version of the latter.

On his next return to Macao, Meares was lucky enough to join the Etches Company who had two of the invaluable licences with which he then despatched Captain Colnett in the *Argonaut*, and Captain Hudson in the *Princess Royal*, with orders that they should now build a factory at Nootka.

Since 1774 Spanish seamen had been exploring northwards along the coast from their established bases in Mexico, and in 1789 two small vessels under Don Esteban Martinez arrived in Nootka Sound and took possession to forestall both the English and the Russians. Martinez found *Iphigenia*, which he allowed to sail, but he seized in turn the *North West America*, *Princess Royal* and *Argonaut* as they sailed into the Sound. The latter two vessels he sent with their crews as prisoners to Mexico where, happily, they were released with a warning to quit the Northwest coast by the Viceroy, newly arrived from Spain. Early in 1790 the British government received an official note from Madrid reporting these incidents and demanding that British vessels should no longer intrude into the Spanish domains at Nootka.

Two or three months later Meares was home to present a memorial to Parliament in which he told at length of the over-bearing treatment his ships had received from Martinez and of the seizure of his lands and factory—as his little warehouse had now become in his eyes.

Things now moved with startling speed towards a major international crisis between the two countries. Naval mobilisation was ordered in England, later known as the 'Spanish Armament', and Vancouver, who, as First Lieutenant, was fitting out in the Thames a new *Discovery* of 340 tons for a voyage to the Pacific, found his vessel overnight turned into a ship for receiving men from the 'hot press' which was now on, as press gangs made their way through the Thames-side waterfront. Vancouver himself was sent to the Channel Fleet.

Spain, surprised by the violent British reaction, soon yielded, and with the opening of diplomatic negotiations the storm passed as rapidly as it had arisen and the Nootka Convention was signed. Both countries would continue to trade on the Northwest Pacific Coast north of 'the area permanently occupied by Spain'. Buildings and land seized at Nootka were to be handed back and reparations paid.

To receive these properties at Nootka the British formed the happy plan of sending out Vancouver in command of *Discovery* which was again prepared for sea. During the course of his voyage he would be able to conduct considerable surveys, for which a set of instructions was given to him emphasising the importance of a renewed search for a Northwest Passage from the Pacific to the Atlantic.

Vancouver was a good 'picker'; as his First Lieutenant he had Zachary Mudge, under him being Lieutenants Peter Puget, Joseph Baker with Joseph Whidbey as Master, all of whom are commemorated by named features on the Pacific coasts of Canada or the United States. A small armed tender, the *Chatham*, a two-masted brig, accompanied *Discovery* with Lieutenant William Broughton as her Captain, and with James Johnstone as Master—two more names not easily overlooked on charts of the North Pacific.

Vancouver did not pick and did not welcome Archibald Menzies, a naval surgeon, as naturalist, and Toweroo, a Sandwich Islander (for return to his homeland), sent onboard the already crowded vessel by Sir Joseph Banks who, as President of the Royal Society, was never far from the planning of any expedition.

Important to the voyage was the later planned despatch of the storeship *Daedalus*, to meet *Discovery* at Nootka, not only for the replenishments she would carry, but because it was hoped that the diplomats would, before her sailing date, have settled more concisely the limits of the area permanently occupied by Spain.

Sailing on 1st April 1791, Vancouver went out eastabout making a landfall on the southwest coast of Australia and discovering and charting King George Sound before sailing on via New Zealand, Tahiti and the Sandwich Islands, all of which he had visited with Cook. At the latter two places he met former acquaintances among the natives, for whom he had a very considerable liking, and he was distressed to find bitter civil war when he reached Kealakekua Bay which, excellent anchorage as it was, held for him the tragic memory of Cook's death.

He made the American coast on 15th December 1792, in 30° N. as ordered, and started his steady, laborious running survey northwards. He employed the now familiar technique developed by Cook, with his own further refinements. All day the ship sailed along the coast if visibility was favourable; reaching or running before the wind the task was comparatively simple, but with head winds constant tacking was needed to keep in sight of the shore. The hours of darkness were spent in the offing, closing the land again at dawn to take up the task where it had been laid down the night before. Every alteration of course had to be noted, every change in speed logged; countless compass bearings and horizontal sextant angles of shoreline and inshore features were taken; the men in the chains were constantly at work with the lead-line; and all was kept on a running plot, for nothing must be left to memory. One thousand, four hundred coastline miles to the north, and nineteen weeks later, Cook's Cape Flattery was reached, and the strait close north of it, which Cook had missed, was entered. A search for the Strait of Juan de Fuca was included in Vancouver's instructions and this was surely it, broad and long, running eastwards into the very heart of the continent. Legend had it that in 1592 de Fuca, a Greek pilot in Spanish employ, had sailed through here to the Atlantic.

Inside the strait a new and more detailed survey technique was developed as the expedition charted the southern shore. Both vessels were anchored when suitable shelter offered and a tented observatory set up ashore for obtaining the gaining or losing rates of the timepieces by observing equal altitudes of the Sun to obtain the chronometer time of its meridian passage every seven days or so and for the fixing of geographical position, and determining of the local variation of the magnetic compass with reference to a true bearing of heavenly bodies. Meanwhile two or more boats, each with an officer in charge, were provisioned for three weeks or so and were despatched along the unexplored coastline ahead. Thus the boats took up the running survey of the intricate coast, proceeding steadily under oars that they might follow closely the trend of the coast, upon which, from time to time, the officers landed to take hand-compass bearings of the direction of the coastline, both forward and back, and of the sides, or tangents, of off-lying islands so that a number of such bearings would determine their positions relative to the shore. The courses and distances covered by the boats were carefully assessed and recorded, so that on return to the ship after a week or two's absence, the work could be transferred to the fair drawing sheet which was kept up-to-date by Lieutenant Baker working steadily away onboard. The vessels weighed anchor and moved forward to the next observatory position which had been selected by the boats, and then another boat party was sent ahead.

As the expedition moved into the innumerable intricacies of Admiralty Inlet and Puget Sound and northwards along the continental shore the boats' crews came to many 'dead-ends' at the terminations of long arms of the sea. There were a few harmless brushes with the Indians, for it was necessary to land to pick berries, hunt game, search for shell fish and brew spruce beer to supplement the rations as they ran short.

In June Vancouver, himself in the boats, was off Burrard Inlet, which he named after an old shipmate of the West Indian days in H.M.S. *Europa*, Sir Harry Burrard, who had been commended while serving in that vessel for bravery in rescuing five men from a wreck during a hurricane. This inlet is today famous, for on its shores lies the great city which bears Vancouver's name. And it was off the entrance that he was extremely surprised to see two ships at anchor, which on closing were found to be the Spanish vessels *Sutil* and *Mexicana*, also employed on survey under the command of Dionisio Alcala Galiano and Cayetano Valdés, the former being able to speak a little English. The meeting was extremely cordial, and the Spaniards, unaware of Vancouver's surveying zeal, offered to work together with the English vessels.

Martinez had not been idle since his arrival at Nootka three years previously. He had dispatched a vessel to northern waters on survey, whilst another small Spanish vessel under Quimper had explored the northern shore of the Juan de Fuca Strait as far as the Haro Strait, named after one of the officers. The following year Galiano and Valdés continued where Quimper had left off. Also, the year before Vancouver had reached the coast, a Spanish world voyage consisting of another *Discovery—Descubierta* under the command of Malaspina—and a consort *Atrevida*, had visited Nootka on their way south from northern waters and had made extensive observations for longitude there, using timepieces made in England by Arnold.

Vancouver learnt from Galiano that Señor Don Juan Francisco de la Bodega y Quadra, a Captain in the Spanish Navy, was now in command at Nootka and awaited his arrival to open negotiations under the Nootka Convention.

The surveying pace was too hot for the Spaniards who, after three weeks, parted amicably, but not before they had generously imparted details of their own work and that of Malaspina and Quimper, which Vancouver used in his chart of the entire coast, and which he showed in red to distinguish it from his own work. This early record of exchange of survey data to the mutual benefit of chartmakers was a forerunner of many similar instances to follow in the years ahead.

Johnstone, in charge of the advance boat parties, forced his way through the narrow tortuous strait which now bears his name, encountering strong tidal streams in the narrower parts, until he was 120 miles ahead of the ships, when he returned to report that he had reached the open sea and that the land to the west must be a vast island. Then began the long and treacherous task of passing the ships through the narrows, alternately assisted and hampered by the strong tidal streams. As they passed northwards they came to an Indian village on the western side of the Strait, at which the natives indicated their awareness of a European settlement at Nootka on the west coast of the Island; native runners were despatched over the mountain trails with the first friendly message of greeting from Vancouver to Quadra.

When the two ships were all but clear to the open sea *Discovery* ran aground and, as the tide fell, she heeled right over to starboard; at low tide she was in imminent danger of sliding sideways into deep water. Desperately shoring up the starboard side with top-masts and spars, the crew prevented the ship from turning com-pletely on her beam ends and with the rising tide she floated off safely. A sketch made by Zachary Mudge shows the vessel with an agonising list and her stern well nigh under water, while canoe loads of Indians look on in amazement. Only calm weather and the determination of the seamen saved the ship.

Vancouver did not wish to reach Nootka before *Daedalus* arrived bringing, so he hoped, a copy of the final agreement with the Spaniards, which he felt he would have to study before commenc-ing negotiations. It was pleasing therefore to fall in with the English fur-trader *Venus* and to hear from her that *Daedalus* was at Nootka, but the pleasure was momentary, for *Venus'* Captain went on to say that Lieutenant Hergest, the storeship's Captain, and Mr. Gooch the astronomer, who was coming to join the expedition, had been murdered by natives on Oahu in the Sandwich Islands. This was a bitter personal blow for Vancouver as Hergest was an old and valued shipmate; they had sailed together as midshipmen with Cook.

Quadra was a surveyor of some experience in Alaskan waters and a naval officer who knew a sailor's requirements; when *Dis-covery* and *Chatham* sailed into Nootka Sound Quadra more than lived up to the name of Friendly Cove,* where he had set his headquarters. Meat, vegetables and even hot rolls were sent off to the ship daily; entertainments, including dining off silver plate, were arranged ashore; Maquinna, the local Indian chief, was included in the social activities organised by Quadra, the genial host of this remote outpost.

Quadra added more hydrographic details of the west coast to Vancouver's chart of the great island, which they named the Island

---

* It is not clear who named Friendly Cove. Strange, a great admirer of Cook and himself an early voyager on the north-west coast in 1786, attributes the name to Cook but there is no further evidence of this.

of Quadra and Vancouver to mark the harmonious relations existing between them. When it came to diplomacy, although the two men remained on amicable terms, agreement escaped them. Vancouver had received in *Daedalus* a copy of a letter sent by the Spanish Foreign Minister to Quadra which ordered that land and buildings, formerly His Britannic Majesty's possessions, be returned to Vancouver. Quadra claimed that there never had been such buildings and that Meares' statements had been fabrications; he himself now quoted statements which he had collected from American and English trading ship captains to affirm this. He stated, however, in his most magnanimous manner, that he was prepared to deliver the Spanish buildings, by now very extensive, to Vancouver without prejudice to the legitimate right of Spain, whilst he would move his establishment to a new station in the Juan de Fuca Strait. This was not what Vancouver had been ordered to accept, and foreseeing the possibility of placing his country in an awkward position he refused the offer and despatched Zachary Mudge by fur-trading vessel to the Typa, the anchorage off Macao, with orders to make his way on to England in an East Indiaman to report the stalemate at Nootka.

With the onset of winter the English expedition sailed south towards the Spanish settlement at Monterey, whilst Quadra sailed there also to act once again as generous host.

Shortly before entering Juan de Fuca Strait on his way north Vancouver had encountered Captain Robert Gray of Boston in his trading vessel *Columbia* who said that he had recently entered a great river south of Juan de Fuca Strait which, owing to offshore breakers and poor visibility, Vancouver had missed on his way north. He was determined to find the rivermouth on the way south.

Both ships approached the line of breakers south of Cape Disappointment, *Chatham* with her shallower draught leading the way. The westerly wind enabled the vessels to overcome the strong ebbing tidal stream.

With the leadsmen calling depths at four fathoms no sign of a gap in the breakers could be discerned. At three fathoms *Discovery* was surrounded by breakers and reluctantly Vancouver hauled to seaward, assisted now by the ebb. At this moment a signal fluttered from *Chatham's* mast but the colour of the flags could not be made out in the gathering dusk.

It could have signified that Broughton had crossed the bar or that he was in dire trouble in the breakers, for he had forced his vessel on over the shallows, the white seas from the gloom around him surging constantly onboard, smashing boats and gear; but at dawn Vancouver saw to his joy through his long glass the little vessel safely anchored within.

Broughton sailed up the river in *Chatham* but, grounding, he decided to proceed by boat for a further week until he reached a point about a hundred miles from the entrance. Here he took possession of the country at Point Vancouver in His Britannic Majesty's name during a little ceremony at which he was assisted by a friendly old Indian chief: however, Gray, the American, had in fact entered the river first, and although he never penetrated far upstream, perhaps today's ownership of the lower Columbia River by the United States can be fairly attributed to the old Boston Captain, while we must admire the superb seamanship and courage of William Broughton.

During a pleasant sojourn in Mexico before sailing for the Sandwich Islands, Vancouver decided to send a second messenger to England, this time choosing Lieutenant Broughton, the command of the *Chatham* being taken over by Lieutenant Puget. Crossing Mexico and sailing from the east coast to England, Broughton was able to explain exactly the details of the impasse which had been reached, for he had been present at all Vancouver's meetings with Quadra.

Vancouver took with him from Mexico cattle for the Hawaiian chief Kamehameha who boarded the ships when they anchored in Kealakekua Bay. Kamehameha now had European advisers, Isaac Davis, sole survivor of a massacre by the natives of the crew of the schooner *Fair America*, and John Young, an English boatswain from the *Eleanora* whom Kamehameha had detained ashore. Unlike many European sailors who were attaching themselves to Polynesian chieftains at this time, these two men offered helpful and friendly advice to their master and to visiting ships.

Kamehameha was steadily making himself ruler of the whole

island chain and he wanted effective, active help. This Vancouver could not give but he tendered much advice, and encouragement, for already he saw the Sandwich Islands as a necessary stepping stone towards the Northwest coast.

Whilst surveying the islands Vancouver visited Oahu, the island where Honolulu stands today, for he had something on his mind: he wished to avenge the death of his old shipmate Hergest. There were a number of local stories, as to who had committed the murders. The local chief, Kahekili, claimed them to have been the action of a roving group of scoundrels, and some of these were brought aboard the English ships by the islanders. Having satisfied himself after a day-long enquiry that they were guilty Vancouver ordered them to be executed by their own chief in a canoe alongside.

Some of Vancouver's officers and men believed this action to be precipitate, and stories circulating later in the islands had it that these men were not the culprits. Whatever the truth may be, Vancouver's decision did in fact result in more circumspect treatment by the Hawaiians towards visiting English ships.

We see developing during Vancouver's voyage the now familiar pattern of the surveyor's year. The summer months were spent in the north, making the most of the better weather, whilst autumn saw the ship's annual return to the Sandwich Islands to lay up the vessels for refitting. With rigging renewed, decks caulked and hulls careened, survey work began again in the New Year, at first in the pleasant conditions in the islands; and with spring a move was made to the Northwest coast.

The spring of 1793 found the expedition again at Nootka, where Quadra had been replaced and the Spanish fortifications had been enlarged. Thus Vancouver stayed but three days before sailing to resume his survey at Restoration Cove. North of here a historic meeting was narrowly missed. On 20th July Alexander Mackenzie, an explorer for the North-West Fur Company, and first white man to cross the continent north of Mexico, came down the Bella Coola River and reached the sea at the head of the North Bentinck Arm near the *Discovery* boat party's halting place of a few days before. The Indians were talking of a visit by 'Macubah'.

The survey progressed up through the Prince of Wales Archipelago and southwards along the west coast of the Queen Charlotte Islands and, with the end of the year, via Monterey to Kealakekua Bay once more.

Here Kamehameha was more powerful throughout the islands and more helpful than ever. Vancouver and he became personal friends and, by a subterfuge, Vancouver arranged an unexpected meeting onboard *Discovery* between the Hawaiian chieftain and his estranged wife which resulted in a happy and enduring reconciliation.

Many islanders came on board, and even a man who was said to have inflicted the fatal stab wound upon Captain Cook was permitted to enjoy hospitality.

Vancouver's idea of cession of the Sandwich Islands to England reached fruition and was concluded between the naval commander and the native chief at an impressive ceremony onshore. But the cession of these islands, which had now been completely surveyed by Vancouver, was never ratified by the Government at home, for, by the time the expedition reached England, the country was embroiled in the Napoleonic wars and was in no mind to burden itself with new colonies. However, Kamehameha finally captured every island in the group, proclaiming himself King Kamehameha I, and for many years he gave special preference to English ships, whose commanders came to expect protection from him on their visits.

In March 1794 Vancouver's two ships went straight to Cook's River in Alaska, which was the second great hope, after Juan de Fuca Strait, for the discovery of the Northwest Passage. In bitter, freezing weather, Vancouver proved it to be but Cook's Inlet, terminating at Turnagain Arm, and then worked eastwards along the Alaskan coast.

Here the expedition fell in from time to time with great fleets of two-men skin canoes manned by Aleuts and directed in their hunting for sea otters by small parties of Russians, many of them working under Baranov, a merchant of great authority on the coast. Baranov and Vancouver are believed to have exchanged messages but never met.

During the first two seasons Vancouver himself had led many of the boat expeditions in the yawl, the cutter or the launch, being absent from the ship on one such occasion for twenty-three days; but in this third season his failing health and the bitter weather combined to prevent his leaving the ship although he made a valiant attempt. The younger officers found it more arduous than before, but at last the survey was progressed through the labyrinth of islands and coastal inlets until it joined up with the previous year's at Port Conclusion, and the great work was done. Here Vancouver gave a day's holiday and an extra allowance of grog. We can sense the 'end of season' feeling and can imagine the satisfaction with which Lieutenant Baker penned the name 'Port Conclusion' on the fair sheet.

At Nootka neither Quadra's successor nor Vancouver had received new instructions, so that negotiation still could not be resumed, but there was sad news that Quadra had died. Christmas was spent at sea on the way south to Valparaiso and the Magellan Strait. The men toasted the memory of Quadra and the health of Kamehameha, who had both done much for the well being of the crews; and they laughed and made fun of the fact that they had sailed from England on 1st April 1791, All Fools Day, on a search for the Northwest Passage that had proved to be illusory; they had no claim to the Government's £20,000 reward for its discovery.

Vancouver was said to have been a stern disciplinarian during this lengthy voyage, and he had even had a Midshipman flogged, although there is little doubt he deserved it. But his personality comes most clearly through to us over nearly two centuries in his relations with Quadra and Kamehameha: to them he was a very human friend. He was a bachelor all his life, perhaps a somewhat lonely man, and during the last two years of his great voyage he was an increasingly sick man. He died in 1798, his journals hardly completed, at the early age of forty-two.

In mid-October 1795 the expedition was home, almost unnoticed by an England at war. The ships had sailed 65,000 miles in four and a half years, whilst the boats' crews had covered 10,000 miles under oars in the course of the survey.

Vancouver had learnt other things than surveying from Captain

Cook. Only six men had been lost in *Discovery*, all from accidents inherent in such an adventure, and none in *Chatham*. Two outbreaks of scurvy had been overcome by attention to Cook's rules—embarking fresh provisions whenever and wherever possible, making sure the men had warm and dry clothing, ventilating and fumigating below decks, airing bedding on deck in fine weather, and employing the men in a relaxed three-watch system all contributed to the well being of Cook's and Vancouver's people. It was unfortunate that neither of these explorers appears to have been aware of the importance of lemon juice in combating scurvy, although the Naval Surgeon James Lind had been advocating its use since 1753. As the physician at Haslar Hospital Lind persuaded the Admiralty to issue lemon juice to the fleet in 1795. Meanwhile Cook and Vancouver had issued malt wort, sauerkraut and portable soup in the belief they had antiscorbutic properties. None of these, however, contain Vitamin C, which we now know is the vitamin which prevents scurvy.

CHAPTER FOUR

Broughton in the Northwest Pacific

Back in England, three years before Vancouver's return, Broughton had been able to relate the details of the stalemate at Nootka and was sent to Madrid to assist personally in the negotiations which led eventually to a final Anglo-Spanish agreement in the Nootka affair. It was not until early in 1795, and after Vancouver had left the Pacific, that Lieutenant Pearce of the Marines, who had sailed north from Monterey with the Spaniards, formally accepted the fortifications and hoisted the British flag at Friendly Cove. It may be added that almost at once the name of Nootka began to fade from the public eye until today only a handful of Englishmen could point to the place upon the map; and even on Vancouver Island, as the Island of Quadra and Vancouver has now become, few can tell one how to travel the road to the remote Indian fishing community at Friendly Cove, where the lofty spruce and firs still crowd down to the shore close to the wooden habitations, little different in their construction from those huts erected by Meares that once caused a national mobilisation in England and resulted in the survey of the western seaboard of Canada.

Cook, Vancouver and Quadra are, however, not forgotten at Friendly Cove, for in recent years the Spanish Government donated to the little Catholic Church in the Indian Village two glass windows, one depicting Captain Cook coming ashore in Nootka Sound and the other, Quadra welcoming Vancouver.

Captain William Bligh's first attempt to carry young breadfruit trees from Tahiti to the West Indies in H.M.S. *Bounty* in order that a new food might be grown for the slaves on English-owned plantations is too well known for further comment here. That he returned again to Tahiti (after being honourably acquitted by court martial of the loss of the *Bounty*), with the ships *Providence* and *Assistant*, and that he successfully carried 680 breadfruit plants half way across the world to Jamaica, is not so well known. For this achievement, when he returned home in 1793, he received the Gold Medal of the Society for the Encouragement of the Arts, Manufactures & Commerce. His ship, *Providence*, had been bought by the Government for this venture whilst still on the stocks, building for the West Indies trade. She was now a sloop of war of 400 tons, carrying a crew of over 100 men, and being sheathed in copper she was well suited for voyages of exploration. Thus, after returning with Bligh, she was selected as the vessel to be sent to the Pacific to take over the task of survey from Vancouver, and who better to send in command than Broughton and Zachary Mudge as First Lieutenant, both of whom had come home as official messengers from the Pacific expedition and were surveyors taught by Vancouver.

Commissioned in the Thames in 1793 with a ship's company consisting, in the Captain's words, of 'young men, who were universally sober, attentive and well-behaved', *Providence* experienced a number of misfortunes. First of all she ran ashore on the Brake Bank on her way through the Downs and, after docking at Portsmouth, parted her bower cable in Plymouth Sound and damaged herself in collision with a transport; so it was not until 15th February 1795, that she finally sailed. The war with France was now in its second year, and *Providence* joined a convoy of 400 ships which had been waiting at Plymouth since mid-October for northerly winds to start the voyage.

Making the usual call at the Canaries for wine and provisions, Broughton sailed on to Rio de Janeiro where he stayed to overhaul the rigging and caulk the decks. Broughton was in company with Captain John Hunter in H.M.S. *Reliance*, and a convoy of ships bound for Port Jackson, where Hunter was to become Governor of New South Wales. Hunter was no stranger to Port Jackson or to the arts of surveying, which latter he had pursued for many years as will be seen in a subsequent chapter. As the Portuguese were being very difficult there was no shore leave, and Broughton spent much time aboard *Reliance* with Hunter, from whom, there can be little doubt, the young commander learnt a great deal more about navigation and surveying.

The easterly route was next taken around the Cape of Good Hope for Port Jackson where *Providence* eventually moored in Sydney Cove for the usual caulking and overhaul of rigging, and a welcome daily collection of vegetables from Garden Island. Tents were set up on Cattle Point for the vital task of rating the chronometers. Then on to Matavai Bay in Tahiti, where, in warping into a safe anchorage, the *Bounty's* anchor was swept up from where it had lain since the mutineers cut their cable on setting out for their final voyage to Pitcairn six years before. As always, the Tahitians were helpful in every way and when he sailed Broughton fired a four-gun salute in their honour, which delighted the gay thronging crowds in the canoes cutting through the water on both sides of the ship. Everyone on board was fit and happy after their stay in the island; only Mr. Crosley, the astronomer, had been disappointed with the visit to Tahiti, for he had been unable to make satisfactory celestial observations on Point Venus because the beating of the surf on the reef near his tent disturbed the quicksilver forming his artificial horizon.

On to Kealakekua Bay, another familiar call in those days for any Royal Navy ship on a voyage of exploration. Here Mr. Crosley was happier, for he was permitted to erect his tents near a morai, which, being tabooed ground, was avoided by all but his personal assistants, and here he observed, on 20th January 1796, ideal equal-altitude sights.

Four timepieces were carried on the voyage and were landed here to obtain longitude. On the 20th January Number 1 made the longitude of Kealakekua Bay 203° 46′ 45″ which differed only by 11′ (about eight miles) from the longitude as obtained by Lieutenant King and Mr. Bayly during Cook's third voyage. This was before the timepiece had been rated and Broughton considered it excellent that his Number 1 timepiece showed an error of only 11′ in 108 days since its rate of going was established at Port Jackson. By the end of January enough observations had been made to obtain a new rate of 6.594″ per day for Number 1 and the longitude by the four timekeepers was now set out thus:

Number 1	203° 47′ 4″
Pocket 2	203° 48′ 19″
Box A, 56	199° 36′ 42″
Box E, 48	204° 44′ 36″
Longitude by King and Bayly . . .	203° 57′ 45″*

Broughton remarked in his journal that Arnold's box timepiece 'keeps so uncertain a rate as to render it useless'. We can guess that this did not earn him any kind words from the Hydrographer when he read it, knowing as we do his preference for Arnold over Earnshaw. We have to assume that Box A, 56, referred to Arnold's watch and Box E, 48, to Earnshaw's watch.

The latitude as observed by Mr. Crosley, being the mean of 6 meridian altitudes of the Sun, was 19° 28′ 9″, and a mean for longitude of 13 observed distances of Aldebaran west of the Moon and computed from Lunar Tables comes to 203° 27′ 30″.

These observations have been set out in some detail for here we see a typical example of the continual building up of accuracy of position which successive surveyors undertook as they revisited the now familiar observation spots at such places as Port Jackson, Matavai Bay (Point Venus), Kealakekua Bay and Nootka. The modern determination of Kealakekua Bay is Lat. 19° 29′ 04″ N. Long. 155° 56′ 09.5″ W. (204° 03′ 50.5″).

Kamehameha was again away on his battles of subjugation, but John Young, now an old friend of the English, who had by this time been six years with his chief, was here, there and everywhere offering assistance with canoes, and supplies of meat, fish and vegetables. The ship's company were permitted shore leave and there they heard many fine things said of Vancouver by the islanders, who showed the cattle he had given them, living happily

* Subsequent research shows that No. 1 and Pocket 2 were both by Earnshaw, A, 56 by Arnold and that the fourth chronometer was also by Earnshaw, though its number should be 248, as given elsewhere in Broughton's account, and not 48.

under a ten-year taboo. Broughton added a pair of goats to those already left by *Discovery*, also geese and ducks, whilst Zachary Mudge generously spared the natives his pigeons.

By the Spring of 1796 *Providence* was at Friendly Cove, now reverted to an Indian village under Maquinna who brought on-board letters left for Broughton by Vancouver dated 1795. A troublesome leak had developed on the last passage so that it was necessary at Nootka to heave down the ship on her beam ends and it was fortunate that a fur trading brig *Lady Washington* offered assistance. The brig secured alongside and all perishable stores were transferred to her and the ship cleared of coal and shingle ballast. The capstan was transferred to the brig and used to haul over *Providence* until her port side was clear of the water almost to her keel. Fourteen feet of the false keel were found to have been carried away, and where a bolt should have held it to the hull, only a bolt hole remained, and this had caused the leak. The carpenter reckoned that no bolt had ever been driven through the hole, which had been overlooked by the builders. Only the copper sheathing covering the bolt hole, now cracked, had prevented the inflow of water. A new bolt was driven and the ship righted after three hours at the four handpumps which were required to clear the water that had flowed in through the upper works whilst the ship lay over on careen. Then the vessel had to be cleaned throughout and dried with fires before reloading commenced.

This episode, regarded by Broughton as but a minor inconven-ience, has been related in some detail to illustrate the tremendous efforts required of seamen in those days and the ingenuity that had to be exercised by officers and men on detached service. To the few modern seamen, among whom I number myself, who have had to discharge by hand into craft alongside without outside assistance the entire stores of a survey vessel in order to lighten her and refloat her after grounding, the magnitude of the task just described is fully apparent. It is not difficult to hear, even across the long years, the epithets used by the seamen to describe the unknown shipwright of Thameside who overlooked that bolt hold-ing the false keel.

Vancouver's letters told Broughton that he had completed the work on the Northwest coast and in order to pick up the threads of the task facing him it was now necessary to sail south to Monterey, where from the now surly Spaniards he gathered that Vancouver had sailed southwards eighteen months before, his men healthy and his ships in good repair. Broughton's instructions were to survey the southern portion of the west coast of South America, should it not have been completed by Vancouver. In view of the Spanish report Broughton had to assume that this work would have now been completed by *Discovery* and *Chatham* and it was obvious that the lateness of his arrival in the Pacific had prevented him from meeting Vancouver. Proceedings after this had been left by his instructions to his own discretion 'to be carried out in such a manner as might be deemed most eligible for the improvement of geography and navigation'.

Broughton had been expecting to meet Quadra at Monterey but he had died two years earlier in 1794. Broughton had been instructed to present two timepieces together with some nautical instruments to Quadra but in presenting Pocket Watch No. 2 and Box A, 56, to the sullen Spanish Governor Broughton records that he most sincerely regretted the loss of Quadra and was 'much hurt to deliver to his executor what I hoped to have done to him in person'.

The type of officers who were sent on surveying voyages at this time interested themselves in the exploration of the globe, and when ashore were likely to read the many current books of voyages in vogue at the time and would follow the reports of expeditions as they appeared in *The Gentleman's Magazine*, the *London Magazine* and the *Scots Magazine*, all of which made a feature of such items. It is not therefore surprising, on reflection, to note that at this point of indecision as to the future employment of the ship the Captain ordered the officers each to set down in writing his own proposals, which happily coincided much with his own—a survey of the coast of Asia from Sakhalin, 52° N., to the Nanking River in 30° N., the only blank area remaining in the North Pacific.

It took *Providence* most of the summer to cross the Pacific and after a terrible storm, which carried away nearly every sail, the coast of Japan was sighted on 12th September 1796. This land was the northern island of the group, now known as Hokkaido, but then as Jeso, so named by Dutch explorers over 100 years earlier to describe the natives—'the hairy ones': and hairy they were when Broughton encountered them when coming to anchor in what he named Volcano Bay. Those who boarded the ship were men of short stature with thick beards, and wherever their bodies were exposed they were seen to be covered with thick black hair. They were friendly but were frequently driven off by a higher class of people whom Broughton took to be the true Japanese; they too were well-disposed but discouraged the Englishmen from landing, being only too anxious to furnish the vessel's wants and see her depart. They brought off a Russian chart and one of their own making, showing the islands, which they exchanged with Broughton for a copy of Cook's general chart of the Pacific.

After the usual observations had been made ashore for position, chronometer rates and magnetic variation, to the obvious displeasure of the Japanese, the running survey was progressed northeastwards along the coast of Jeso and into the Kurile chain where, in 47½° North, a ruined trading post was visited. Only a few crosses marking graves and the wearing of Russian boots by the natives testified to the former Russian occupation.

The weather had been generally foul and the night after leaving this place Broughton fell during the height of the gale and broke his arm. Dispirited, he turned southwards encountering continuous gales of great ferocity which obliged *Providence* to keep well off-shore, and it was not till the first week in November that the weather permitted closing the coast, the southeast point of Nippon (modern Honshu) being eventually sighted. As they came close inshore the crew exchanged words with many fishing craft, and passing the entrance to what is now called Tokio Bay they saw the unforgettable sight of Fujiyama, her snow-capped peak like a vast sugar-loaf rising above the surrounding land.

After coasting along the southern shores of Nippon *Providence* worked herself along the southern side of the island chain between Japan and Taiwan, and across to Macao, where she cast anchor in the Typa, the anchorage off that port occupied by merchant men waiting to navigate up the Canton River. There were always

East India Company ships here, British men of war and fur trading vessels from the Northwest coast. The people of Macao had a thriving business supplying vessels in the Typa, and ashore the Commander was generously received by the Portuguese Governor.

It was early December before Broughton's arm had healed sufficiently for him to get about ashore. During the recent long nights and days at sea in thick and blustery weather he had pondered on the risks he was taking in a single vessel in uncharted waters. If *Providence* ran aground there would be no ship to stand by. Cook had learnt this lesson on his first voyage when aground in *Endeavour* on the Barrier Reef and ever since it had been Admiralty policy to send two ships in company on voyages of discovery. Perhaps the pressure of wartime needs had resulted in *Providence* sailing alone. However, Broughton was now resolved to find a tender before he sailed again and his wanderings ashore in Macao eventually led him to Lark's Bay. Here lay a robust little 87-ton schooner, *Prince William Henry*, her owner proudly claiming that it was common knowledge that she had made the record passage from China to the Sandwich Islands. Broughton bought her for £1,500.

With charts of the Japanese coast drawn, and the winter over, *Providence* refitted, and the newly acquired schooner fitted out, Broughton set off in April 1797 full of confidence, with an extensive programme ahead of him. He coasted the east side of Taiwan and then planned to run along the northern side of the island chain to Japan so that he might fix the coastlines he had not observed on the southern passage at the end of the previous year.

On the evening of 17th May *Providence* was on a northeasterly course, with the wind on the port side, making four-and-a-half knots. Before dusk the mate of the watch climbed to the masthead and, although he could see an island to the southeast, all was clear to the north and east. Broughton decided to stand on till 8.00 p.m., and then to tack to windward till daylight.

At 7.30 p.m. white breaking water was sighted ahead by the look-outs who called to Lieutenant Vashon, the Officer of the Watch. But before any action was taken the ship was aground, and Broughton, feeling the shock, hurried on deck. Here he found the helm aweather and the sails still full. Quickly the men were on deck and the sails braced aback. At first she lay pretty steady and made little water, but the wind from the northwest increased and *Providence*, on a dead lee shore, began to pound on the coral reef on which she lay to such an extent that any attempt to haul her off by the schooner, which had now anchored to windward, would have caused the vessel to sink in the deeper water, for holes in the hull had now caused the sea to rise within her to the orlop deck.

With the rising moon the wind increased and the crew could see the curling white breakers bearing down upon the vessel. There was nothing to be done but to transfer officers and men by boats to the schooner, which took from 10.30 p.m. till midnight. The schooner had both anchors down in foul ground bordering the reef and it was an anxious time weighing them. Hardly was one anchor home than the other cable parted. A groan of relief went up from the overcrowded decks of the tiny vessel as the sails filled and she drew clear into deep water.

At dawn the grey seas were breaking over Broughton's dear *Providence* and the master went in the longboat to her lee side to collect cordage, sails, and even more vital, the kedge anchor, for the schooner had but one left.

The island to the south Broughton calls Typinsan (modern Miyako Shima) and towards it they now made their way, navigating in through extensive shoals to be happily received by the natives. Wrecks were obviously no novelty to the islanders of Typinsan: ships' timbers were incorporated in their houses and several skulls lay in caverns along the shoreline.

When the time came to part, Broughton as a survivor was hard put to it to reward the islanders for all the food and care they had provided; he gave them a drawing of *Providence*, a telescope, and the longboat fully rigged. Two local boats piloted the schooner through the reefs and she set out on her tedious voyage to the Canton River; with rainy weather and 112 men onboard, there was a sodden mass of humanity above and below decks.

Arriving at the Boca Tigris Broughton was happy to find thirteen large East Indiamen anchored in the Canton River and to his surprise there was Captain Hayward in command of H.M.S. *Swift* preparing to sail for England. He had been a Midshipman in *Bounty*, loyal to Bligh with whom he had been cast away on the famous boat voyage. He had been selected to sail with Captain Edwards in *Pandora* in the search for the mutineers whom he would recognise. Now he offered to carry home forty of Broughton's overcrowded crew. The story has a tragic ending for Captain Hayward, survivor of Bligh's boat voyage and of the wreck of the *Pandora*, lost his ship with all hands in a tropical storm on the voyage to England.

Many would have been daunted by the loss of their ship and returned to England, but zeal had, since Cook's days, been part of the make-up of every officer employed on survey work. Broughton selected thirty-five men for the schooner, and sent the remainder who did not join *Swift* to the East Indiamen for passage home. He was determined to continue his discoveries even in the small schooner which he now stowed with provisions at the Typa, filling every hole and corner, that he and his crew might live at sea for five months. Again he set out, this time coasting the west of Taiwan, north of Typinsan, along the south and east coasts of Nippon, arriving once more at Endesmo Harbour in Volcano Bay, at the southern end of Jeso.

The Japanese came as before to keep the lower orders away, and they were surprised to find Broughton in such a small vessel and wondered what had become of *Providence*. They were again courteous, but as on the previous occasion keen to see him move on. From one of them Broughton obtained another, better, map of the complete coastline of the Japanese islands, but with strong injunctions that he should not disclose from whom it had been procured. This he used to outline in yellow hairline on his charts the western coasts of Japan which he had no time to explore.

Passing through the straits which separated Nippon from Jeso the schooner sailed north into the Gulf of Tartary, the whole eastern shoreline of which Broughton sailed along and delineated by running survey. He found the western entrance to what was later called La Perouse Strait between Jeso and Sakhalin and, like La Perouse, when he reached 52° North he encountered extensive shallows which led him to believe that no navigable channel existed through the Straits of Tartary, despite the efforts of Mr. Chapman, the master, searching ahead in the boat with lead and line.

Turning south Broughton mapped almost the entire east coast of Asia down to Quelpart Island off the south point of Korea and made a chart of the harbour at Chusan. This was a magnificent achievement in so small a vessel as an 87-ton schooner.

Broughton set off for home in November 1797 by way of the Straits of Malacca and Trincomalee where the schooner was paid off on 28th May 1798. But his charts had gone before him, taken by Zachary Mudge who had sailed from the Typa in an East Indiaman, for scribbled in pencil on the original drafts, beautifully drawn by Lieutenant Vashon, is the notation 'Rec. May 11th, 1798'. Poor Vashon was 'discharged per sentence of court martial' only five days before the schooner paid off at Trincomalee, for, had he put his helm alee as soon as the breakers were reported that night off Typinsan, Broughton believed *Providence* would have run clear—her loss had to be accounted for.

CHAPTER FIVE

Terra Australis

We have seen how Commander Broughton, outward bound for the North Pacific in his ship *Providence*, fell in with Captain John Hunter in *Reliance* when the latter was on his way out to New South Wales to take over as Governor from Captain Arthur Phillip, R.N. in 1795. To the Master's Mate in *Reliance*, the sight of his old ship *Providence* brought a flood of memories and a renewed feeling of the excitement he had experienced at the age of eighteen when he had sailed in her through the intricate reefs and amid the racing currents of Torres Strait.

Matthew Flinders had accompanied Captain Bligh on his second and successful breadfruit voyage from Tahiti to the Caribbean. He had at that time been placed in charge of the precious time-keepers, and had received instruction in navigation and chart drawing as well as tongue lashings from his Captain, who was then making his second passage of the infamous straits.

In fact it was Flinders' enthusiasm for exploring and chart making which he had acquired in *Providence* that was the direct cause of his present appointment. He had contrived to get onboard *Reliance*, for he knew that once on the coast of New South Wales he would have all the exploring even his enquiring mind desired.

His Captain, John Hunter, was a surveyor of repute. He had commanded *Sirius* in 1787, when a fleet had taken the first ship-loads of convicts to New South Wales; and he had, during the establishment of the colony, surveyed Port Jackson, finally chosen for the first settlement, as well as Botany and Broken Bays, the

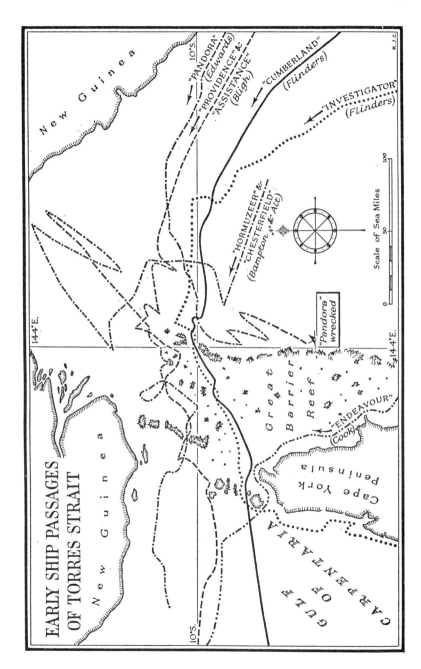

EARLY SHIP PASSAGES
OF TORRES STRAIT

alternative sites. He had an adventurous time off the coast of New South Wales, losing his ship at Norfolk Island, where he had been then marooned for a year. And now, at his own request, he was again on his way out to Port Jackson this time as Governor, for he was an enthusiast for the new colony.

With Flinders in *Reliance* was his younger brother Samuel. The ship's surgeon George Bass was, like Flinders, fascinated by exploration.

Reliance reached Port Jackson in September 1795 and before we follow Flinders and Bass on their exploring voyages along the coasts of New South Wales it will be well to review the state of European knowledge of the emerging continent which came to be known as Australia.

A glance at *The World Sailing Ship Routes*, which is still published by the Hydrographic Office as Admiralty Chart No. 5308 shows that ships sailing via the Cape of Good Hope to the Indies ran along the latitude of 40° South until their longitude was deemed sufficiently great for them to turn northwards for Sumatra or Java. Hence in the days before the timekeeper it was not unlikely that vessels carried on too far to the east and thus sighted the barren western shores of the continent on their northward run. Probably Dirk Hartog was the first Dutchman to do so when sailing that passage in his vessel *Eendracht* in 1616. Others fell in with the western shores during that century, including Dampier, the English sailor who voyaged with the buccaneers, but whose early descriptions of Western Australia reached the highest standards of navigational reporting, and Vlamingh, another Dutchman, both of whom had laid down parts of the coastline.

Little exploration was achieved on the western coast in the next hundred years and Van Keulen's chart, republished by Dalrymple at the end of the eighteenth century, relied almost entirely for its material on these earlier navigators.

During the seventeenth century, a number of vessels of the Dutch East India Company were sent from Batavia (Jakarta) to explore the north coast of Australia, passing along the south coast of New Guinea and circling southwards to touch upon the Arnhem Land of the emerging continent; or probably, in the case of

Tasman, southwards around the shores of the Gulf of Carpentaria. But the Dutch East India Company did not easily give away its secrets and it was by no means certain in England in 1795 whether Carpentaria was indeed a great gulf or the entrance to a wide strait.

In 1627 the Dutch ship *Gulden Zeepaard*, outward bound along latitude 40° South, overran even more than was usual and, heading north, encountered the southern coast of the continent east of Cape Leeuwin, which she then explored for a thousand miles, to the eastern side of the Great Bight. As the vessel was carrying a wealthy merchant named Pieter Nuyts, the land was named after him.

Over 150 years elapsed before further exploration here took place when Vancouver, on his way to the North Pacific in 1791, closed the coast at the southwest point of land and named it Cape Chatham, after his tender, under Broughton's command. Discovering an anchorage in spacious King George Sound, he broke off his survey at Termination Island, six degrees further eastward, in order to push on to far distant Nootka.

This part of the coast, so long unvisited, now received its full share of exploratory activity for, in the very next year, the French Rear Admiral d'Entrecasteaux, with his expedition in the ships *la Recherche* and *l'Espérance*, in search of La Perouse, who was missing without trace since 1788, made the coast near Cape Chatham. With M. Beautemps-Beaupré, the geographical engineer, laying down the survey, the expedition worked along the coast till they reached the barren waterless shores of the Great Bight, when D'Entrecasteaux, too, hastened on to his main task in the Pacific.

The continent now seen to be contained by the coastlines already described, and largely first discovered by the Dutch was appropriately known as 'New Holland', but it was without a clearly defined eastern limit. The whole of the eastern coast from Point Hicks to Cape York had been discovered and laid down by Captain Cook during his first incomparable voyage in *Endeavour*, and to the hinterland he had given the name of New South Wales. Whether this was part of the great continent of New Holland or was separated from it by an ocean channel running southwards from the Gulf of Carpentaria was not yet clear. What Cook had clearly established was that a strait encumbered with islands and reefs divided the north tip of his New South Wales from New Guinea. Since he had passed through Torres Strait in 1770 a small number of adventurous spirits had followed. It had always been a hazardous business, for narrow waters, rapid currents, countless reefs, hostile natives and waterless shorelines combined to make it a formidable, sometimes deadly, passage. It was Bligh's oft-repeated threats of the hardships to be endured when *Bounty* came to follow Cook's tracks through Endeavour Straits (between Cape York and Thursday Island) that did much to bring Fletcher Christian to his fateful decision.

Bligh himself made the passage twice, once in an open boat as a castaway, and later in *Providence*. This second passage took Bligh nineteen days through the reefs from 'Bligh's Entrance' in the Pacific to 'Bligh's Farewell' in the Indian Ocean. 'Perhaps no space of 3½° in length presents more dangers than Torres Straits,' wrote Flinders who had taken daily part in Bligh's navigation.

Both Bligh's passages of the Strait were remarkable for the careful views, precise notes and clearly drawn tracks, which, considering especially the distress he and his men were suffering during the first voyage, establish him in the very forefront of surveyors of his time.

The only other ship masters known to have accomplished the passage of Torres Strait prior to 1795 were William Bampton and Matthew Alt in their vessels *Hormuzeer* and *Chesterfield* who, sailing together from Norfolk Island in 1793, decided to attempt the passage by a northerly route. They took seventy-two days, and encountered a great deal of trouble with the natives, losing the mate of the *Chesterfield* and a boat's crew. This passage, the first by a merchantman, gave little encouragement to others to follow. Instead, vessels bound homeward from the new colony at Port Jackson continued to use the tedious route northabout New Guinea, for it was necessary, if fair winds were to be carried to the Cape, to take a departure into the Indian Ocean from the vicinity of Timor or Java.

Off the other, southern extreme of Cook's New South Wales

lay Van Diemen's Land, discovered and named after the Governor General of the Dutch East Indies by Abel Tasman in 1642 with his vessels *Heemskerck* and *Zeehaen*. During the course of that same voyage he made the first recorded European visit to the shores of 'Nieuw Zeeland', as he so named it, and made the first unhappy contact with the Maoris, who killed some of his people in a boat in what Tasman called Murderers Bay (now Golden Bay). The next European to visit Van Diemen's Land was the Frenchman Marion du Fresne in search of the southern continent in 1772, who also later had a tragic encounter with the Maoris. The following year, yet another sufferer at the hands of the warlike natives of New Zealand, Captain Tobias Furneaux in *Adventure*, who had parted company from Cook in *Resolution* on the second voyage, discovered Adventure Bay, a well sheltered anchorage in the south of Van Diemen's Land. This bay had a plentiful supply of wood and water and served as a reliable port of call for subsequent exploring expeditions.

From here Furneaux sailed northwards to determine whether Van Diemen's Land was joined to New South Wales. This task was performed inadequately and Furneaux neither proved nor disproved the existence of a strait between the two.

Arriving in *Reliance* at Port Jackson in September 1795, Flinders and Bass had plenty of scope for their exploring enthusiasm, whenever they could be spared from official duties in their ship. To examine the coast of New South Wales to the north and south from Port Jackson, and further to extend Furneaux's exploration between Van Diemen's Land and New South Wales were obvious first tasks, but a vessel to make the voyages was not easily forthcoming. Strangely, the two young men did not at first receive encouragement from the new Governor who, we must assume, was too busily engaged in taking over his duties to give his attention to exploration: they has to use a small boat, about eight feet in length, which Bass had brought out from England in *Reliance*. They named her *Tom Thumb*. To assist them they engaged a young lad also anxious for adventure.

In this small craft these three made two voyages southward along the coast; they had many adventures at sea, as they were bound to have in such a minute boat, and ashore much tact was required in handling the natives, which included Flinders giving a number of them a haircut to distract them from perceiving that his firearms were still useless as a result of a recent swamping of the boat.

By 1797 the two adventurers, by their efforts, had impressed themselves on the authorities at Port Jackson and the Governor provided Bass with a whaleboat and a crew of six volunteer seamen for a further voyage south and west. Provisioned for only six weeks, Bass returned eleven weeks later having augmented his rations from land and sea. He had minutely examined the coastline 300 miles southward past Point Hicks, Cook's furthest south sighting, and thence 300 miles westward until he discovered the spacious haven of Westernport. The heavy swell and the strength of the tidal streams led him to believe that he was in a strait separating the mainland from Van Diemen's Land.

Meanwhile Flinders had received permission from the Governor to sail in the schooner *Francis* with Captain Hamilton who was returning his wrecked ship the *Sydney Cove* on Preservation Island, one of the Furneaux group, which lay in the eastern approaches to Bass' supposed strait. Whilst the crew were recovering what they could of the wrecked cargo, Flinders made a five-day boat trip through the islands.

A party had stood by the wreck for six months, housed in tents and feeding on the short-tailed shearwaters which they took from their burrows at night and ate after smoke drying—described by Flinders as 'passable' food. These early European consumers of the 'mutton bird' apparently ate the grown birds, whilst the modern 'mutton bird' is the young squab—'passable' I believe, however, to be a flattering description of this southern delicacy, much eaten by both Maori and Pakeha in New Zealand today.

After a further spell of duty in *Reliance* for a voyage to Norfolk Island, Flinders got the ear of Governor Hunter again, and this time he and Bass convinced him of the desirability of a well planned voyage which should penetrate westwards through the group of Furneaux's Islands and the supposed strait, returning to Port Jackson southabout Van Diemen's Land. The colonial sloop *Norfolk* was provided with a crew of eight volunteers for this voyage which was a complete success, the vessel returning to Port Jackson on 11th January, 1799, only eleven days after the elapse of the twelve-week absence which had been planned. The two explorers had found and surveyed an extensive river harbour on the north coast of Van Diemen's Land, rounded the islands lying off Cape Grim, the northwest point, and returned as envisaged around the southern extremity, including an exploration of the Derwent River where Hobart stands today. Governor Hunter named the northern port after the newly appointed Hydrographer, Dalrymple, the strait after Bass, whose conjecture on his earlier voyage had now been fully vindicated, and approved the name of 'Hunter's Isles' off Cape Grim.

Bass then returned to England and Flinders alone in *Norfolk* made the last of these excursions from Port Jackson, this time to the north where he explored as far as Sandy Cape and surveyed Hervey's Bay which lies behind it.

Disappointingly no sizeable river had been found between 24° and 39° S. for such a discovery would have hastened the opening up of the interior of the country.

In 1800 *Reliance* arrived home in England and the discoveries of Flinders and Bass were soon published. Thus at the end of the century the sketchy picture of a continent had been built up in large measure by the Dutch and the English; likely to be one whole, yet it was still possible that a great passage of the sea divided it in half. The picture had become clearer in the southeastern corner of the continent as exploring voyages crept outwards from the only European settlement yet established.

Flinders was now through with trifling voyages from Port Jackson, and wanted nothing less than a ship and a crew for the circumnavigation of *Terra Australis*. He took his plans to Sir Joseph Banks, the recognised enthusiast for any such ventures, who in turn put pressure in the right quarter. Earl Spencer, the First Lord Commissioner of the Admiralty, was impressed and royal sanction for the voyage was obtained. Flinders was to be in command, and was shortly promoted to the rank of Commander. On his promotion Sir Joseph Banks wrote as follows (19th February 1801): 'I think you should now ask for Leave to come to Town to overlook the provision of instruments that will be necessary for your purpose. I wish to see you before I make any application as I do not think you ought to Follow the Precedent of Capt. Vancouver who went without an astronomer.'

The ship chosen was the *Xenophon*, renamed *Investigator* for the voyage. She was a north-country-built ship such as Cook would have chosen, and newly coppered. She was ordered to fit out at Sheerness Dockyard, a fortunate choice in that Mr. Whidbey, who had sailed as one of Vancouver's officers, was the Master Attendant there and knew exactly what was required of a ship sent on survey work; he gave much advice on stores and equipment.

The crew were chosen from young volunteers and Flinders was extremely pleased with them.

Astronomical and surveying instruments were supplied in plenty, as were articles for barter with the natives such as cloth, mirrors, axes and knives, now standard issue for exploring vessels. Most of the known books of South Sea Voyages were supplied and Joseph Banks presented the *Encyclopaedia Britannica*.

The East India Company showed their interest by presenting £600 to the Captain, officers and scientists 'for their tables'. Banks advised how this should be apportioned.

Mungo Park, the African traveller, was first chosen as naturalist, but Banks finally appointed Robert Brown, a young Scotsman, a graduate of Marischal College, Aberdeen, who made a great success of the voyage. He was assisted by an Austrian, Ferdinand Bauer, as botanical draughtsman. 'It is fortunate for science that two men of such assiduity and abilities have been selected; their application is beyond what I have been accustomed to see,' wrote Flinders to Banks, who was consolidating the tradition that hand-picked men of science should accompany every surveying expedition.

It was planned to bring back a great many plants from the voyage and a gardener, Peter Good, was also appointed and took with him a portable greenhouse for erection on the poop.

John Crosley, the astronomer who had sailed with Broughton, was appointed but left the *Investigator* at the Cape owing to illness; from then on Flinders was assisted by his youngest brother Samuel with the astronomical work, a somewhat unfortunate arrangement as will be seen.

Westall, a competent landscape painter, and John Allen, a miner sent to collect geological specimens and of whom we hear little, completed the civilian team.

Fowler, a former First Lieutenant of *Xenophon*, was appointed to these duties in the newly-named ship, Flinders' brother was second Lieutenant and John Franklin was one of the Midshipmen; all hailed from Lincolnshire.

In 1800 the French Republic had applied for and received from the First Lord of the Admiralty a passport for two ships of discovery to visit the South Seas; this meant that, war or peace, Royal Navy ships would not molest such vessels. Now, a year later, a French passport was requested for Flinders and his *Investigator* and, knowing that the French exploring ships were probably well on their way to *Terra Australis*, Flinders was desperate to be off. But now occurred embarrassing domestic and navigational troubles.

Flinders had married Ann Chappell, a Lincolnshire girl, in April 1801 and had planned to take her with him in *Investigator* to Port Jackson where she could set up house while he explored the continent. Banks had not been overjoyed on hearing the news of this arrangement as he felt that in some way it would detract from Flinders' dedication to his task, nor were Their Lordships pleased, for it appears to have overstepped regulations recently introduced, and on an inspection of the ship they were nettled to find Mrs. Flinders sitting quietly in the Captain's cabin 'without her bonnet'. Advice from Banks, who was in close touch with the Admiralty, resulted in Flinders writing to him as follows: '. . . and I foresee that, although I should in the case of Mrs. Flinders' going to Port Jackson have been more particularly cautious of my stay there, yet Their Lordships will conclude naturally enough that her presence would tend to increase the number of and to lengthen my visits. I am therefore afraid to risk Their Lordships' ill opinion and Mrs. Flinders will return to her friends immediately our sailing orders arrive.' Modern surveying wives will see in these words an attitude they may feel has been carried into the present day.

At the end of 1801, *Investigator* sailed from Sheerness only to run on the 'Roar', a sandbank northeast of Dungeness unmarked on the chart supplied to Flinders by the Admiralty. Flinders got his ship off without damage and many a man would have said nothing, but fearing lest another vessel suffer if the shoal was not charted, he reported the matter only to receive adverse criticism from Their Lordships, with whom the domestic scene they had witnessed in the captain's cabin a few weeks before still rankled.

Investigator was again delayed, awaiting instructions at Spithead, but this enabled Flinders to enrol a valuable man as Master. John Thistle had first sailed with Bass as a volunteer from *Reliance* in the whaleboat to Westernport: later Thistle had accompanied Flinders on both voyages in *Norfolk*. He had been promoted from before the mast to be Midshipman and then Master. Thistle had arrived in England only three weeks earlier after six years away, but he reported to Flinders at once as ready to sail. One day while waiting to come off to the ship from the Hard at Portsmouth, Thistle and the captain's boat's crew visited a fortune teller who, after informing them of the obvious, that they were to go on a long voyage, stated that Thistle would be lost at sea and that the others would be later shipwrecked.

On 17th July, the instructions and the French passport arrived and the following day *Investigator* was away. Broadly, the instructions, which were signed by Their Lordships with an appendix on wind and weather by the Hydrographer, directed Flinders to proceed to New Holland to make a complete examination and survey of the whole coastline. He must first close the south coast in the vicinity of King George Sound, making it a harbour for refreshment, and then sail eastwards along the coast to Bass Strait. He must search for and examine any opening likely to lead to an inland sea or strait.

When necessary to refit the ship he should repair to Port Jackson where he might expect to find a tender, *Lady Nelson*, recently sent especially from England for survey work, and which he should take under his command. Then he must repair to the Northwest coast where, from the extreme height of the tides observed by Dampier, it seemed probable to Their Lordships that valuable harbours could be discovered; then the Gulf of Carpentaria, then Torres Strait, then the East coast. Next, in order to refresh the men and to give variety to the painters, Westall and Bauer, he was to visit the Fijis and after that lose no time in returning to England for further orders. Well did Their Lordships set the precedent that the greatest merit of any Hydrographic Instruction is that it should be incapable of completion lest a single day be lost by its early termination!

Flinders' published journals show a great advance on the stilted professional styles of Vancouver and Broughton. For the first time a naval surveyor writes for the general public and he introduces many fascinating incidents far removed from the daily progress of discovery and chart making.

In August on the passage south to the Cape he writes: 'On 27th, in latitude 6° North and longitude 17½° West, a noddy was caught, and next day a swallow was found dead in my sleeping cabin. This poor little bird had been our companion for three or four days before, and had become a favourite. It was generally seen darting past the lee scuttles and ports, apparently after flies which were carried out by the streams of air; sometimes it alighted upon the boats which hung on the ship's quarters, and more than once rested itself in the cabin where, at length, it was found dead.'

He mentions Crossing the Line. 'On the 7th, (September), our latitude was 0° 43' north and we expected to cross the equator some time in the following night. It was a part of my plan for preserving the health of the people, to promote active amusements amongst them, so long as it did not interfere with the duties of the ship; and therefore the ancient ceremonies used on this occasion, were allowed to be performed this evening; and the ship being previously put under snug sail, the seamen were furnished with the means, and the permission, to conclude the day with merriment.'

That Flinders was a second generation disciple of Cook there is no doubt. On 16th October he writes: 'At this time we had not a single person in the sick list, both officers and men being fully in as good health, as when we sailed from Spithead. I had begun very early to put into execution the beneficial plan, first practised and made known by the great captain Cook. It was in the standing orders of the ship, that on every fine day the deck below and the cockpits should be cleared, washed, aired with stoves, and sprinkled with vinegar. On wet and dull days they were cleaned and aired, without washing. Care was taken to prevent the people from sleeping upon deck, or lying down in their wet clothes; and once in every fortnight or three weeks, as circumstances permitted, their beds, and the contents of their chests and bags, were opened out and exposed to the sun and air. On Sunday and Thursday mornings, the ship's company was mustered, and every man appeared clean shaved and dressed; and when the evenings were fine, the drum and fife announced the fore castle to be the scene of dancing; nor did I discourage other playful amusements which might occasionally be more to the taste of the sailors, and were not unseasonable.'

At the Cape Mr. Crosley set up his observatory in tents and instructed Samuel Flinders in the duties he would have to perform on Mr. Crosley's imminent departure. 'The road from Simon's Town to a place called the Company's garden, led close past the observatory; and this was the sole ride or walk in the neighbourhood, which the inhabitants and the gentlemen belonging to the ships in the bay could enjoy. From those of the first rank, who took their morning's ride, to the sailor who staggered past on a Sunday, and even the slave with his bundle of fire wood, all stopped at the observatory to see what was going on. Ramsden's universal theodolite, set up for the purpose of observing transits, excited its share of attention from the curious. Some wanted information, some amusement, and all would have liked to see how the sun appeared through the telescope.'

CHAPTER SIX

Flinders' Circumnavigation
of Australia

On 6th December 1801, Flinders sighted Cape Leeuwin and ordered the cables to be bent in readiness for anchoring. He started at once a running survey to the eastwards along the south coast, for despite the fact that this had already been laid down, he had to sail that way and he was too conscientious a man to let slip an opportunity for improving the chart.

Wales, Cook's astronomer, had remarked upon the fact that the variation of the compass changed with the heading of the ship as well as with geographical position. Flinders had studied Wales' remarks and was interested in discovering the cause. By patient observing, commenced now and continued throughout the voyage, Flinders realised that the change of variation with the ship's heading must be due to the altered relative position of the iron in the ship's structure, and he further proved this by moving the compass from the binnacle to the taffrail and noting that a change of variation resulted. His orders were, therefore, that the compass must always be used from the binnacle position when taking bearings for laying down the coastline. After he had returned to England and arranged for tests in a number of vessels he realised that he could make a table showing the value for deviation, as we call it today, for every heading of the ship, and he set about correcting the thousands of bearings he had recorded throughout his voyage. He realised, too, the importance of keeping movable

metal away from the vicinity of the compass and discovered that
the effects of the iron in the ship's structure forward of the poop
could be counteracted by vertical bars of iron close abaft the
compass. That the 'Flinders bar' today is on the foreside of the
binnacle merely reflects the changed position of the modern
compass which is usually sited on a navigating bridge well
forward.

Flinders entered King George Sound in the dark with confidence using Vancouver's chart, and anchored within. Here the
painters and the botanists got ashore, a survey of the harbour was
put in hand and the ship's rigging, masts and sails were prepared
for the arduous voyage eastwards. On leaving, Flinders tried to
keep so close inshore that breaking water on the coastline could
be kept continually in sight from the deck, whilst he himself was
often at the masthead with the glass. All bearings were meticulously
recorded and before turning in he made a habit of completing the
rough chart for the day. The ship would then move to seaward
for the night, endeavouring to return at daylight to the same point
to pick up the sinuous thread of white water once more.

He was well through the Great Bight before he had passed
beyond the earlier tracks of Vancouver, D'Entrecasteaux and
Nuyts and found himself exploring a virgin coast. He was not one
to underrate his predecessors and he generously used their names
and indicated on his charts the discoverers of each stretch of
coastline.

Flinders constantly hoped for a great river and he took the
salinity of the seawater whenever he suspected from the appearance of the shore that an opening was at hand, but in this he had
many disappointments; not until he neared the great gulf at 136°
East did he encounter strong tidal streams which gave some hope
that they were nearing the desired strait. But tragedy was at hand
and the headland on the western side of Spencer's Gulf, Cape
Catastrophe, is a reminder of the true forecast of the 'Pompey'
fortune-teller.

Water could not be found in the vicinity and Mr. Thistle in the
cutter was searching the beaches till dusk, when he was seen to
be making his way back to the ship. As he had not arrived half

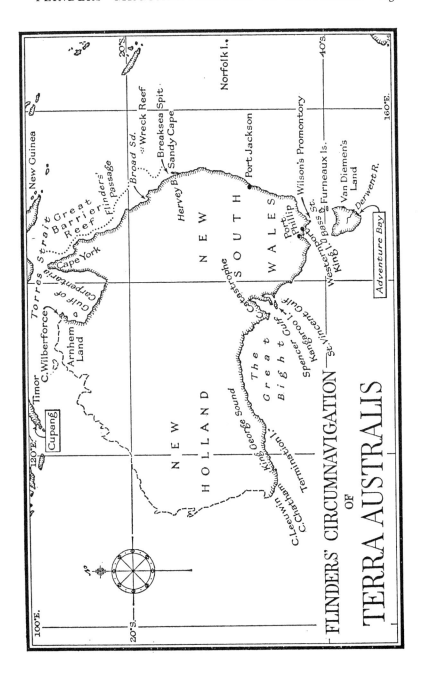

FLINDERS' CIRCUMNAVIGATION
OF
TERRA AUSTRALIS

an hour later Lieutenant Fowler was despatched in another boat
into the night in search of the cutter. Two anxious hours had
passed with only the occasional distant flicker of Fowler's lantern
to be seen, when Flinders ordered a gun to be fired as a recall.
Those peering into the darkness could see that the First Lieutenant's boat was alone, and shortly afterwards he was onboard to
report that he had experienced dangerous tide-rips and overfalls
which had nearly capsized him in the position where Thistle had
been last sighted. A strong tidal stream running to the southward
would have carried any disabled boat to seaward. It was a long,
anxious night onboard and when the first light of dawn made it
possible to search the grey waters Flinders got the ship underway
and sailed over to an anchorage nearer to the mainland and to
where the cutter had disappeared. There were indeed dangerous
tide-rips to be seen but no sign of the cutter. Whilst the ship's
boats set out to search the coast, Flinders himself went to the
high point at the southern end of the mainland which he was so
soon to name Cape Catastrophe. From this height he 'examined
with a glass the islands lying off, and all the neighbouring shores
for any appearance of our people, but in vain; I therefore took a
set of angles for the survey, and returned on board; and on
comparing notes with the different parties, it appeared that no
further information had been obtained of our unfortunate companions.'

This was a desperate blow to Flinders for Thistle had sailed so
long with him now; as well as a personal friend he had lost a
competent surveyor. But losses by act of God were inevitable on
such expeditions and the work must go on relentlessly.

Investigator now moved into the great gulf and opening on the
port hand was a fine harbour which Flinders decided to examine
in detail, and to set up a shore observatory for which young
Flinders was sent ashore with tents, timekeepers, and the necessary
astronomical instruments for rating them. A party was sent to dig
pits for water, for none was to be found at the surface; another
party with axes went in search of wood. Then Flinders set to on
the survey of Port Lincoln, as he now named the harbour, and
the Lincolnshire officers attending him showered homely names

upon the many features—Cape Donington, Grantham Island, Spalding Cove, Louth Isles, to mention but a few.

No open beach or level stretch of clear ground being readily available for measuring a base, and the general alignment of the port being too far from the north/south direction to permit base measurement by differences of observed latitudes, Flinders fell back to the gun and pendulum method to measure an eight-mile base from the ship at anchor to a station on Boston Island.

The naturalists roamed the countryside in search of specimens; Westall painted a view of the port from Memory Cove where Flinders had set up a copper plate commemorating the names of those lost with Thistle; the ship was refitted under Lieutenant Fowler's direction; and Flinders himself had the satisfaction of observing a solar eclipse which would in time substantiate the position observed by his young brother—in fact the now familiar routine was completed which over the next fifty years became the standard practice when a good harbour was found. These anchorages, laboriously surveyed and fixed, became part of a steadily increasing network of established positions about the world to which intervening coastal and oceanic surveys were adjusted and connected.

To make such a network possible it was necessary to expend every effort to establish the position with the utmost care; of Port Lincoln Flinders wrote:

'The latitude of our tents at the head of Port Lincoln, from the mean of four meridian observations of the Sun taken from an artificial horizon was 34° 48' 25" S.'

'The longitude from thirty sets of distances of the sun and stars from the moon was 135° 44' 51" S.'

Now came the work of fitting in the intervening coastline he had delineated since leaving the previous established position at King George Sound. The rates of acceleration or deceleration of the timekeepers had been carefully measured by daily observations of equal altitude over a period of six days at Port Lincoln. Flinders now compared these with the rates obtained fifty-seven days previously at King George Sound and employed a rate accelerating in arithmetical progression between these two to give the longitude

of Port Lincoln. This differed by 7′ 25″ from the position fixed by
the lunars and so he then re-worked the longitudes for all coastal
features laid down between the two places by applying to each a
proportion of 7′ 25″ commensurate with the total elapsed time in
days since quitting King George Sound.

To complete the routine observations now common to every
established geographical position ashore the magnetic variation
and dip of the needle were measured, the nature of the daily tides
was recorded with their range in height, whilst maximum and
minimum daily temperatures were recorded.

The gulf which stretched away northwards proved a disappointment when it terminated after 185 miles of exploration. Naming
it Spencer Gulf, Flinders sailed south to discover and land upon
Kangaroo Island where great numbers of these animals made no
move to avoid being slaughtered with ease by the sailors. Half a
hundredweight of heads, tails and forequarters were boiled daily
for soup, and kangaroo steaks were freely consumed—this was a
magnificent feast for men who had enjoyed no fresh meat for four
months.

A second large gulf, upon whose eastern shore Adelaide lies
today, was next explored. By subsequently naming this gulf after
St. Vincent, and the peninsula separating it from Spencer Gulf,
Yorke Peninsula, Flinders flattered three successive First Lords of
the Admiralty at once.

It was now April 1802 and Flinders decided that with the onset
of winter he must press on for Port Jackson. He navigated to the
open sea through a channel between the eastern end of Kangaroo
Island and the mainland which he aptly named 'Backstairs Passage'.

At 4.00 p.m. on Thursday 8th April, a white rock to the
southeast was reported from aloft, but this was soon to be a sail
and all hands were on deck to peer across the waters at this
unusual sight, and quarters were manned.

As the vessels closed, the British colours were hoisted and in
reply the stranger, according to Flinders, 'showed a French ensign,
and afterwards an English jack forward, as we did a white flag'.
Baudin had in fact, for some unknown reason, hoisted the former

French naval ensign, a rectangular white flag, which had been superseded by the tricolour in 1794.* The two nations were at war and both vessels were suspicious of each other. Flinders veered his vessel round as the Frenchman passed under his lee to keep his broadside towards her, when the French vessel was seen to be *le Géographe* of which Captain Nicholas Baudin was known to be in command.

Flinders had a boat lowered and, with his boat's crew sporting their newly made kangaroo-skin caps and with Mr. Brown accompanying him as interpreter, he drew alongside and boarded the Frenchman.

The passports were exchanged, but Baudin gave but a cursory glance at that of Flinders, commencing at once, and freely, to tell of his discoveries and misfortunes.

He had been exploring Van Diemen's Land where he had lost touch with a boat's crew, now probably wrecked; and later, in Bass Strait, his consort *le Naturaliste* had parted company in a gale.

Only next day, when Flinders again visited Baudin to present him with an up-to-date chart of his discoveries, did the latter become aware of the identity of his visitor, and he then retracted some of the hard things he had said the night before about the English chart of 1800 which he had been given for the voyage.

Flinders promised to look out for the missing boat's crew and for *le Naturaliste*, and to inform the latter to repair to Port Jackson, to which he had cordially invited Baudin. The vessels parted and Flinders sailed onwards to King Island, at the western end of Bass Strait, of which he had heard from whalers at Port Jackson three years before. These enterprising sailors had soon followed up the reports they had heard from Flinders and Bass of abundant seal stocks on the shores of the islands of Bass Strait.

Flinders was thrilled, too, at finding and entering an inland sea (subsequently named Port Phillip, present site of Melbourne), but

---

* I am grateful to Ingénieur Général Jean-Nicolas Pasquay, the Hydrographer of the French Navy, for obtaining for me an extract from Baudin's journal in which the French navigator wrote 'On vit, *du* Geographe *monter puis s'abaisser le pavillon blanc, puis pavillon et flamme anglaise*'.

he was later to find that he was not the discoverer, for Lieutenant Murray in the *Lady Nelson* had found this spacious shelter only ten weeks earlier.

In early May Flinders was amongst familiar landmarks as he rounded Wilson's Promontory and on 9th May entered Port Jackson to anchor in Sydney Cove, with every man fit and on deck to work the ship into port. The inhabitants of Port Jackson expressed themselves amazed at the health of those who had just made such a long voyage, and the ruddy, apple-cheeked complexion of the sailors reminded them of old England. Perhaps the name 'Pommie' was coined that day.

le Naturaliste was already in port and Baudin's missing boat's crew had been recovered by the sealing brig *Harrington* in Bass Strait. On 20th June *le Geographe* arrived off the port, her crew in a desperate condition from scurvy—only twelve of her company of 170 men were capable of duty and *Investigator's* boat was among others who went to help the wretched vessel in.

News of peace between France and England having been received in the colony, there was nothing to prevent the authorities at Port Jackson from giving the Frenchmen succour, except of course the general shortage of beef and fresh provisions, which the new Governor Philip Gidley King and his subordinates did their utmost to overcome: this meant going short themselves, including Flinders and his crew.

The usual refitting of *Investigator* went forward; the portable greenhouse was erected on the poop in a modified form; a new cutter was built to replace the one lost with Thistle; and provisions were embarked.

The *Lady Nelson* which awaited Flinders at Port Jackson had been specially built for surveying rivers and shallow waters, having a shallow draft, and three drop keels for ocean sailing which could be retracted for inshore service. She had been brought from England by Lieutenant James Grant, had done some useful work on the south coast and was now under the command of Lieutenant John Murray and ready to accompany *Investigator*.

Mr. John Aken joined *Investigator* as the new Master, and nine convicts 'of good character' were received onboard to make up a deficiency in numbers. Two natives were also engaged: one was Bongaree who had sailed in *Norfolk* with Flinders, and whose presence had done much to bring about friendly intercourse with the native inhabitants on the sparsely populated coastline.

The two vessels sailed northward in July 1802 to continue the circumnavigation and for many a mile Flinders was following in Cook's *Endeavour* tracks. 'He reaped the harvest of discovery, but the gleanings of the field remain to be gathered,' wrote Flinders who saw his duty in extending the detail of Cook's overall discovery. The gleanings were considerable and could be described only in an entire book devoted to Flinders; suffice it to say that he investigated every bay and inlet in hope of finding a river, sketched a great deal of the coast and sounded as he went.

With the Master in a boat searching for the channel, *Investigator* rounded the end of Breaksea Spit off Sandy Cape, passed within the shallow reef-protected water and anchored to await the lagging *Lady Nelson* which, an indifferent sailer, was commanded by an officer 'not accustomed to make free with the land' as Flinders was. Sailing too far off the coast in search of safety, Murray had been hindered by the stronger south-going stream encountered here.

The coast was now further examined northwards to Shoalwater Bay. The surveyors and the botanists enjoyed much time on shore and Flinders himself anxiously searched the beaches for signs of wreckage; it was his belief that La Pérouse had been lost in the waters of New Caledonia, and if this was so it was possible that evidence in driftwood form would have reached these shores.

A geographical station was established at Broad Sound, for Flinders was anxious to rate the timekeepers before setting out for Torres Strait and the unexplored shores of Carpentaria. Whilst Samuel Flinders was set to this task his brother went on a survey expedition in *Lady Nelson*. He returned a few days later to find that Samuel, in his efforts to obtain lunar distances and compute them, had neglected to wind the timekeepers which now lay silent in their cases. After heated words these were set going, only for Flinders to return after a second absence to find a similar state of affairs. As the timepieces had once before been let down by Samuel on Kangaroo Island this was a horological hat trick which tried

Flinders hard. Four days' rates had been secured before the time-keepers stopped and as these now agreed closely with those for the first twenty-four hours of the newly started pieces, Flinders had to accept them and the loss of time already entailed, but with how good a grace we do not know, for he makes little of it in his journals as well he might, considering it almost a family matter.

It was now Flinders' intention to quit the coast, find and pass to seaward through a break in the Barrier Reef and make direct for Torres Strait by the open sea in an effort to complete the passage before the onset of the contrary northwest monsoon of which he was clearly aware. It took fourteen exasperating days to find such a gap, sailing and searching by day, anchored and dragging anchors by night, for the tidal streams flowed at alarming rates through the tortuous passages between the reefs, which formed not a solid barrier but a great loosely scattered jigsaw pattern, green-covered at high water, brown and black-studded with 'negro heads' at low. Shadows thrown by the clouds made their own 'reefs', as did the eddying of the tidal stream. With one eye on the whaleboat sounding ahead and the other on the 'lee-wardly' *Lady Nelson* in danger astern, Flinders crept onwards and at last thought he had found an opening. Here he took the decision that had been formulating in his mind and ordered Lieutenant Murray to return with his vessel to Port Jackson; but hardly was the brig out of sight astern than white water ahead once more showed that *Investigator* was still within the reefs. Two further days of trial and near error resulted before Flinders really felt the open ocean heave beneath his feet.

The general pattern of the Great Barrier Reef was now clear to Flinders, unfathomable ocean without but studded with extensive and dangerous reefs rising steeply from the ocean bed; within was sheltered shallow water suitable for intricate coastal navigation. He recommended entry at Breaksea Spit where the southern end of the reefs terminates close to the land, for by the latter's visible proximity this entrance was easier to locate than Flinders' Passage which, although five miles wide, had no land for guidance—only a good position from observation of heavenly bodies and a keen look-out for a gap in the white wall of breakers could ensure safe entry.

Flinders warned: 'The commander who proposes to make the experiment must not, however, be one who throws his ship's head round in a hurry, so soon as breakers are announced from aloft; if he do not feel his nerves strong enough to thread the needle, as it is called, amongst the reefs, whilst he directs the steerage from the mast head, I would strongly recommend him not to approach this part of New South Wales.'

Since passing through Torres Strait with Bligh, Flinders had studied the details of the few other passages which had been made and now resolved to see how expeditiously the voyage might be done. He entered by 'Pandora's Entrance' on 29th October 1802, lay two nights at anchor and reached Prince of Wales Island on the afternoon of the 31st and, had he wished, could have passed clear of Booby Island before dusk. Thus he believed that if this route were carefully followed, the perilous passage of but a few years previously could now be made with safety and certainty in three days. Flinders' clearly worded instructions for the passage removed much of the former danger.

Now followed the arduous and lengthy task of sailing around the whole coasts of the Gulf of Carpentaria, a coastline so remote that to this day a deal of the detail shown on Admiralty and Australian charts stems direct from Flinders' work.

For the most part the inshore waters proved shallow, the Dutch 'rivers' but lagoons, and the coastlines barren and sparsely populated. Elusive turtles were now the source of fresh provisions but at last at Bountiful Island a feast of turtles, comparable with the feast at Kangaroo Island, was enjoyed.

As the vessel made her way southwards and then northwestwards along the gulf's shores, a leak, which had festered long as a running sore, broke out into something more damaging. When the wind was on the beam, and the ship heeling over, up to ten inches of water an hour had to be pumped from the hold; finally there was nothing to be done but to place the vessel on careen at Sweers River, and whilst observing and surveying was put in hand ashore, the carpenter and his mates inspected the hull and submitted an official report to Flinders upon the poor state of the vessel. They had bored into the timbers and found many completely rotten. They believed that if the ship met with a heavy gale and worked her timbers, or if she happened to get driven ashore in anything but calm weather, or even if an attempt was made to heave her down on her beam ends on a good beach, she would go to pieces. Mr. Aken, with his knowledge of ships of this type, judged that she would last barely six months more. This then was a desperate predicament in which Flinders and his men found themselves on one of the remotest shores of the known world.

Flinders steadily proceeded with the laying down of the Gulf of Carpentaria, which he completed at Cape Wilberforce three months later, and as he went he studied how best he might employ the remaining three months of his vessel's life. He finally decided that he must sail directly westabout to Port Jackson: this was a bitter moment for Flinders who now saw his chance of completing the circumnavigation survey of the continent slipping through his fingers.

Flinders searched his mind for some means of continuing. Finally he decided to sail for Cupang where he hoped to find a ship sailing for Europe, in which he could despatch Lieutenant Fowler to the Admiralty with an account of his proceedings and with a request that he be sent out to Port Jackson with a suitable vessel to continue the work. If things moved smoothly, Fowler could be back at Port Jackson with another vessel as soon as Flinders' crew were refreshed from their present labours!

At Cupang the sickening news was received that a vessel homeward-bound from India had passed through but ten days before and no other was expected. Provisions were poor and expensive and, as a legacy of the place, the officers and men, already much fatigued, took with them a fierce epidemic of dysentery which resulted in eight deaths.

To reach Port Jackson it was necessary to complete the circumnavigation of the continent, but not as Flinders had always planned, as a close coastal survey voyage, but sailing far out at sea clear of dangers as the urgency of his vessel's defects dictated. Southwards off the west coast of New Holland and then eastwards through Bass Strait *Investigator* sailed to the haven of Port Jackson.

With this turn of events Flinders' great surveys really terminate, but his subsequent adventures during his attempts to reach England with his charts must be briefly told, if only to show how the Hydrographic Office, so newly established, was denied from now on the services of one of its brightest stars.

Investigator being quite unfit for further service the Governor provided H.M. Armed Vessel *Porpoise* for Flinders' passage home, appointing Fowler in command. A portable greenhouse was erected on deck and the great collection of plants transferred from *Investigator*. In August 1803 *Porpoise* sailed in company with two merchantmen, *Bridgewater*, of the East India Company, and *Cato*.

Flinders looked forward to shepherding this little convoy through Torres Strait and thus spreading the news of the quick passage home, but this was not to be for, although they sailed well to the eastward of the Barrier Reef direct for Pandora's Entrance, disaster overtook them on the night of 17th August. First *Porpoise* and then *Cato* struck an unknown reef and spent an agonising night battered by the breakers before the majority of both crews were able to escape in the boats to a low island about a mile away. Here they erected tents made from sail-cloth and collected salvaged provisions from the wrecks. Only the *Bridgewater* escaped, but strangely her Captain made no effort to return at daybreak to rescue the survivors but pursued his course unmindful of the curses of those now marooned on the reef. They faced an indefinite sojourn on a completely barren stretch of coral sand 300 yards long, two or three feet only above sea level and over 100 miles from the nearest known land, Sandy Cape.

Fowler proposed that Flinders, with a picked crew, should attempt the journey to the mainland and then southward to Port Jackson to raise the alarm and find a relief vessel. Naming the cutter *Hope*, Flinders set out inauspiciously on a Friday with the Commander of the *Cato* and a crew of fourteen men; and after much privation they reached Port Jackson. 'The reader has perhaps,' wrote Flinders in his journal, 'never gone 250 leagues at sea in an open boat, or along a strange coast inhabited by savages; but if he recollect the eighty officers and men upon Wreck-Reef Bank, and how important was our arrival to their safety, and to the saving of the charts, journals, and papers of the *Investigator*'s voyage, he may have some idea of the pleasure we felt, but particularly myself, at entering our destined port.'

The Governor was surprised at his dinner by the two unshaven and sunburnt officers and as soon as he had overcome his distress he arranged that the ship *Rolla* would be engaged to call at Wreck Reef on her passage to Canton whence the crews of *Porpoise* and *Cato* would find a passage home. To Flinders the Governor gave a small colonial schooner named *Cumberland* that he, with a dozen volunteers from his former crew, might pass through Torres Strait and sail direct to England with the precious charts and journals.

Six weeks to the day after Flinders left in *Hope* a watcher on Wreck Reef sighted *Rolla's* top-gallant sail above the horizon and a few hours later Flinders was being cheered as he stepped ashore to experience one of the happiest moments of his life.

Flinders took with him in *Cumberland* Mr. Aken, Master, and Mr. Charrington, boatswain of *Investigator*, his servant and seven men, a cask containing his mineral and shell specimens, chests containing his charts and papers, and the one timekeeper still functioning.

Young Samuel Flinders, unhindered by the winding of more than one clock, had taken sixty sets of lunars on Wreck Reef which gave Flinders an excellent departure and *Cumberland* sailed away. The passage through Torres Strait to Cupang was now simply routine to Flinders and by mid-November he had left there for the Cape. But once in the open Indian Ocean the motion of the long swell increased the flow of water into the cranky vessel to such an extent that the pumps, which were badly worn internally, were unable to cope with the situation. Increasingly Flinders became aware that he would not reach the Cape without caulking the hull and re-boring the pumps, for both of which operations he required a sheltered harbour. Unaware that Britain and France were again at war, and happy in the belief that his passport was still valid, he decided to make for the French-held Île de France (now known as Mauritius), but beforehand he set down methodically, as was his way, his reasons for doing so, for Governor King had been averse to such a visit.

Cumberland's appearance off the island caused a flutter amongst the military ashore. The vessel's reception in Port Louis was cold, reflecting the renewed outbreak of hostilities, and Flinders was surprised and indignant to find himself placed under arrest and shortly taken before Captain General Decaen.

Decaen had been one of Napoleon's most dashing generals, and it was as a reward that Napoleon had sent him to India during the brief peace which followed the Treaty of Amiens to receive back Pondicherry from the British and become its Governor. However, the British had heard that the peace was at an end and refused to surrender Pondicherry to Decaen, who was then ordered by Napoleon to take command on Île de France, where he now felt remote and forgotten and strongly resentful towards his old enemies.

He interviewed Flinders roughly and haughtily and pointed out the inadequacy of the passport which had been made out specifically for *Investigator* and did not, in the Governor's view, cover the insignificant *Cumberland*.

Flinders was removed from the ship and placed under open arrest in an insalubrious café in the town where, in a stuffy room and attacked by mosquitoes and bed bugs, he spent the days and nights raging at the overbearing attitude of Decaen, and comparing his treatment of him with the generous hospitality that had been offered to the two French exploring vessels at Port Jackson but two years before.

To Flinders in this room on the day after the interview with the Governor came an invitation from Madame Decaen for him to join them at their table for dinner that night. Here Flinders may have made one of the two mistakes which kept him so long upon Île de France, for he haughtily declined the invitation to sit at table with one who had treated him so cavalierly but twenty-four hours before—and haughtiness was not the way to treat Decaen if you were already his prisoner. The other mistake that Flinders made came to the eyes of those of the Governor's staff who were now paging through Flinders' journals which they had taken into custody; for among the reasons Flinders had set down in his journals for visiting Île de France was that he might see in what state the island had been left by the French Revolution, and gain a practical knowledge of the periodical winds, for he visualised the island as a base for his renewed voyaging off the western shores of Terra Australis. This simple reason, set down without ulterior motive, made sinister reading for Decaen.

The tale of Flinders' detention on Île de France is a long, sad one of hope deferred, for there were many influential persons in England, India and even in France who worked for Flinders' release, he being a man of science and outside the war. And of these persons, Sir Joseph Banks probably worked as hard as any at the task, despite the fact that every one of his precious plants had perished on Wreck Reef and his gardener had died long since at Port Jackson.

Having reported the news of his prisoner to the authorities in France, Decaen could not release him until he received orders. Communications were slow, the years rolled on, and by the time permission had been finally granted the Royal Navy were in-vesting Île de France and Decaen believed that Flinders now knew too much about the island's defences for him to be returned. So he stayed on, at first moving to the Garden Prison, whence his officers and his crew were one by one repatriated; later he was allowed to reside and work at 'Mesnil aux Roses', the beautiful home of the French de Chazal family who owned the St. Antoine Sugar Plantation.*

But Flinders was allowed access to his papers, his journals and his charts, many of which he painstakingly re-drew so that today the great majority of his original works in the Hydrographic Office bear the legend 'Drawn on the Île de France'. And when he eventually received his release in 1810 after six and a half years' captivity, all his charts and journals were returned to him with the exception of Volume III, which contained those damaging reasons for visiting Île de France. Mauritius fell to the Royal Navy only six months after Flinders' departure.

---

* I am indebted to Dr. Robert L. Fisher of Scripps Institution of Oceanography for this information. Whilst working in oceanographic research vessels in the Indian Ocean in the 1960s and early 1970s Dr. Fisher was often entertained at 'Mesnil aux Roses' by Jean and Alix de Chazal Bassaic, descendants of Flinders' generous hosts.

Some have said that Flinders' release was held up in order that Freycinet, who had sailed with Baudin and was compiling the charts, might get the French explorations of *Terra Australis* published before Flinders, but if this was so, and there is little evidence to support the supposition, then Freycinet made poor use of his advantage for it was only after Flinders' return to England that the French work was published. The discoveries that Flinders had described to Baudin in *le Geographe* so many years before appeared as 'Terre Napoleon' for the southern coast, and 'Golfe Bonaparte' and 'Golfe Josephine' replaced Spencer and St. Vincent, but only briefly until Flinders' great atlas was published. Its very completeness, and the generous indebtedness acknowledged whenever the work of others was included, swept all competition aside. Flinders was the great explorer of Australia, the name he now gave to the encircled continent and by which it became increasingly known.

Flinders' reunion with his wife after nearly ten years is touchingly evoked in a letter by John Franklin, who had sailed with Flinders in *Investigator*, and came to meet Flinders in London.

'My dear Sir,

Some apology would be necessary for the abrupt manner I left you, except under the peculiar circumstances that my departure was taken. I felt so sensibly the affecting scene of your meeting Mrs. Flinders that I could not have remained any longer, in the room, under any consideration . . .

Captain Flinders being in England seems to me even now a mystery—had I not seen the well known countenance I still might doubt: after the unjust and unexpected detention you have suffered, all things may be reconcilable to some minds—and persons may doubt without deserving the charge of obstinancy.

At our meeting I was much agitated—and might perhaps have given the wrong answers to the enquiries you made after the old *Investigator*s—I will endeavour to refresh my memory—and state how they are disposed of—etc. The old ship lies at Plymouth cut down nearly to the water's edge; they were near losing her during their passage—in the gales off Cape Horn.'

From that day on until he died three years later his wife did all she could to nurse Flinders' failing health. He did not spare himself in his stupendous efforts to complete his atlas and his published journals, and they constitute an enduring record of his great work and human endeavour.

CHAPTER SEVEN

Hurd: The First Naval Officer Hydrographer

In the foregoing chapters we have followed the world-wide voyages of Vancouver, Broughton and Flinders. That Broughton ran on Brake Bank in the Gull Stream and that Flinders grounded on the Roar Sand, close east of Dungeness and unmarked on the chart provided for his use by the Admiralty, and each within a day or so of sailing from the Nore for the uttermost ends of the earth, focuses attention on the inadequacy of the charts of home waters at the end of the eighteenth century.

To follow the progress of charting at home, it is necessary to go back to the survey off the north coast of Kent by Lieutenant Murdoch Mackenzie and his cousin Graeme Spence, employed by the Admiralty for this work. Their endeavours resulted in the old southern approach route to the Thames (past Reculver Cliff and across the Kentish Flats to the Nore) being abandoned for a deeper channel further offshore which had been revealed by the survey; named Queen's Channel, it was buoyed by Trinity House in 1775.

The two surveyors had then been sent to Plymouth to resume their work there, where the results enabled the entrance channels to be buoyed and shore batteries to be sited by the engineers to command the approaches.

By 1788 Spence had taken over from Mackenzie as chief surveyor to the Admiralty.

From time to time Spence was employed directly by Trinity

House to assist them with the judicious placing of light vessels including the *Owers* and the lightships necessary for safe navigation of the Gull Stream; the lighthouse at Portland Bill was among those Spence assisted in siting. At this time Trinity House were not the sole owners of such aids to navigation, there being a number of private owners of lighthouses who obtained satisfactory monetary returns from shipping by way of tolls.

In Dalrymple's early days as Hydrographer Spence was set to surveying the coastal waters from South Foreland to Beachy Head, including the intricacies of the Goodwin Sands, and the compiling of detailed reports on the possibilities of Dover and Rye Harbours for defence purposes.

By the end of the century the importance of delineating the northern approach route to the Thames was realised and Graeme Spence surveyed the shipping route southwestwards through the King's Channel and East Swin, and over the swatch-way into the West Swin. Then he continued northeastwards to Orfordness and Harwich, where in 1801 he enjoyed the signal honour of piloting Lord Nelson in *Medusa* through the inshore channel between the Roughs and the Naze which he had but recently discovered and which today, marked by the Medusa Buoy, is still known as the Medusa Channel.

Spence retired to the Hydrographic Office in 1804 with the grateful thanks of Trinity House who added a bounty for his pioneering work in opening up the new entrances to the Thames; and until shortly before his death in 1812 he was employed in writing up the directions of both his own and Mackenzie's surveys.

In those days written directions for navigation formed an integral part of necessary hydrographic information and in furtherance of this Their Lordships instructed H.M. Ships, during the Seven Years War, to keep Remark Books containing such information. In 1804, in order to encourage a higher standard in these Remark Books, Dalrymple was instrumental in instituting a system by which a satisfactory receipt had to be given by the Hydrographer before pay could be drawn by the Captain. Not all captains saw that to remark upon the coasts of many harbours visited was a

part of their duty, and it was some time before they began to
record their opinions of the most desirable tracks to follow at
different seasons of the year. But as time passed and the Hydrographic Office assimilated the experience of great numbers of
practical seamen and, condensing it, passed it out for public use,
it was realised that Dalrymple's institution of the Remark Book
had been of prime importance as a step towards safer and speedier
navigation.

Since 1795 Dalrymple had been progressing with his task of
sifting the available material in the Admiralty and arranging for
the engraving of the more useful items so that copies could be
produced. Many of the charts of harbours and anchorages were
of too large a scale and required reduction, whilst the smaller scales
covering the oceans required compilation from many different
track charts. Dalrymple was a perfectionist with a very modest staff
and only one copper printing press, yet in 1800 he had printed
and published the first Admiralty Chart entitled 'Sketch of the
Road on the N.E. Side of the Island Houat in Quiberon Bay by
Thomas Moore, Master of H.M. Ship *Diamond*. Published by
Order of The Lords Commissioners of the Admiralty by A. Dalrymple, Hydrographer to the Admiralty, November 1800'. This
chart was to be followed by eleven more charts the following year.
During the period up to 1808 Dalrymple planned and had engraved for use by the Fleet a scheme of about thirty large-scale
charts covering both sides of the English Channel. Those on the
French side were based on French charts, now more readily available, whilst those on the English side relied upon the surveys of
Murdoch Mackenzie Junior, Graeme Spence and Lieutenant
Murray. The latter having returned from Australia had been
employed since 1803 in a ship named *Sorlings* on surveys from
Winchelsea to Selsey Bill. Dalrymple realised that it would also be
necessary to buy charts from the commercial chart sellers to
complete the set of world cover required; in this he saw himself
hampered by his freely admitted lack of knowledge of the coasts
of Europe and North America, and suggested that a Charting
Committee of naval officers be set up to advise him on the selection
of the charts. Their Lordships appointed such a committee in 1808

composed of Captains Sir Home Popham, Edward Henry Columbine and Thomas Hurd, all of whom had carried out surveys,
Columbine in the West Indies, Popham off southwest Africa and
in the Red Sea and Hurd more extensively.

There is clear evidence that Hurd, like Cook, had learnt his
surveying from the army engineer Holland under whom he had
worked on the North American coast in the years 1771 to 1774.
Subsequently, after an exciting period as a lieutenant in a most
successful frigate, *Unicorn*, in which he had amassed prize money
on both sides of the Atlantic, he was employed as Surveyor
General of Cape Breton.

In 1788 the Ordnance Board in London requested Their Lordships to appoint a naval officer to accompany Captain Durnford,
R.A., to Bermuda where he might carry out a nautical survey
whilst Durnford made a plan of the island. Their Lordships
selected the Surveyor General of Cape Breton.

Since losing the American War of Independence there had been
little succour for British men-of-war on the American coasts, and
after the outbreak of war with the French in 1793 the movements
of our vessels were passed freely to the enemy by the local authorities. Only Halifax was secure, but in winter hard weather delayed
refitting work above decks, and this base lay 2,000 ocean-miles
from the Caribbean, the centre of activity against the French.

So in 1795, hearing that Lieutenant Hurd had found 'safe and
secure anchorage among those islands for the whole Navy of
England', Admiral Murray, commanding the North America
Station, visited Bermuda in his flagship *Resolution* in search of a
new base for his squadron.

He found Hurd ready to pilot him through the Narrows, into
Murray's Anchorage and across the lagoon to Grassy Bay where,
in the shelter of Ireland Island, Hurd proposed a refitting basin.

Admiral Murray was delighted with all he saw and urged upon
Their Lordships the need to adopt this as his base from which his
vessels could sail swiftly and secretly to any part of his station.

Hurd was promoted Commander, ordered to erect landmarks
and lay channel buoys; to build ships of local cedar, all of which
he commanded in turn to extend his surveys; and to train for the

Fleet Bermuda pilots, well versed in the local channels, which he did by training three slaves who subsequently obtained their freedom for this task. Hurd laid the foundation of Bermuda naval base which served the Royal Navy until it was finally abandoned in 1950.

In 1797 Hurd requested to return to England, to make fair copies of his works, 'which I am unable to do in any reasonable time without assistance, my sight and health being too much injured by having been so many years exposed to the sun in this hot climate.' He had completed his Bermuda charts by 1801; they consisted of two sheets, each six and a half feet square, of intensely detailed work. For the next two years he pestered Their Lordships for employment.

With the collapse of the Peace of Amiens in 1803, Admiral Cornwallis resumed the blockade of Brest, employing an inshore squadron under Sir Thomas Graves which was constantly under way within the labyrinth of islets and rocky outcrops only a few miles from the French mainland.

In March 1804 the 74-gun *Magnificent* struck an isolated danger in this area and became a total loss alerting both Graves and the Admiralty to the urgent need for a complete survey of the Bay of Brest. Captain Hurd was appointed to carry out this work and arrived with his instruments in June 1804. Graves made available to him what ships or boats could be spared from the exigencies of the blockade but the frequent changes in shipboard accommodation and of boats' crews, the poor visibility, westerly weather and the difficulty of landing on the islets so close to the enemy's lookout posts combined to make the survey an extremely arduous one. Nevertheless, by the time Hurd returned to Plymouth in September he had made a great number of theodolite observations to lay down the islands and rocks, and had sounded a sufficient number of channels between them to prepare a 'Nautical Survey in the Bay of Brest'. Although Hurd returned to the area in 1806 the survey off Brest no longer, as a result of the Battle of Trafalgar, had priority.

Hurd had been granted the assistance of a draughtsman and the use of a table in the Hydrographic Office to complete the vast

and intricate survey sheets of the Bermuda lagoon. Doubtless as
he lay stretched across the paper to achieve the intricate penwork
hour after hour, he listened to, and took mental note of, the
activities of this office under Dalrymple's direction, so that in him
the committee had a surveyor who could add office acquaintance
to his naval and seagoing experience.

The first disagreement the Committee had with the Hydrographer arose over D'Entrecasteaux's charts, the complete set of this
great explorer's work having fallen into the hands of the Royal
Navy * some years previously.

Including as they did the charts resulting from D'Entrecasteaux's great Pacific voyage in search of La Perouse, there were
ample data here for the correction of British charts; and in modern
times of war such a windfall would be hailed with triumph and
immediately put to use. But in the Napoleonic Wars, desperate as
they were, the two nations were still living in an age where
scientists did not go to war, and surveyors were still scientists. Both
Flinders and Baudin had so recently carried, as had D'Entrecasteaux, passports to protect them from enemy interference whilst
engaged on their scientific voyages. That Napoleon had himself
now ordered Flinders' release from Île de France was proof enough
for Dalrymple that Decaen's disregard of Flinders' passport was
but a temporary lapse in international scientific relationships. Dalrymple, himself a Fellow of the Royal Society, was indeed a
scientist, and believed fervently that the niceties of these relationships should be maintained regardless of war, and so, after making
copies of D'Entrecasteaux's charts, he had returned the originals
to France. Nor did he think it right to use the copies at this stage
to correct British charts, so they were stored in a locked press, the
key of which he kept on his person.

The practical naval officers of the Committee were unimpressed
with this high-minded attitude (at a time when losses of naval
vessels by shipwreck were eight times greater than those imposed

---

* The French vessel *Houghly*, in which D'Entrecasteaux's papers were being
returned to Europe, was taken off St. Helena by a British Squadron under
Commodore Essington, about the year 1795.

by the enemy), but even when they suggested that the charts should be used only to correct longitudes and not for detail of depths and coastline Dalrymple would not budge and an impasse was reached.

From this point onwards relations between the Hydrographer and the Committee deteriorated, and it became necessary to obtain directions from higher authority for Dalrymple to co-operate.

Dalrymple complained that the Committee were doing far more than advising on chart coverage, and their first report bears this out. They considered how, by making the best use of the surveys available in the Admiralty, and by purchasing from chart sellers, the Hydrographic Office could make up sets of charts for world-wide use by the Fleet. They recommended that the best scheme would be to provide sets of charts for each naval station, the outfit to be supplied in a box. They had considered all the available sheets in great detail and estimated that it would cost initially about £11,000 to outfit the Fleet in this manner. They further recommended that completed chart boxes should be kept by the naval commissioners at Sheerness, Chatham, Portsmouth and Devonport, and it was proposed that the Admiralty now attempt to buy back the copyright of the many charts which had been made by naval officers and were now sold by various chart sellers.

The programme was an ambitious but realistic one, requiring much energy to implement, and thus it was a logical step to place a younger man in charge of the Hydrographic Office. So in May 1808 the Admiralty Board decided to remove Dalrymple from office. William Pole, The Navy Secretary, tried to break it gently to Dalrymple by saying that the several new arrangements suggested by the Committee would call for great and continual exertions on the part of the Hydrographer, and Their Lordships believed that at his advanced period of life it would not be possible for him to undertake them. Dalrymple was severely shocked and died within a few weeks of being superseded by Captain Hurd in 1808.

Dalrymple's relations with the Navy over many years had never been of the happiest: he did not get on with naval officers, and was probably too scientifically inclined for most of them.

However, the clear-cut style of the lettering of Admiralty charts today reflects the workmanlike engravings published under Dalrymple's direction which were such a notable advance on the over-flowery, decorated, yet often highly inaccurate charts on sale in the City.

Dalrymple had written and published a great deal, from charts to scathing pamphlets, and from this mass of material one can learn much about the man. His successor wrote little and was not noticed by contemporary writers, so that by comparison Hurd is a shadowy figure. But undoubtedly he was the man for the job of Hydrographer at this time; he was a practical naval officer with no pretensions to science, in fact the only Hydrographer of the nineteenth century, with the exception of Admiral Washington, who did not become a Fellow of the Royal Society. His very lack of scientific leanings was help to him in his task, for he could concentrate upon mundane matters such as the preparation of chart boxes, and this he tackled with vigour, even to the extent of supervising in person their despatch to the naval ports by stage-coach so that the Navy at war might be speedily supplied. In January 1809 Hurd was able to report that 113 boxes of charts had been issued since he took over in June and that he was introducing a system whereby boxes were returned by ships changing from one naval station to another for inspection and replenishment before re-issue.

Vigorously did Hurd pursue every piece of hydrographic information—we find him re-opening correspondence with the embittered Des Barres, now Governor of Prince Edward Island, in an attempt to get the full set of his charts; writing to a whaler captain, in prison in King's Bench for debt, to purchase the copyright of his Kerguelen chart; seeking coastal maps which were now becoming available through the Board of Ordnance as a result of Colonel Mudge's survey of England; and, what some considered sharp practice, purchasing Dalrymple's copper plates from a scrap-metal dealer for a song, after the Admiralty and the East India Company had refused to buy at the price proposed by Dalrymple's executors.

Hurd was concerned about the surveys of home waters. In 1809 we find him pressing Their Lordships to provide a Mr. Chapman with a convenient vessel, a good chronometer, a spyglass, a sextant by Troughton, a quicksilver horizon and an improved azimuth compass that a survey of the East Coast, northwards from the Thames, might be put in hand, for lives were constantly being lost for lack of a chart to guide shipping through the maze of sand-banks.

A tiny gunbrig was specially built in Deptford Yard and appropriately named *Investigator*; but Mr. Chapman's health failed shortly after the brig was commissioned and the Hydrographer was forced to seek a new captain. George Thomas, Master, was eventually chosen in 1810. He remained continually surveying for the next thirty-six years.

It is a fortunate chance that William Mogg was appointed clerk in charge of the stores and commissary department in *Investigator* for he kept a good journal and L. E. Tavenor has recently brought to light interesting detail from Mogg's manuscript which is in the library of the University College, Southampton. Mogg gives an account of the early life of Thomas, which in view of his great service to naval hydrography is worth recording. Probably the most important point about his youth was that he was educated at the Blue Coat School, completing a year in the mathematical class. In 1796 he went to sea in a whaler to the South Seas. After being wrecked and picked up by an American whaler young Thomas and a coloured boy, San Domingo Jack, were set ashore at their own request on Mas-a-Fuera with firearms and provisions.

After almost a year Jack met his end by falling over a cliff in pursuit of goats and Thomas lived on alone, employing himself by killing seals and curing their skins. Three years later a vessel touched at Mas-a-Fuera and the crew were astonished to find the lone inhabitant and willingly embarked him with his valuable cargo of skins. Although the captain claimed half the skins in return for a passage to China, yet Thomas's portion was worth over £2,000. He arranged a passage in a ship from the Typa to England, but as he came within sight of England, keenly anticipating the spending of his money, the vessel was boarded by the press gang and poor Thomas found himself transferred to a frigate bound for the coast of Holland. Here good fortune took a hand, for the captain

was also an old Blue Coat Boy and, hearing of the seaman's skill
with the sextant, promoted him to schoolmaster. George Thomas
was therefore, when finally discovered by Hurd, an obvious choice
for command of *Investigator* and this officer must be numbered
among the more successful catches of the haphazard press gang
system.

With George Thomas committed to the intricacies of the East
Coast, Hurd next looked to the approaches to the English Channel, which included the dangerous reefs of the Channel Islands
that had to be negotiated by vessels inward bound, and often with
but a poor idea of their position. Here Hurd was again fortunate
in obtaining the services of Commander Martin White who had
entered the Navy in 1793. He had seen a great deal of war service
but was chosen, as far as can be ascertained, for surveying in
H.M.S. *Fox*, as an officer having personal navigating experience
in the western approaches.

Whilst Hurd was getting into his stride at home the more
enlightened naval Commanders-in-Chief abroad had realised, as
surveyors have often realised since, that the closing stages of a
victorious war, whilst ships and men are still plentiful, is a time
when a surreptitious harvest of charts may be gleaned before the
cold economic winter that so surely follows. As early as 1811
Commander Francis Beaufort had been sent by the Commander-in-
Chief in the Mediterranean to explore in the frigate *Fredericksteen*
the remotest part of that sea, the southern coast of Turkey known
then as Karamania. This survey was finally terminated by a brush
with a party of Turks urged on by a fanatical dervish, who attacked
the surveyors as they embarked from the shore in a boat. A shot
fired by the dervish most seriously wounded Beaufort in the hip;
had this Moslem's aim been more exact, England would have been
deprived of her greatest Hydrographer of the Navy.

Again in the Mediterranean, the decision of Admiral Sir Robert
Hall to employ Lieutenant Smyth to carry out surveys in the
Sicilian gunboats under his command advanced the career of
another naval officer who was to gain fame in scientific fields, and
laid the foundation for the mapping of the greater part of the
Mediterranean by officers who served with him.

In 1809 the Right Honourable John Wilson Croker, LL.D., F.R.S., had been appointed Secretary to the Board of Admiralty, a post he was to hold for twenty-one years. As the Hydrographic Office was not yet a separate Admiralty Department it came directly and closely under the Secretary. Croker was an energetic and ambitious man and we can feel increasingly his hot breath on the back of Hurd's neck with the coming of peace in 1815 and a surge of economy as vigorous as anything we know today. During the years 1812 to 1817 the Navy dwindled in numbers from about 145,000 men to 20,000. It is thus of singular merit on Hurd's part that despite the lean times and close supervision by the all-powerful Secretary, he was able in the next nine years to lay the sure foundations of the Hydrographic Office.

The review of the state of the world's charting with the advent of peace, which Hurd laid before Croker in 1814, is an important document, the foundation upon which the Hydrographer laid his plans. He represented 'the great deficiency of our Nautical knowledge in almost every part of the World, but more particularly on the coast line of our own Dominions, and also with the hope that the present favourable moment for remedying these evils will be made use of, by calling into employment those of our Naval Officers whose scientific merits point them out as qualified for undertakings of this nature . . .'

Hurd then enumerates the areas which he considered ill charted—the whole of the China and Eastern Seas between Kamchatka and Van Diemen's Land; a great deal of the north and west coasts of New Holland; the eastern side of the African continent, and much of the west coast; doubtful shoals and islands laid down on the passage from the Cape of Good Hope to New Holland which made it a much feared undertaking; lack of Spanish charts of the South American continent from the River Plate to Trinidad; the southern shores of the Mediterranean were little known; the Syrian coast, the Greek Archipelago and the eastern side of the Adriatic were similarly unknown; and finally our own shores, particularly the Firth of Forth, the northern and western coasts of Scotland, the Shetlands and the coasts of Ireland except for Dublin and Cork Harbours. Well could Hurd conclude in 1814:

'At all events such an undertaking would keep alive the active services of many meritorious Officers whose abilities should not be permitted to lie dormant, whilst they can be turned to National benefit, and would also be the means of acquiring a mass of valuable information that could not fail of being highly advantageous to us in any future War, and would otherways redound to the Credit and Glory of this great Maritime Empire, whose flag flies triumphant in every part of the World.'

Much of Hurd's correspondence deals with pleas by officers who had returned inadequate Remark Books pleading that he would give them a certificate in order that they might draw their pay. ('I am in receipt of your Remark Books which I wish had been a little more bulky.') This generally unsatisfactory state of affairs proved to Hurd more than anything else that the majority of naval officers were unsuited for the detailed work required to prepare sailing directions and compile charts, and that special officers whose hearts were in the work were required. A corps of officers, selected for their mathematical and navigational abilities to carry out the Hydrographer's instructions worldwide, was gradually built up by Hurd. The founding date of what has become known as the 'Royal Naval Surveying Service' may be taken as 7 January 1817, when a Board Minute established special rates of pay for officers specialising in hydrography.

As Hurd expanded his service he found it increasingly difficult to get Masters, Masters' Mates or Midshipmen having the sufficient basic mathematical knowledge to act as surveying assistants or to find Lieutenants and Commanders suited to take command of vessels to be employed largely on scientific work. There were many disappointments; those in command constantly complained of the inadequacy of their assistants whilst they themselves were often to receive from Hurd the admonishing letter. These letters, carefully worded so that they infer shortcomings, but do not condemn so utterly that the officer's will to work is broken, set a pattern for his successors which they have followed into the present day. 'I hasten to acknowledge the receipt of your two letters of 21st May and 26th December last, as well as of the Packages containing your labours up to those periods, which I should not hesitate to say were comparatively trifling did not I know the weakness and inefficiency of your means, as well as the various obstacles you have to encounter in carrying out a scientific work so replete with difficulties.' Thus did Hurd write to Mr. Holbrook, Master, surveying in Newfoundland in 1819. Again to the same officer in 1820 he ends his letter, 'It is also necessary I should point out that the figures used in your Charts are of so diminutive a size it is very difficult to make out what the soundings are, and I will therefore thank you in future to have them enlarged.'

There were disappointments too with equipment. Dickinson's patent floating mark buoys, due to some defect in the moorings or construction, went adrift in the strong tidal streams of the Thames Estuary and caused Mr. Thomas much vexation. De Mayne's ship *Kangaroo* being struck by lightning in the Bahamas, his two timekeepers ceased to function and replacements had to be despatched to that distant station; these had to be sent to New Providence for, had they been taken in a vessel of the Fleet to Port Royal, de Mayne would have had to go there to get them and, meeting with the King's Ships, would certainly have been diverted by senior officers to troop carrying or other duties unconnected with surveying.

There was also difficulty in adjusting the earlier naval surveys with the new, and with the coastline of the Ordnance Survey at home, where it was being progressed under Colonel Colby's direction. An example may be cited when a survey by Joseph Whidbey, now Commissioner for the Construction of the Plymouth Breakwater, showed that recently completed work failed in any way to agree either with the coastline as depicted by Mackenzie and Spence or that of the recent Ordnance sheets, so that Commander White in *Shamrock* was despatched thither to observe from the breakwater terminals with a theodolite to all prominent objects so that the new breakwater might be laid down on the charts.

Steadily Hurd made progress with his direction of the surveys, even trivial items most necessary to the surveyor having to be passed by the Principal Officers and Commissioners of His Majesty's Navy before they might be purchased. Having been admonished by them for excessive expenditure on candles in his vessels Hurd set down in reply, 'as the duty of the Surveying Officers on all open and fine-weather days is occupied in making the necessary Remarks and Observations proper for that purpose they are of course constrained to commit to paper in the evening whatever has been the results of the day that they may be of free liberty to proceed on the following one without the risque of confusing their work. In executing this the most troublesome part of their labours a strong light is absolutely necessary and must therefore be made up either in quantity or quality of the articles alluded to.' The unchanging pattern of the surveyor's day was already clear.

In December 1819 Hurd reported to the Board the state of the surveys. Mr. Thomas was still with the *Investigator* in the Thames approaches; Lieutenant Hewett in *Protector* was carrying out surveys off the Norfolk coast to the limit of visibility and was delineating many of the shoals in that dangerous area; Captain White in *Shamrock* was employed in the English and Irish Channels; Mr. de Mayne in *Kangaroo* was in the West Indies; Mr. Holbrook was still struggling on in Newfoundland with local craft; Captain W. F. W. Owen had commenced a survey of the Great Lakes of Canada in 1815 on the cessation of hostilities of the American War; whilst Captain W. H. Smyth pursued his task in the Mediterranean, now in the sloop *Aid*. Many of these officers had young assistants whose names were later to shine in hydrographic history—White had Denham; de Mayne had Barnett; Lieutenant Bullock was on his way out with a small vessel, the *Snap*, to support Holbrook, for it was Hurd's desire to get exact positions of the many headlands in Newfoundland that he might use the excellent surveys of Cook and Lane which had been made without the benefit of timepieces.

The following year was to see success by Thomas in fixing dangers far from land in the Thames approaches for, undaunted by the failure of Dickinson's patent floats, he had been planning other ways to fix Long Sand and Kentish Knock shoals with reference to the mainland. Starting with Ordnance triangulated positions on the Essex coast he was now able to use in his offshore triangulation a navigation beacon which had been erected on the Gunfleet Sand, the Sunk Light Vessel and temporary stations marked and occupied at low water on Sunk Sand and on the Long Sand and a convenient stranded wreck on Kentish Knock twenty miles distant from the shore. Thomas's soundings of the intervening waters then fell neatly into place. This technique of using temporary stations on sandbanks to bridge the long gaps between light vessels and conspicuous wrecks opened up new possibilities for extending surveys across the shallow waters off the English coasts.

Hurd could be satisfied with progress at sea but in the office things were not as satisfactory as he could wish. In addition to John Walker as Hydrographer's Assistant and Walker's son Michael as an extra clerk and draughtsman, the remainder of the staff consisted only of one clerk, two engravers and a copperplate printer. Naval officers, paid by the week, were employed from time to time in the office to complete the drawings of their charts but Croker personally made certain they dallied no longer than they need.

Not only were the civilian staff inadequate in number to cope with the surveys sent in from sea but they were very badly paid: Walker, as Assistant Hydrographer, getting but £209 per annum although he had served the Department over twenty-five years in this post, whilst the remainder ranged down to about £109 per annum. Since 1816 it had been Hurd's plan to place the Admiralty charts on sale to the public so that they could be used by the mercantile interests of the Kingdom and by navigators throughout the world, and further, that by their sale his department might become self-supporting and able to pay its employees more suitably without detriment to the public purse. This he had frequently urged in official communications to Their Lordships, but to no avail. Hurd was somewhat mortified therefore in 1821 to have referred him by Croker for action just such a scheme, but proposed by a rather unsuitable chart seller named Faden, the self-styled 'King's Geographer'.

It was Faden's proposal that he should be the sole agent for the sale of Admiralty charts and although Hurd grasped the opportunity to put into practice his long-planned scheme, he insisted that other chart sellers, who had been more generous than Faden in handing over copyrights of charts formerly published on behalf of naval officers, should also be offered agencies. Once this had been accepted by the Board, it was Hurd's task to compile a catalogue of charts for sale. This, the first Admiralty chart catalogue giving a list of Admiralty charts and the names of agents, was published in 1821 and set the seal on Hurd's great work, for his health had recently been declining and he died in 1823.

Hurd will be remembered for his recognition that surveying was a specialised task requiring officers of a scientific and mathematical bent, that these officers should be permanently retained and specially paid and that particular ships should be allotted for their use. Officers in command of survey ships began to receive regular hydrographic instructions, prepared by the Hydrographer to meet his charting needs and issued under the authority of Their Lordships.

Hurd is truly the Father of the Surveying Service, which since his day has comprised those vessels of the Royal Navy specially commissioned to carry out the Hydrographer's tasks at sea.

CHAPTER EIGHT

Owen Commences
his African Survey

A fellow prisoner with Matthew Flinders on Île de France for the
last two years of that unfortunate officer's confinement was Lieutenant W. F. W. Owen who, until his capture by the French, had
led a full life in the Navy since 1788 and had carried out surveys
of the Maldives during a long period of distinguished service in
the East.

By 1815 Owen was a post captain in charge of a survey of the
Great Lakes of Canada, for the unsuccessful British naval actions
on the lakes during the American War of 1812 had demonstrated
our lack of geographic and hydrographic knowledge in the vital
boundary area between Canada and America.

Owen, assisted by Lieutenants Alexander Vidal and Henry
Bayfield and Mr. John Harris as Master among others, had their
headquarters in 'Hydrographic House', Kingston, where Mrs. Harris looked after a very happy team, doing their cooking and their
mending and other family chores.

In 1816 Owen joined Captain Peter Heywood at the Hydrographic Office where both advised Hurd in the establishing of the
Surveying Service, and Owen exercised his knowledge of Portuguese in translating charts and sailing directions of that country.
Both Heywood and Owen were deeply religious men, both had
travelled and surveyed widely, both had suffered imprisonment,
one in the Île de France, the other in 'Pandora's Box'; whilst Owen

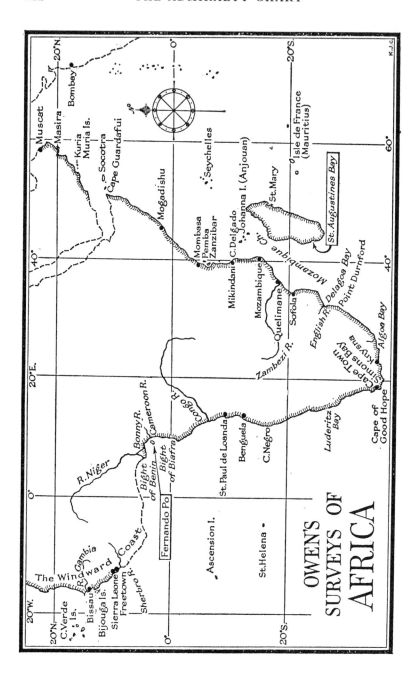

OWEN'S SURVEYS OF AFRICA

had been promoted for his conduct at the Mutiny of Spithead, Heywood had been court-martialled for his part in the *Bounty* affair, but had happily been pardoned and still bore on his throat the native tattoo marks he had received when living with the mutineers among the islanders of Tahiti. Both, years later, were offered the post of Hydrographer of the Navy.

Whilst Owen had been on the Lakes, the first surveying expedition organised by the Admiralty to the continent of Africa had sailed in the schooner *Congo* to explore the river of that name. After penetrating 280 miles upstream, Commander James Tuckey and five of his officers died of a fever, which terminated the survey and set a dismal precedent to be followed on a grander scale by many surveying expeditions to the great continent before the nature of malaria was understood and its terror conquered by quinine.

In 1806 the British captured the Cape of Good Hope, and in 1820 the British settlers were established in Algoa Bay, so that eyes were again turned to Africa and to the possibility of trade expanding northwards along the eastern shores; this area was known only to a handful of survivors from vessels employed on the trade to India which had been driven upon this inhospitable coast. Those who had survived the violence of the breaking rollers on the beaches and the hostility of the African tribes had sometimes, after incredible hardships, reached the Portuguese trading posts.

Three centuries earlier the Portuguese had built and maintained fortresses along the coastline northwards into the Arabian Peninsula, where they had fortified the natural harbour of Muscat. But now the Imam of Muscat claimed sovereignty over the whole east coast of Africa as far south as Cape Delgado, and his dhows, making use of the changing monsoons, traded regularly to Mombasa, Zanzibar and other ports southwards as far as Mikindani.

The hydrography of the area under Arab control was even more sparse than that southward through the Mozambique Channel, for it was the practice of vessels bound to and from India to shun the coast, calling only at Johanna in the Comoro Islands, where a friendly population had built up a modest reputation for providing an adequate, if noisy, provisioning service.

Dalrymple's successor as Hydrographer to the East India Company, James Horsburgh, had compiled a directory of the eastern seas which had a good name for reliability, but even this was much in error for the East Coast of Africa. A survey of that portion of the coast under Arab control made by Smee of the East India Company in 1810 was of too small a scale to be of any real value.

Not only was Britain beginning to look for an expansion of her own trade along the East Coast of Africa but she was also interested now in suppressing the existing trade of others, for in 1807 the British Act abolishing the Slave Trade had been passed, and although this act had primarily been aimed at the trade from West Africa to the West Indies, yet there was also very considerable activity on the East Coast of Africa.

Both Arabs and Portuguese engaged in the Slave Trade, but whereas the Arab slavemasters went themselves far inland to take their slaves, marching them roped together to the coast and shipping them by dhow via Madagascar, the Portuguese were content to buy them from the Arabs or from the victors in African tribal warfare, to be held in barracoons in the Portuguese seaport settlements to await shipment in American, Portuguese or Brazilian vessels to Cuba and Brazil.

A treaty of friendship between Britain and Portugal of 1810 offered co-operation in suppressing the export of slaves from East Africa, and in the early 1820s British naval officers stationed at Mauritius were engaged in making treaties with King Radama of Madagascar, the King of Johanna and the Imam of Muscat for abolishing the slave trade, although the latter still permitted direct coastal slave trade between Africa and Arabia.

In 1821 preparations were being made at the Admiralty for a formidable expedition to survey the whole East Coast of Africa from the Cape of Good Hope to Cape Guardafui (now Raas Caseyr), including off-lying islands and the lesser known parts of Madagascar, during which survey a full report was to be made on the hinterland and the natives.

In command of this task was placed Captain Owen, whilst some of the Lieutenants of the expedition—who were now drawn from the newly established surveying service—are today household

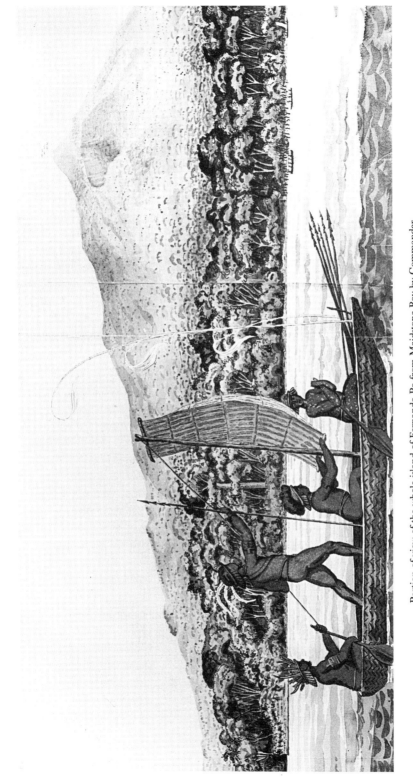

Portion of view of the whole island of Fernando Po from Maidstone Bay by Commander
T. Boteler, H.M.S. *Barracouta*, 1827. The original, held by The Hydrographic Office, measures 1 ft. high by 11 ft. 6 ins long.

words among their modern successors—Vidal, William Mudge, Thomas Boteler and Richard Owen. Officers from the general service were also included in the ships, of course, and these were soon somewhat critical of surveyors' 'humbug' as they referred to the niceties of quadrant observations, the consciously delicate handling of the chronometers, the careful nailing of the quarter-deck around the compass with brass instead of iron, the frequent conversational references to Flinders' new-found deviation of the compass on every occasion that the vessel but slightly altered her heading, and the regular larding of discussion with mathematical formulae. These were all preoccupations of the young gentlemen who had elected to serve as surveyors, but in no way detracted from their capacity for hard work, for the task was already for them a scientific vocation.

The *Leven*, a ship-sloop, was chosen for Captain Owen, whilst Commander William Cutfield accompanied him in the small brig *Barracouta*. Whilst at this time the Lords Commissioners exercised operational control from the Admiralty, up till 1832 the Navy Board in separate premises dealt with administration, victualling, and ship construction, etc. And whereas Owen had no complaint about his officers, the fitting of the ships for this laborious survey was far from satisfactory. The narrator of Owen's expedition, writing after the ships had returned, wrote: 'During the equipment of this expedition both Captain Owen and his officers were con-stantly exposed to the frivolous annoyances so often complained of in the administration of our civil departments of the Navy. No office ever defeated the intention of its projectors so perfectly as the Navy Board; for instead of expediting the equipment of His Majesty's Ships, they threw every obstacle in the way, either by an ingenious misconstruction or wilful delay.'

Two additional four-oared gigs were supplied to each ship and these extra boats, in which so much of the surveyor's time has to be spent, were given names—*Melville*, after the First Lord Com-missioner who had signed the Hydrographic Instructions, *Croker*, the redoubtable Secretary to the Admiralty, *Hurd*, the Hydro-grapher, and *Troughton*, the maker of so many of the instruments provided for the expedition. This naming of boats established a practice which has been followed ever since in the surveying service; but today it is usual to name the ship's sounding boats after earlier surveying ships, and in fact the wheel has come full circle for the sounding crews of H.M.S. *Owen* twenty-five years ago spent their long days in the *Barracouta* and *Leven* and others named after the ships of Owen's squadron.

Despite the Navy Board, Owen insisted upon and obtained three iron cables for each ship instead of one.

New surveying techniques to be employed on the voyage included the use of Sir W. Congreve's rockets which, when fired vertically, could be expected to obtain heights in relation to the size of the rocket used. Before sailing from England various sizes of rockets were launched from Shooter's Hill, the elevation of their explosion being observed by theodolite from Woolwich Warren, a known distance from the launch site. Thus the height reached by each size of rocket was calculated so that Owen would later be able to choose a suitable rocket which would be visible from two stations in his African Survey.

The purpose of the rockets was to measure the meridian distance between two stations by observing the explosion time of the rocket by chronometer at each position. Owen described the method as 'a ready and simple method of measuring the difference of longitude between two places not very distant'. Another successful use of the rockets was when they were employed horizontally to drive off a strong attack by Hollontonte natives upon Lieutenant Vidal when he was making night observations for position with a theodolite ashore at Delagoa Bay.

There are many references to the use of the traditional gun for base measurement, sometimes mistaken by important native chiefs for a salute, to which they replied; whereas when a gun salute might have been expected Owen usually despatched a Lieutenant ahead by boat to explain that this courtesy could not be offered for fear of disturbing the all-important battery of chronometers.

The Massey Patent log was carried, which, although patented in 1802, seemed to be regarded even in 1821 by surveyors as a new device which added greatly to the accuracy of their running surveys, for exact distances run could be measured by hauling in the log and reading the recording dials. Three brass fins attached to a hollow copper tube imparted a rotary movement to the log, which system, modified so that it might be read onboard, has lasted to the present day as a basic method of measuring distance run at sea.

Lisbon was visited on the voyage out, and an immediate gift of a survey of the Cape Verde Islands (recently made by Vidal on a previous voyage in *Leven*) to the Minister of Marine put the authorities in a suitable mood to provide Owen with a letter to the Governor of Mozambique permitting survey work in the Portuguese African territory.

The expedition touched at the Canaries and the Cape Verdes, and located and fixed the positions of the lonely islands of Martin Vaz and Trindade, dangers which had been reported in widely different places over recent years.

A visit to Rio de Janeiro enabled Owen to purchase a tender of a suitable size and draught for entering the rivers which were to be explored upon the African coast. An American steamboat was obtained which, named *Cockburn* after another of the Lords Commissioners and rigged as a schooner, was towed by *Leven* to the Cape, not without considerable damage to the smaller vessel, which required immediate repairs on arrival in Simon's Bay.

At the Cape, and particularly in Table Bay, the squadron officers immediately became aware of the lack of seamanlike precautions that were being taken by the new British authorities to safeguard shipping where the most violent storms were a not infrequent occurrence. There was no service for the supply of spare anchors and cables to those in need, and the many vessels using the new iron cables subjected these to such heavy stresses in the great Atlantic swells that they parted and the ships drove ashore to leeward in every storm which blew. It was common knowledge at the Cape that unprincipled men, having insured their vessels for high premiums, chose Table Bay for the termination of their voyage.

Owen advised his vessels to employ only a shackle or so of cable next to the anchor, to take the chafe and friction of the seabed, to which should be spliced a very considerable length of hempen cable; moored thus, the vessels of the squadron rode out many a gale off the exposed coasts of Africa where great ocean swells are ever ready to join with the stormy winds to drive vessels ashore to their destruction.

A British Observatory had recently been established at the Cape and many observations had been taken by Fearon Fallows, the Astronomer, but Owen, who used Cape Town as the meridian from which to measure all his longitudes in Africa, felt the need for further observations. Whilst he busied himself here, and the *Leven* waited for *Cockburn* to be repaired, *Barracouta* set out along the coast to the east and Lieutenant Vidal took the remaining officers under his instruction for a survey of False Bay.

An incident during the False Bay survey illustrates, perhaps, a typical attitude of a seaman finding in the early days of life in a survey ship just what he had let himself in for. Towards dusk on a blustery afternoon Vidal and his boat's crew became swamped and were cast ashore south of Gordon's Bay, and were guided into camp there by a party of fellow surveyors employed in firing rockets for a meridian distance measurement from Simonstown. However, William Smith, the coxswain of the boat, paid no heed to the beckoning rockets and eventually made his way to Cape Town, where he was later apprehended as a deserter. Confronted by Captain Owen he confessed that he 'ran away from dislike to engaging in so arduous a service, subject to such exposure, varying from the ordinary duties of a seaman and without any further reward than if he were onboard a guardship in an English port'. During the next two years he performed many laborious services without a murmur until he died of fever.

For interpreters along the coast, Owen arranged to receive from Robben Island six Kaffirs who, having entered the boundaries of the colony, had been lucky to be made prisoners. They came aboard in a dismal state, clothed in filthy skins with hands tied. Once released, clothed in seaman's rig and allocated to messes for victuals, they proved to be sterling fellows of whom Jacob, a former chief, and Fire, a warrior, were outstanding, and popular alike with officers and men.

On the last day of August 1822 *Leven* and *Cockburn* sailed east for Delagoa Bay and a rendezvous with *Barracouta*, awaiting them there, having taken the first positive steps in the great continental survey in her passage along the shores of the Cape Colony. Her officers had made their running survey; they had remarked upon the fishing potential of the Agulhas Bank and the vast saltpans ready at hand ashore for preserving the fish; they had noted the possibilities of a port at Knysna; they had seen the new settlement at Port Elizabeth; and in the survey of the natives which had been required of them they reported that the country from Keiskama along the coast to Delagoa Bay was in possession of several tribes of warring negroes. These did not appear to be the original inhabitants but conquerors from the interior who had replaced each other in succession; the great chief Chaka was in the ascendancy at the time and his ruthless methods were steadily depopulating the area. In a review of Owen's *Narrative*, Lieutenant Wolfe wrote in 1833, 'The state of these countries, which have scarcely had any intercourse with civilised nations, is a direct proof in refutation of the theories of poets and philosophers, who represent the ignorance of the savage as virtuous simplicity—his miserable poverty as frugality and temperance—and his stupid indolence as a laudable contempt for wealth. How different are the facts! We ever found uncultivated man a composition of cunning, treachery, drunkenness and gluttony.'

In October all three ships of the squadron were in English River in Delagoa Bay, where a Portuguese trading post was situated but whose inmates admitted that they could offer no protection to the survey parties for they held no authority beyond the range of their guns.

Three large streams debouched into the main river entrance where friendly natives had been for many years in the regular habit of supplying English whalers, thus giving the place its name. It was now Owen's plan to survey the three minor rivers to the extent of their navigation and here he first met the great scourge that was to remain with him to a greater or lesser degree throughout the whole of his coasting voyages of Africa.

Midshipman Tambs had been with the parties in the rivers. He had been hurled from his boat by a hippopotamus and a night or so later, clothed only in his nightshirt, had, with his sword, driven off a party of Hollontontes attacking the camp, emerging unscathed from both adventures; but back onboard on the evening of 24th October 1823 he took suddenly ill and died of fever within a few hours.

A week later Captain Lechmere, who had, in order to learn the art of surveying, accompanied Captain Owen on the voyage as a companion, came off from the observatory ashore in a sorry state. His fever rose until his cries brought Owen to his cotside. To overcome the woeful sound of his distress Owen sang the ballad 'Here a sheer hulk lies poor Tom Bowline'; pathetically true even to the end when at the words 'His soul is gone aloft!' Lechmere expired with a long guttural sound.

To relate the fatal fevers which now took place among the officers and men from *Leven* and *Barracouta* who had been in the rivers would be as tedious as it would be dismal to describe the foreboding and nervous panic of many others who daily expected to be struck down. Suffice it to say that by the end of November the attendance at a funeral had become a dreaded daily duty. The effects of the deceased, sold by auction, as is naval custom, sometimes changed owners twice in one week.

Owen, who had given compassionate leadership during this melancholy period, now decided that the two larger ships should make for the open sea, leaving only *Cockburn*, whose crew had as yet suffered no casualties, commanded by Richard Owen to progress the survey of the remaining river and the bay.

Owen also had Captain Cutfield brought onboard *Leven* from *Barracouta* in an effort to save his life but he too succumbed and Lieutenant Vidal took command of *Barracouta*; whilst both Mudge and Boteler received promotion as First Lieutenants of *Leven* and *Barracouta* as a direct result of the fever's destruction.

Setting course southwards, the now familiar running survey was resumed, plotting on a scale of a half inch to a mile. New-found features ashore or under the sea were easy to name for the men who continued to die onboard, and each was made immortal—'in fact there is not a remarkable spot between English River and Morley's Bank that does not record the fate of our departed

shipmates.' The coast was followed south to Point Durnford, happily named this time after the young officer who delineated it,
before foul weather drove the ships from the coast and they stood
away for the east coast of Madagascar where the ships spent two
weeks, including Christmas, at St. Mary's, a French settlement.

Victualling at Johanna Island, in the Comoros, the vessels
reached Mozambique where hospitality offered by the Portuguese
Governor extended to the establishment of an observatory on the
roof of his palace; but here, too, the Portuguese held sway only in
the immediate environs. The northeast monsoon being favourable,
the ships now surveyed their way southward to meet up again in
English River with *Cockburn*.

As the two ships sailed southwestward across Delagoa Bay the
officers with their spyglasses could see *Cockburn* at anchor in the
river with two small merchantmen. But even the rattle of the cable
as *Leven* came to anchor elicited not a sign of movement on the
decks of the vessels at anchor. Hurriedly a boat was lowered and
Mr. Williams sent across to *Cockburn*, where he stepped on to the
empty decks and went below to find Mr. Tudor and a native cook
in their beds, too feeble to raise a smile of welcome, whilst a few
hours later young Richard Owen and two officers were found sick
onshore.

Undoubtedly these terrible losses had been brought about by
malaria, but at this time the fever was attributed to the miasma
that rose from the low-lying river banks and from the acres of
mud which lay uncovered in the estuaries at low tide. It is tragic
to realise how near the officers were to understanding the true
cause; Richard Owen reported that the mosquitoes in the
Mapoota, which was the river he had been exploring, had been
a dreadful scourge and that often those who had been most
worried by mosquitoes had been the first to die; Captain Owen
never believed that bleeding, the naval surgeon's only recourse,
was helpful for fever, and in fact Richard Owen's surgeon had
died with his lancet still in his own arm. Whilst at St. Mary's the
officers had met a Frenchman who had lived there in native style
for many years, and noted that he took large quantities of quinine,
which he reported an infallible remedy for fever.

The Portuguese had been proving troublesome towards the remaining crews of two trading vessels, insisting that they trade with the natives only through them, whilst King Kapell of Temby on the south side of the river opposite the Portuguese was most anxious that Owen should arrange a treaty between himself and King George IV, that he might cede a large area of land to the British. This Owen accepted with little hesitation, for at heart he was an empire builder as well as a surveyor.

An immediate and minor product of this treaty was permission for 'English Bill', a garrulous native with a few words of whaler's English, and twelve of his companions to join the squadron to make up for some of the many seamen who had died.

On subsequent visits to Temby Owen had to re-hoist the British flag which had been lowered in his absence by the Portuguese. It was two years before Earl Bathurst, reading in Downing Street Owen's reports, was convinced of the rightness of the treaty; it lasted, however, till 1872 when, as a result of an agreement between Portugal and the Transvaal Republic on their common boundary which ignored Britain's claim to Temby, Britain entered into a long wrangle with Portugal. This finally went to arbitration before the President of the French Republic who decided in Portugal's favour and Owen's little piece of empire disappeared for ever.

The squadron now departed for the Cape, Lieutenant Johnes, temporarily in command of *Cockburn*, having the misfortune to lose the vessel, but without loss of life, on Muizenberg beach, having attempted to make harbour in Simon's Bay at night.

Here in the dockyard an office was taken over and between April and the middle of June no less than nineteen Double Elephant*-sized fair charts were drawn by the officers and forwarded to England.

Meanwhile 'English Bill' was much in demand in Cape Town with his local knowledge of Delagoa Bay, and three vessels were fitted out for trading to that port by his lavish hosts. He was seen at Green Point races, at Government House, at the ball which was

---

* Double Elephant is a size still used in describing chart paper today. It measures 40 ins. × 26¾ ins.

held onboard *Leven* with dancing until dawn, and often Owen used to catch him as he was sneaking off to bed and keep him talking far into the night, so amusing was his conversation and so engaging his manner.

Before the squadron again left the Cape for the East Coast Owen purchased a schooner, the *Albatross*, to replace *Cockburn* as tender, again with Richard Owen in command. When the squadron sailed they took with them Mr. Threlfall, the first missionary to Temby.

Northwards from English River Owen split up his squadron to complete the whole coast as far as Cape Delgado and the three vessels, after making a rendezvous at Sofala three months later, sailed in company to Mozambique, where Owen presented the Portuguese Governor with a complete set of charts, much to his satisfaction, although he must have known, as Owen now surely did, how little of the territory he really ruled and how little attempt was being made under the Treaty of 1810 to reduce the slave trade, as the crowded barracoons, most particularly at Quelimane, testified.

Mr. Forbes, the botanist, and two companions had been landed by Vidal at Quelimane to explore the Zambezi, an expedition during which all three succumbed to fever. *Barracouta* had an exciting time both at Quelimane and at Sofala. At the former place the vessel had found herself anchored outside the bar at night with a rising sea and swell, the rollers even sweeping one man overboard, who was rescued by a rope thrown to him by a fellow seaman. At dawn it was clear that there was no chance of weighing and making to windward and as the tide was now at its height Lieutenant Boteler, who was in command in the temporary absence of Vidal, buoyed and slipped the cable and ran for the bar. As the shallower water was reached the whole sea was a boiling whiteness, whilst the roar of the breakers burst upon the ears, until suddenly the ship rode into the calm water within.

When the survey of the river and roadstead in Quelimane was complete *Barracouta* was navigated over the now peaceful bar to find the anchor buoy missing. However, it was the surveyor's invariable habit to fix the anchorage position with horizontal quadrant angles, a practice new to the boatswain. 'Damme,' he explained with a squirt of tobacco juice, 'I never heard of an anchor being picked up with a quadrant before.' But before the voyage was out he too was using the quadrant to progress the work.

Barracouta's arrival at Sofala was not so fortunate, for a local mulatto pilot put the vessel on the bar from which she was dislodged only after much laying out of kedge anchors and throwing the guns overboard. Whilst these latter were being recovered the pilot who, since the grounding, had been extremely morose, went berserk and stabbed the surgeon who had been trying to cheer him. Bleeding himself, the surgeon relieved the acute pain of the wound below his heart and eventually recovered. The pilot was never brought to justice for the ship's surgeon refused permission for a local surgeon to 'probe the depth of the wound' as part of the build-up of evidence.

Having completed the Portuguese section of the coast, it was now Owen's intention to commence work on that part north of Cape Delgado, and Vidal in *Barracouta* was ordered to take *Albatross* under his command, sail northwards as far as Patta in 2° South and then to survey his way south. Meanwhile Owen in *Leven* (which was the better sailer), decided to make direct for Bombay where he could charter a vessel with provisions for the squadron and despatch her to Mombasa; he could see a copy of Smee's survey of the African coast; he could send completed charts to England in an East Indiaman, and then proceed to Muscat to inform the Imam of the activities in which his squadron was engaged. Knowing Owen, we should also expect him to bring up with the Imam the subject of slaving on the coast. He would also be able at Bombay to get replacements for his men, for despite the hard discipline for which the Navy had a reputation, seamen when abroad preferred service in H.M. Ships, and they would readily quit merchantmen for this purpose.

The officers and men of *Leven* found the cultivated life and the lively trade of Bombay a great tonic after the dreariness of the African coast where the only trade of note was that of slavery. Not since Cape Town had everyone enjoyed life so much.

Christmas Day 1823 saw *Leven's* arrival at Muscat, anchored amidst a forest of dhows' masts in the cove below the white forts, built but long abandoned by the Portuguese. The town was one huge, filthy, thriving bazaar where Indians of every caste were encouraged by the Imam to pursue their trade.

Captain Owen received some trifling gifts from the Sultan, gave his usual present of the New Testament in Arabic in return, and was supplied both with a pilot and an interpreter for the Arabian and African coasts. The Sultan's return call onboard *Leven* caused some pandemonium for a great many pigs had been taken onboard in Bombay and it was imperative that they should be out of the ship before His Moslem Highness should set eyes upon them. Every pig was put into the boats, which were towed away temporarily out of sight. It was a still morning and the pigs were greatly agitated so that the whole cove echoed and re-echoed with the squeals of these unclean beasts for over an hour before the royal visit.

On New Year's Day Owen sailed south along the coast of Arabia. When coasting inshore the vessel was followed by a motley crowd of Arabs mounted on camels, hoping against hope, the pilot said, that the ship might be wrecked and that they would be at hand for the looting.

Past Masira and Kuria Muria Islands, Captain Owen was stricken by a disease called in these parts 'blat', his first illness of the voyage. Consequently the vessel quit the mainland, coasted the north side of Socotra and commenced the survey of Africa at Cape Guardafui (now Raas Caseyr), when Owen was once again on deck.

Now followed a run down the long barren Somali coast, to Mogadishu, a calling place for dhows. Further south a letter from Vidal informed Owen that the coast had now been surveyed southwards and he was able to hurry on.

Arriving at Mombasa, Owen was surprised to see a fleet of dhows of the Imam of Muscat apparently blockading the port, whilst British colours flew from the fort. The Sheikh of Mombasa was opposing the Imam's claimed right to rule the city and he had tried, without avail, to persuade Captain Vidal to permit him to fly the British flag. This question he now put to Owen, offering to place his whole country, including the Island of Pemba, under protection of the British. To this Owen assented, provided the slave trade was abolished in Mombasa by the Sheikh.

Owen was delighted to have secured such a fine British base for anti-slave trade activities and, sending the Third Lieutenant, Johannes Jacobus Reitz, ashore as Governor with one Midshipman, a Corporal of Marines and three seamen as his staff, sent for the Commander of the blockading squadron and ordered him to raise the siege.

Having, as he thought, thus easily secured a second piece of British Empire, Owen sailed confidently southward, never thinking how little this gift was to be appreciated by those in authority at home, when they received another report of territorial acquisition from one whom they had sent as a chart-maker.

In March, exactly as arranged, all three vessels made rendezvous in Mozambique and as Vidal had reached his target at Cape Delgado, the whole East Coast of Africa was now complete.

It was imperative to pause now for another drawing of fair charts which, there being no facilities available ashore at Mozambique, had to be drawn in the Captain's cabins of the two larger vessels, the only adequate spaces onboard, and with all the inconvenience that this entailed for Owen and Vidal.

The whole 6,000 miles of the East Coast of Africa having now been virtually completed, only the great island of Madagascar remained, and some work in the Seychelles group and at Mauritius. Owen again divided his forces; whilst Vidal with *Barracouta* and *Albatross* worked on the west coast of Madagascar Owen, with occasional visits to the Seychelles and Mauritius whence he could despatch reports and receive mails, concentrated on the east coast.

In November the squadron assembled at Mombasa, only to hear the melancholy news that Reitz had died of fever on a trip up country and that Commodore Nourse, the Commander of the Cape Station, had appointed a Lieutenant Emery from his flagship to continue as Governor. Nourse himself, a good friend of Owen, had died of fever after sleeping ashore at Zanzibar.

On Christmas Day 1824, Captain Owen, feeling that his great task was nearing completion, and with the thoughts of his ship's company turned towards home, arrived at the Seychelles where a letter of further instructions from the Admiralty awaited him. He was, on his homeward voyage, to survey the West Coast of Africa from the Congo to the Gambia Rivers. Vidal and Mudge, who had earlier experience of parts of the West Coast during *Leven's* previous commission, were able to state that as far as fever was concerned there was little to choose between the two coasts. This was heavy news for any Captain to have to break to his men on Christmas Day. It is happy, however, to record that the French inhabitants of Mahé, who had been treated leniently by the British after the capture of the island in 1806, now offered generous hospitality to the Englishmen, who found the ladies 'graceful and pleasing' and 'that morality was not among their leading virtues'. Perhaps the West Coast of Africa was forgotten for a time by the men ashore from *Leven*.

Death still struck as the crews pursued their work in Madagascar; here fever was not so frequent for there were not the great rivers to explore, but dysentery was ever present and two young midshipmen were murdered by natives whilst coastlining Grave Island on the west coast.

However, there were happier incidents onboard and three natives of *Leven* were born, for there were at least five English women in the squadron. When Mrs. Gregory died soon after the birth of her child, Owen took over custody of the infant, for its father had previously died of fever. It must be assumed that the care of the baby fell to one of the other women among the crew.

There was much satisfaction for Owen whilst working in Madagascar for here he was in touch with the military activities of King Radama who, in attempting to suppress the slave trade, had many enemies. On one occasion Vidal was able to transport a party of Radama's troops along the coast by sea that they might reach the seat of rebellion in time to quash it. On another occasion Owen himself captured a slaver near St. Augustine's Bay; flying a small Portuguese flag, with a Swiss captain and a varied collection of officers, the vessel was bound for Brazil with 172 slaves. The story of her recent activities in collecting slaves was easily obtained, for among her crew was a deserter from *Leven* who, in his anxiety to escape Owen's punishment, was eager to be as informative as possible.

Owen took *Soleil*, the slave ship, to Mauritius where there was a Vice-Admiralty Court for the condemnation of slavers. But this triumph was completely overshadowed by the instructions recently received from England by the Governor at Mauritius. The Imam of Muscat had not taken lightly the turning away by Owen of his blockading fleet of dhows outside Mombasa. He had been busy through his British contacts in India reminding the home government of his treaty signed with Captain Moresby in 1822 whereby his coastal slave trade to Arabia was preserved. The British Government rejected all that Owen had obtained at Mombasa and the young naval Governor, Lieutenant Emery, was eventually taken off and the British flag lowered in 1826.

Subsequent events bore out Owen's wisdom in proposing the taking over of Mombasa as a protectorate. Slaving continued along the coast after Emery had left and it was necessary for Britain to take Mombasa all over again in order to continue the crusade against slavery—which, as Lecky once said, 'may probably be regarded as among the three or four perfectly virtuous pages comprised in the history of nations.'

Before Emery died in June 1889 at the age of ninety-five he expressed himself happy in the knowledge that the whole coastal strip, including Mombasa which he had briefly governed, had been granted to the Imperial British East Company.

A brief visit to Delagoa Bay on the way south to the Cape did nothing to raise Owen's spirits, for here he found a new Portuguese Governor once again interfering in the trade between English vessels and the natives of the land Owen had accepted for Britain, and again he had to make a strong gesture; on this occasion the squadron prepared to demolish the fort before the Governor would release the English merchant brig *Eleanor*. And there was evidence from the gloomy natives that slavers were now regularly visiting English River and Owen feared that the men of Temby who had sailed with him so long, and whom he was now putting ashore, would perhaps next put to sea against their will in shackles on the long desperate voyage to Brazil.

CHAPTER NINE

The African Survey
Completed

At the Cape, which was reached by the Squadron on 28th
September 1825, the familiar chart drawing and ship refitting
routine was put in hand. Only Mumgatawney, from Delagoa Bay,
and one or two other natives now remained onboard, for 'English
Bill' had landed at Delagoa, whilst Jacob was now right-hand
man to the great chief Chaka, to whom his knowledge of
Europeans was valuable, and poor Fire had been killed in an
affray onshore. Captain Owen had once again to recruit, and
almost succeeded in obtaining the services of twenty Irishmen
who walked off their ship in a body to sign on in *Leven*, claiming
to have been taken from their country by force—did slavery extend
even to Ireland? The Master of the vessel took the case to court
and Commodore Christian, who had now succeeded Owen's
deceased friend Commodore Nourse, ordered the men to be
returned to their ship.

Nor was the new Commodore helpful with officers, for he
appointed officers from shore, untrained in survey work, over the
heads of those whom Owen had hoped to promote as a reward
for their faithful service during the long drawn out survey of the
east coast.

The new instructions received from home ordered the survey
to begin only when the Congo River was reached, but as the
squadron was passing northwards in any case Owen made plans

that either he in *Leven* or Vidal in *Barracouta* would keep in sight of the shore by day, and each would attempt to sight different parts of the coast. The two vessels were to rendezvous at Luanda south of the Congo before making plans for the next stage and, meanwhile, *Albatross* was sailed via Ascension to await Owen at Sierra Leone.

The best account of the voyage northwards to Luanda is given by Vidal. On 26th October he sailed from the Cape, his crew cheerily singing 'Homeward Bound' at the capstan as they weighed, for at last they felt the ship was heading in the right direction, and they ignored for the moment the many tasks in fever-infested rivers that lay between them and England.

'The neat farmhouses of the Dutch, so numerous in the vicinity of the Cape, with lofty highland scenery that surrounds them, gradually disappeared, and was succeeded by a wilderness of sterile granite hills, above which, in the distance, the lofty peaks of an inland range of mountains occasionally showed themselves.'

On 21st November the officers saw through their spyglasses the remains of the cross erected by Bartolomew Diaz on Angra Peguena and anchored their vessel in the bay beyond (now Luderitz Bay). Vidal himself landed, for although there was a high wind it was off the shore, raising sheets of spray but no sizeable waves; with a small party he scaled the headland—fine blown sand lashing their faces. Vidal made observations with the theodolite for position at the site of the cross, which had suffered damage, perhaps by human hands, and the inscription was worn beyond legibility.

The next landmark worthy of remark was Cape Negro in 15° 41' South where the first palm tree, the first hut and the first solitary native for many hundred miles were seen; and here, too, were the remains of a small marble cross erected by Diaz.

Benguela, the most southerly Portuguese settlement on the west coast, was reached—a wretched place of little trade and few livestock, but with an abundance of lions and other carnivores which even entered the town in search of food. This was extremely satisfying to the newly arrived Portuguese Governor who had particularly sought an African post so that he might gratify his love of the chase, apparently acquired during an education at Reading in England!

Relations between Portugal and her former colony Brazil being strained at this time, there was some nervous apprehension in the Portuguese settlements of an attack from sea, which explains the rather unfortunate entry by *Barracouta* to Luanda: although a local pilot had been embarked, the battery commander fired three shots which fell very close to the vessel. This called for a vigorous protest by Vidal on landing, who demanded satisfaction for an insult offered to the Flag of His Britannic Majesty.

The Governor was extremely apologetic and the same mistake was not repeated when *Leven* arrived a day or so later. Both Owen and Vidal were then daily table guests of the Governor at this beautiful old crumbling city.

Here the vessels parted again, *Barracouta* to work northwards and westwards around the Gulf of Guinea and *Leven* for Ascension and Sierra Leone.

Freetown had, as the name implies, been founded by the British Abolitionists in 1787 as a refuge for liberated slaves where they might be given useful employment. There were many difficulties in running such a grandiose and distant scheme from England without governmental backing but with much foreign criticism, and in 1808 the town and the surrounding district were taken over by the British Government as the colony of Sierra Leone. As a logical step, in 1817 a Court of Mixed Commission was set up to condemn slaving prizes brought in by the cruising vessels of the Royal Navy. The Governor was also given some responsibility for scattered British trading stations both here on the 'Windward Coast' as it was called, and along the thousand-mile stretch of coastline eastwards to the Bight of Biafra.

The Îles de Los and the Banana Islands had recently been acquired by the British Government as these formed strategic outposts to the north and south of Freetown, and a survey of the new possessions was Owen's first task when he reached the Windward Coast. He had completed work at Îles de Los, had called at Freetown to collect *Albatross* which, with Richard Owen still in command, had been working in the river, and was at the Banana

Islands when he was interrupted by the arrival of the Governor
of Sierra Leone with a small squadron of colonial vessels. He was
bound on an expedition to the Sherborough River to destroy the
slaving establishments of a notorious slaver called James Tucker,
and he wished Owen's assistance. Such work was close to Owen's
heart and he transferred to *Albatross* and led the squadron, for in
this smaller vessel the river could be navigated.

After some searching, Tucker's quarters were found far up the
Kittan River and Lieutenant Mudge took over the lead in the
smallest of the colonial schooners. He forced his way upstream,
landed a shore party and, successfully overwhelming the armed
men guarding the stronghold, burnt the place to the ground with
only one or two of his men wounded.

Of course Mudge had combined a running survey of the river
with his punitive mission, but even this short sortie upstream took
its toll as soon as the crews got back to sea. Major General Turner,
the Governor, died of fever, as did three midshipmen and several
seamen. It was the same sad conclusion to every river expedition,
however brief and for whatever purpose.

Owen next moved to the archipelago of the Bijagos Islands,
which thrusts far out to sea off the coast of Guinea beyond the
mouths of the Rio Grande and Jeba Rivers. The Portuguese station
at Bissau was situated on the north side of the Jeba estuary.

Owen had added one of the colonial vessels to his squadron,
perhaps with permission but perhaps without, now that the Governor was dead.

Here Owen had a chart made by the French navigator Baron
Roussin, but its complete unreliability was not apparent until
Owen found himself hard and fast aground in *Leven* and able to
walk round her on the sands at low water. Repairs to the hull
were conveniently made but only the comparative calm of the
weather when she refloated on the next tide with the aid of kedge
anchors saved a perilous situation.

Two Europeans, Antonio and Lawrence, who came off to the
vessel by canoe when they saw her predicament, were more value
to Owen than Roussin's chart and they acted as his pilots while
he remained in the group.

Lawrence was the son of an Englishman who had come to the islands in 1787 with Captain Beaver, R.N., to form a settlement at Beaverport. Only the ruins of this venture remained, and young Lawrence now kept his own native trading post where he lived in a certain style, a professed Christian with four native wives.

One day a boat came from Bissau with news that the Portuguese garrison had revolted and the Governor sought Owen's help. *Leven* at once sailed to Bissau and her arrival, together with a ceremonial landing by the Captain with a guard of marines, and the firing of a salute onboard, despite the chronometers, caused an immediate collapse of the mutiny.

On 17th May, as had been arranged by Owen with the authorities at Sierra Leone, the new Governor, Mr. Kenneth Macauley, arrived in the colonial steam vessel *African* to which Lieutenant Richard Owen was now transferred with two Midshipmen and a boat's crew for the survey of the Gambia River. By the first of June *Leven* was back in Freetown awaiting *Barracouta*.

Since leaving Luanda Vidal had experienced a busy time, constantly harassed by shortage of provisions and water, for *Barracouta* was small and ill-equipped with store rooms and constantly needed replenishment, not an easy task on the African coast in those days.

Barracouta entered the River Congo on Christmas Eve, but it was New Year's Day 1826 before, with the advent of westerly winds, she began to make headway upstream against the strong current.

Once inside the river it was necessary to anchor and land to obtain wood and water, and here it was that the first contact was made with the native chiefs of the Congo. Umbrellas and red nightcaps were signs of affluence in this society, whilst a strange mixture of European clothes, many of great age, adorned the persons of the chiefs who were additionally slung about with inconveniently shaped fetiches of every kind, including boxes of considerable size said to contain bones of deceased forefathers.

The leading men had many certificates to testify to their honesty and capacity for fair dealing although they had few goods with which to trade. One certificate was signed by Lieutenant Hawkey who had later perished, together with Captain Tuckey, during their ill-fated attempt to survey the river in H.M.S. *Congo*. As the natives could see no purpose in charting the river, in fact could not comprehend what was being attempted, they believed that Vidal was in search of slaves.

Lieutenant Boteler in the pinnace was sent to examine the north side of the river, whilst Mr. Charles Robinson in the gig went to the south bank. It was not long before Boteler's crew were in trouble. The boat grounded in shallow water, and, as surveyors will, they jumped out and hauled the lightened boat forward toward the deeper water beyond. At once, seeing the English sailors at a disadvantage, a fleet of canoes was launched by the natives from a nearby village, and by the time the pinnace was afloat again an attack was imminent. 'The scene was one of fearful interest,' wrote Boteler, 'each individual in the crowd of canoes vying with the others who should first seize upon our devoted little party . . .' A brass gun was rapidly mounted on the chart table and the sail hoisted, while each man loaded his musket and seized his cutlass. Three times did Boteler fire over the heads of their pursuers with his musket, and once with the brass gun, which only led the natives to cheer and press on with more vigour; only when the leading canoes were within a few yards did he order the men to fire their musketry which effectively turned them back, for so close were they that many must have been wounded.

Thirteen miles from the entrance, with the river still wide and navigable before him, Vidal had to turn back, for both time and his stores were running out and it was a long way to Sierra Leone.

Northwards from the Congo a number of places were visited and surveyed, each having its own mafula, or chief, living usually in some style but interested only in selling slaves and drinking rum, and baffled by *Barracouta* which appeared to be neither a slaver nor a man-of-war. Such men were Prince Jack of Kabenda, King Passol of Cape Lopez, King Qua Bon and King Glass of the Gabon River and Jack Romondo of Corisco.

'You go here, you go dere, you send boat ebery where. Gaboon man look um dat too much fear. Who you be?' So enquired Tom Qua Bon, brother of the King, as he boarded the ship clad in the lace coat of an English mail coach guard. Each community had a 'tradesman' such as Tom, who came bearing a sheaf of testimonials to place himself as a middleman between the purser and the natives.

Off the Cameroon River *Barracouta* sailed into a thick fog, brought on by the 'harmattan' wind, and whilst she lay at anchor thus unable to proceed with the work a boat was sent into the river to see if any foreign vessels were anchored there which might have provisions for sale. Only one small English brig was found and she was unable to provide, and on the way back the boat had the misfortune to ground on a sandbank on the ebb tide. Whilst aground, three men set off wading to find the deepest channel to follow with the boat when she floated. Suddenly two slipped in and the third plunged in to save them for, as was common in those days, they could not swim. One was rescued but the other, an elderly marine, was swept from view in the swift current. This was particularly galling to Vidal, for in four years of constant boatwork off the treacherous shores of Africa no man had been lost in this way.

The provision situation was now so serious and the haze so prevalent that there was little point in waiting for clear weather, so in early March Vidal set sail for Fernando Po, the high island seventeen miles or so off to the westward which they had kept in view for some days prior to the 'harmattan'.

Both Portugal and then Spain had formerly colonised Fernando Po, but now the natives were in undisturbed possession and at once created a very favourable impression by their friendliness and willingness to trade succulent yams and abundant poultry.

The natives were totally unlike those on the mainland, being honest, robust with ringlets of dark hair falling below curious straw hats and having but a leaf or two to cover the nether portions; they were festooned with snake skins, monkeys' paws and other animal remains. Strangest of all, they eschewed the taste of rum.

Refreshed in considerable measure by their contact with these people, the ship's company returned to the coast of Africa with renewed vigour to take up the survey of the Bonny River.

An English squadron but three years before had made a

spectacular attack upon slave ships loading in the Bonny River, and when King Peppel saw *Barracouta* he feared another such attack although the seven English ships anchored this time in the river were innocently loading palm-oil for Liverpool. When the survey boats pushed upstream the King ordered all loading of the English ships to cease and the captains had, in turn, to beseech Vidal to desist from work or placate Peppel.

At a table groaning with meats and bottles of liquor in the 'palace' Vidal soothed King Peppel and relations became friendly, if uneasy, for Peppel believed that the passage of the survey boats upstream was for the purpose of locating and destroying his fleet of war canoes hidden there.

Palm oil trade was here in the Bonny taking on a greater importance than the slave trade and today palm oil has in turn given way to petroleum which has now been found in this part of Africa. Always the shallow bar at the river's mouth has been a barrier to trade as in so many of the rivers hereabout. In the old days it was customary to make a human sacrifice to the 'Spirit of the Bar' when this was shoaling; today a mammoth dredging programme has been required to admit the tankers to Port Harcourt in the Bonny River.

The bar had only recently been placated, a fine youth had been chosen and lodged with the King for many months; attended by servants and fed on the finest foods, he became a favourite of all, quite unheeding of his fate to come. On the appointed day he was persuaded to go with the principal men of the town on a fishing trip to the bar. Here he was suddenly cast overboard and left to the sharks as the canoe made rapidly for the shore. Ships can now carry eighteen feet over the bar.

Three days before Vidal left the Bonny another English ship arrived from Liverpool with mails for *Barracouta* onboard, and news from the Admiralty that Vidal had been promoted Post Captain and that Mudge, First Lieutenant in *Leven*, was promoted Commander. This had a quite astounding effect on every member of the crew for it showed that the squadron was still remembered in England and in some odd way it seemed to bring home suddenly nearer, and spirits were strangely exalted as the ship sailed into the fever-dreaded Bight of Benin. 'There's one comes out for forty goes in.' Boteler, Vidal's First Lieutenant was also promoted to Commander a few months later.

Here again in the Benin River human sacrifices were made to the 'Spirit of the Bar', but to no good purpose for there was only twelve feet of water here, exposed also to the westerly weather. So the palm oil calabashes remained full and unwanted as the Liverpool ships sailed on to the Bonny and New Calabar.

Between New Calabar and the Benin River the officers remarked the presence of many great rivermouths as they sailed round Cape Formosa, and some at least wondered if indeed these were not all the mouths of one great river. It took Lander, years later, to prove that in fact this was the delta of the great River Niger.

Before sailing for Sierra Leone Vidal paid a second visit to his former anchorage at Fernando Po where he and his men were heartily welcomed by the people, eager again to trade. 'Oop, Oop,' they cried as they proffered yams and goats in return for precious hoop iron. Many came aboard, and even the King was persuaded to be brought off by boat. Nervousness overtook him half way to the ship and he leapt overboard although quite unable to swim. A marine at once dived from the boat to the rescue and towed him to the shore where a delighted populace showered gifts upon the saviour of their King, the King himself remaining unmoved throughout, although half drowned and full of sea water.

A terrible gale which took away the main-top and mizzen mast smashed from the davits a survey boat which had entered half the rivers in Africa, but *Barracouta* reached Sierra Leone safely on 4th June where the crew of *Leven* manned the rigging and cheered her into harbour. *Albatross* too was here, Lieutenant Richard Owen, her Captain, being still absent in the steamer *African*, but in a few days this vessel returned, also bringing with her the Governor who had accompanied Lieutenant Richard Owen on his survey of the River Gambia 180 miles upstream to Macarthy's Island.

It was a great day when the squadron sailed for home under the command of their tough old chief Captain Owen, bronzed and weatherbeaten after five years' relentless work on the coast of Africa.

Yet one more death was to occur: that of Midshipman Owen Tudor of the *Albatross*, who had contracted fever in the Gambia River on this last trip with Lieutenant Richard Owen. He was laid to rest in the fort at Porto Praya in the Cape Verde Islands alongside Captain Bartholomew, a former Commander of *Leven* from whom Vidal, the senior surveying assistant, had completed the survey, resulting in the surveys presented by Owen to the Portuguese at the outset of the present great commission. Thus were the graves of the English surveyors scattered in the Atlantic Islands as well as all along the 30,000 miles of African coastline which the men of the squadron had now charted on 300 fair sheets.

As the ships sailed home the officers discussed all they had seen and crystallized, as men will, their impressions of a long commission. They had seen the crumbling mellowed forts of the Portuguese; every native tribe set against another to obtain slaves for barter; petty native Kings apeing Europeans and seeking their advice on matters of war and trade; the beauty and fertility of the Cape Colony; the swift sailing buggalows of the Arabs plying a vigorous trade from the clove islands of Zanzibar and Pemba to the arid shores of Arabia; and as a background to all this had been the human inner thought of every man as he wondered whether he would survive the scourge of fever to see his native shores again.

Scurvy, the disease of the long sea voyages, had been largely conquered long since, but now a new plague whose very cause was as yet only guessed at was the enemy of every seaman who landed upon the shores of tropical Africa or thrust inland by boat along the great rivers which were the highways to the interior. Owen doubted whether his losses would have been greater even without a surgeon, for their recognised treatment of bleeding the patient only appeared to hasten the end.

The squadron paid off at Deptford in September 1826, but before doing so the officers decided upon a plan which they at once put into action. This was the presentation to Captain Owen of a unique and magnificent punch-bowl in the form of a globe of the earth surmounted by Neptune and supported by figures representing the four continents as evidence of Owen's widespread surveying activities. The wording on the plinth beneath the bowl testifies to the leadership which Owen gave in a harsh age and on a long and hazardous enterprise—'Presented by the Officers of His Majesty's Ships *Leven* and *Barracouta* to Captain William FitzWilliam Owen as a tribute of esteem and grateful acknowledgment for his unremitting kindness and attention to their welfare and likewise in token of the very high sense they entertain of his eminent abilities.'

In 1949 when a new surveying ship was named *Owen* and commissioned for service in the Persian Gulf, Captain Owen's great-grandson Rear-Admiral E. O. Cochrane presented the punch-bowl to the ship, one of the finest trophies any H.M. Ship ever received. It was lodged in the Commanding Officer's cabin but made its frequent appearance at the successful completion of every major survey performed by the officers and men of that ship, being then filled with punch so that Owen's still enduring leadership could again be toasted and remembered.

Captain Owen had hardly been reunited with his wife and his two daughters, aged six and seven years, when, as a result of Vidal's enthusiastic reports of the natives and produce of Fernando Po, he was appointed to H.M.S. *Eden* with the object of establishing an English settlement there, whither it was planned to move the mixed Commission Court for the suppression of the slave trade from Sierra Leone, Fernando Po being considered healthier and more strategically placed. Unfortunately the dangers to health were as great on Fernando Po as elsewhere in Africa—all but three of Owen's gunroom officers and forty-six of his men died of yellow fever, and the happiest outcome of this failure was that Owen and his own family, who had sailed with him, survived. It was at Fernando Po that he received by the same mail a letter offering him the post of Hydrographer of the Navy and despatches announcing Admiral Beaufort's appointment to that post. Owen's letter of congratulation to Beaufort in these circumstances leaves one with the feeling that he was too good for this world.

It is happy to relate that Captain Owen returned to the Canada that he had grown to love during his survey of the Canadian Lakes. In 1835 the family estate on Campobello Island, in the Gulf of

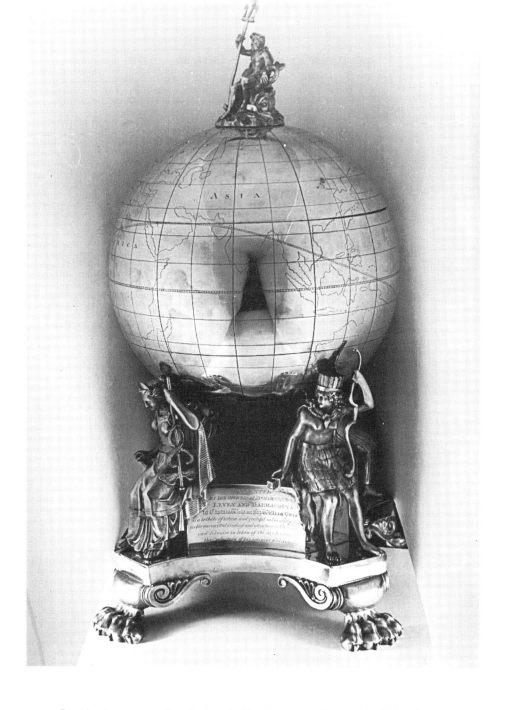

Punchbowl presented to Captain Owen by his officers on conclusion of the African Survey.

Fundy, came into his possession and later that year he and his family settled there, from where he conducted a survey of the Bay of Fundy in his declining years. He died, a Vice-Admiral, at the age of eighty-three, at Saint John, New Brunswick.

CHAPTER TEN

The Northwest Passage

In following the tracks of the African Squadron we have overrun our story. Their return to Deptford in 1826 was little noticed outside official circles, for the enthusiasm of the whole nation was now turned upon the Arctic where even the Hydrographer himself, Captain Parry, had been employed in leading his third expedition in search of the Northwest Passage, that quick seaway to the East which nearly every European sailor believed must exist. It would be a happy alternative to the rigours of the Horn or the tedious passage by the Cape.

Parry had succeeded Hurd as Hydrographer upon the latter's death in 1823 and his absence in the far north left the Hydrographic Office and its inadequate staff to the mercy of the First Secretary to the Admiralty, Croker, who was ever at pains to limit the addition of surveying assistants, whether civilian or naval.

But happily there was a Second Secretary, and throughout Croker's long reign this post was held by John Barrow. Whereas Croker was a politician, a journalist, a man-about-town and a harsh critic of the naval staff, John Barrow was a geographer of wide vision and enthusiasm having, in his youth, travelled widely, in a whaler to Greenland and with the Embassy staff to China and the Governor's Staff to Southern Africa. Croker's post was that of an M.P. whereas Barrow's was that of a civil servant.

Appointed as Second Secretary in 1804, it was inevitable that a man of Barrow's enthusiasms should become friendly with elderly Sir Joseph Banks, and in fact the mantle of that great instigator

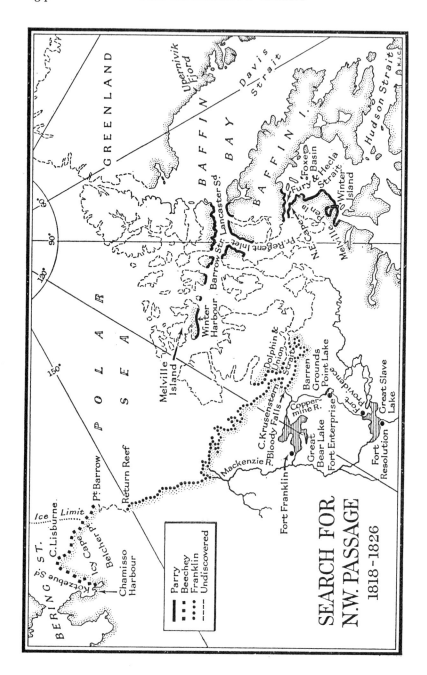

SEARCH FOR
N.W. PASSAGE
1818-1826

of naval expeditions fell upon the shoulders of Barrow, and remained there until he finally retired from the post of Second Secretary to the Admiralty in 1845.

In 1817 Banks informed Barrow that a whaling friend of his, William Scoresby, had reported that for the last three years the Greenland Sea had been free of ice, an unusual circumstance. To Barrow this meant that the time was ripe to renew attempts to find a Northwest Passage to the Pacific, a venture which had received little attention since the American War of Independence.

The Hudson Bay Company and their rivals, the Northwest Company, were consulted, as were whaling skippers and fishermen sailing to the Davis Strait. All agreed that conditions were uniquely favourable and Banks and Barrow prepared a plan for northern exploration which, endorsed by the Royal Society, was laid before Lord Melville, the First Lord. Two ships under Commander John Ross were to search for the Northwest Passage and two ships under Captain David Buchan were to voyage via Spitzbergen towards the North Pole. Each expedition, and every one which followed during Barrow's reign, embraced the sciences—astronomy, navigation, hydrography, meteorology and magnetism. 'Knowledge is power,' said John Barrow, quoting Queen Elizabeth, and added, 'These voyages produce officers and men not to be surpassed, perhaps not equalled, in any other branch of the service.' If the First Secretary was often critical of the surveyors, reviewing their appointments to the Admiralty for chart drawing weekly, the Second Secretary gave them unstinted praise.

Sailing with Commander Ross in *Isabella* in 1818 was his nephew James Clark Ross, who was to spend a large proportion of his life in Polar Seas and rise to the greatest eminence in their exploration, whilst in command of the consort *Alexander* was a man of exceptional talent, Lieutenant William Parry.

Parry had been serving on the North American Station when volunteers for Tuckey's ill-fated Congo Expedition had been called. However, in his own words, 'he was ready for hot or cold' and was a willing volunteer for *Alexander*.

It was 200 years since Luke Foxe had penetrated Hudson's Strait and explored Foxe Basin and since Baffin had passed north through Davis Strait to Baffin Bay. Over the years vessels of the northern trading companies had become familiar with Hudson Bay, whilst Scottish whalers had hunted northwards from Davis Strait. The Northwest Passage seemed likely to lie on the western side of Baffin Bay or Foxe Basin; few doubted its existence.

The Ross expedition tried the western side of Baffin Bay and in sailing into Lancaster Sound had their feet in the door. But an effect of cloud or a mirage convinced the leader that a great range of mountains barred the way and, whether or not he meant to define the role of the First Secretary in exploration, he named these 'Croker Mountains' and turned for home.

Only for two brief summer months were these northern seas free of ice, so that in order to pursue any protracted exploration it was necessary to winter in the ice; accordingly the vessels *Hecla* and *Griper*, sturdy bombs that were to sail for the second attempt under Lieutenant Parry, were prepared for this eventuality.

Parry was in *Hecla* with Captain Edward Sabine, R.A., as astronomer, and Lieutenant Matthew Liddon was in command of *Griper*. Both Frederick Beechey, First Lieutenant in *Hecla*, and James Hoppner, First Lieutenant in *Griper*, were sons of Royal Academicians so that the expedition was to be well illustrated. James Ross appears among the Midshipmen. This was Beechey's second voyage to the Arctic for he had sailed with Buchan and wrote an account of that voyage many years later.

Parry had been sceptical of the Croker Mountains and confidently entered Lancaster Sound again on 1 August 1819, and by sailing westward in ice-free water, was able to rename Croker Mountains fittingly as 'Barrow Strait'. Excitement ran high as the empty sea encouraged the ships' companies in the belief that they had already entered the Polar Sea, with only a simple, if long, passage ahead of them as far as Cook's Icy Cape, and a certain entry through Bering Strait to the Pacific.

However, ice floes soon began to impede their passage both in Barrow Strait and in a broad inlet opening to the south, which Parry investigated and named Prince Regent Inlet. On returning again to Barrow Strait the ice had cleared and they were able to push on westward.

The southern side of the channel became increasingly encumbered by ice spreading westwards until only a narrow passage remained between the ice and the complex chain of rocky islands that unfolded along the northern side.

About the longitude of 100° West of Greenwich the compass needle became increasingly sluggish and then, from having recorded a westerly variation of 129°, swung through south to show an easterly variation, indicating to Parry that he had passed to the north of the magnetic pole. And when 110° West was reached, 'Bounty Cape' was named on 'Melville Island', for the reaching of this longitude entitled officers and men to share a government bounty of £5,000.

Navigation in the ever-narrowing passage between ice and the rocky shore had become increasingly difficult. By 9th September the ships were completely beset, and on freeing themselves made their way slowly back eastwards, for it was essential to get the vessels moored in the lee of a point of land to avoid the steady eastward flow of ice at the beginning and end of the winter. Eventually, in order to reach the haven of Winter Harbour, it was necessary for the men to saw a channel through the ice for a distance of 4,000 yards along which the vessels could be warped.

Once within the point the vessels were made snug; the yards and topmasts sent down, the upper deck roofed over, Sylvester's patent stove and its ventilation extensions erected and special clothes and comforts issued. Lieutenant Beechey was made stage manager for the production of a monthly play in which officers and men, including Parry himself, took part whilst Sabine was made editor of *The North Georgian Gazette and Winter Chronicle*. Many illiterates were among the crew, and for these nightly school was arranged.

Ashore Sabine established an observatory where magnetic observations to record seasonal and diurnal changes in variation could be made, and the effect upon the magnetic needle of Aurora Borealis noted. Pendulum experiments to record the earth's gravitational pull were also made by finding the exact length of a pendulum which completed its swing in one second.

Hunting parties occasionally went out, but game was scarce in the barren wilderness and soon only a brief walk ashore was permitted in order that the men might neither be lost nor exposed to frostbite.

Despite ten months of such confinement, and the close proximity of officers and men in a harsher age, punishments were seldom required; nor did the men take advantage of their unique position when joining the officers in social activities such as play-acting.

This was Parry's design for wintering in the ice, which he was to follow with success on two subsequent occasions. Perhaps this organisation of closely confined human relationship through the long dark winters was this great man's foremost gift to his profession as a surveyor. On 30th October when Parry landed from the vessels at Peterhead and headed south by stage coach for the Admiralty, he had lost only one man, from a disease contracted before leaving England.

The next year Parry, now a Commander, was off again; he in *Fury*, with Commander George Lyon in *Hecla*. This time the search for the passage was to be made through Hudson's Strait to the western side of Foxe Basin.

Repulse Inlet, north of Southampton Island, was found to be a dead end, and the vessels made their way northward examining every inlet, the ice steadily closing in with the onset of winter, and by 6th October they were frozen in at Winter Island.

Parry's winter routine was again established with two interesting improvements on the previous expedition; onboard the men enjoyed the displays of a phantasmagoria, an anonymous gift from a lady in England; and ashore they enjoyed the company of a very friendly tribe of Eskimaux who built their winter ice houses near the ships.

The Eskimaux were often onboard and one woman in particular, Iligliuk, became a regular visitor to the ships and showed such a superior intelligence that Parry finally encouraged her to draw a map of the land to the north. Having taught her first to box the compass for the four cardinal points, she was given a pencil and, watched breathlessly by half a dozen surveying officers, all skilled draughtsmen, she traced a firm line away north-wards from Winter Island. Then, suddenly, to the excitement of the onlookers, she brought the line sharp round to the westward and then southwards at what she described as 'three or four days' sledge journey' westwards of her starting point. The vessels must be on the east side of a peninsula around the north of which a passage existed. The remaining months of the winter were filled with mounting excitement.

In early July the ships got away from their winter berths, but once clear of the land were terribly buffeted by countless ice floes, all driving strongly southwards in the current. Both these stout bombs withstood the terrible battering, increased as it was by gales, and gradually, by making use of every puff of wind and open stretch of water, the vessels were coaxed northwards towards the strait that Iligliuk had indicated.

At last high land was sighted to the northward and a gap to the westward, but as the ships reached the strait it was clearly blocked with old ice from one side to the other. And here, 'at the very threshold of the Northwest Passage' as they thought, the crews spent the month of August inching their ships forward along the winding narrow ice-free channels of the 'Fury and Hecla Strait', reconnoitred by the land parties sent ahead for that purpose. But by the end of the month all was at a standstill.

Three exploring parties were sent westwards over the ice, whilst on the shore abreast the ships a massive stone cairn was built on 'Northeast Cape'. The land parties indeed found, as Iligliuk had said, that the strait eventually opened into the sea to the west, but so cluttered was the channel with islands, and so swift a current was driving ice through to the east, that it seemed unlikely that a ship would ever make the passage.

Early October saw the expedition back at Lerwick and Parry travelling south to report to the Admiralty, where he found the post of Hydrographer vacant, Hurd having died a few months previously.

Captain Buchan's expedition towards the North Pole in 1818, which had reached 80½° North, is noteworthy for the officers who obtained their first Arctic training in his company. These included

Lieutenant Franklin in command of the consort *Trent*, whom we last encountered greeting his old captain, Flinders, on his return to England in 1808, Lieutenant Beechey and George Back, the Mate, all three of whom played leading parts in the further attacks on the Northwest Passage which now developed. Beechey had drawn views of Spitzbergen during the expedition.

When Parry had set out on his first voyage in 1819, a modest land expedition under Lieutenant Franklin had been sent across the wastes of Northern Canada to explore and survey the shores of the Polar Sea in preparation for the arrival of Parry's ships from the east; and for sheer hardship and heroic comradeship it stands high in the annals of the exploits of naval surveyors.

On the face of it, such an expedition was simple to arrange as the party could travel from London to the trading posts on the Great Slave Lake under the auspices of the Hudson Bay and Northwest Companies. As the expedition developed, however, it became apparent that the intense rivalry of these two companies, the unreliability of the Canadian voyageurs, and the measles and whooping cough epidemic rife among the Indian hunters would combine almost to defeat Lieutenant Franklin, Dr. John Richardson, Midshipmen George Back and Robert Hood and Able Seaman John Hepburn, who composed the entire party who sailed from England.

Back nearly missed the ship altogether for, landing at Lowestoft where the Company ships anchored to await favourable winds, he had not sufficient cash to meet the exorbitant charges of the local boatmen when a gun fired from the ships announced an immediate departure on a favourable wind. After travelling by night and day, by coach and ship, he strode mud-bespattered, into the ballroom at Stromness where a farewell dance for the ships' companies was in progress. The Hudson Bay Company had a depot at Stromness and many Orkneymen had served them in Canada, so that Franklin was here able to engage boatmen familiar with the swift rivers and tedious portages of the long haul from York Factory on Hudson Bay to the trading posts a thousand miles to the north-west.

After a perilous voyage through the ice of Hudson's Strait, Franklin's party landed at York Factory, where he called upon the

Governor of the Hudson Bay Company, and also upon the senior members of the North-west Company, both of whom had knowledge of the expedition and were anxious to provide all the aid they could. The fact, however, that the latter were under detention by the former gave Franklin an early clue to the unhappy relationships existing between the two companies. Although the expedition was always at pains to avoid taking sides in any disputes, yet this rivalry was undoubtedly one of the causes of the non-arrival of vital stores once the expedition had travelled to the northern limits of normal company operation.

For the present Franklin had his Orkney boatmen and was loaned birchbark canoes for the long, long voyage to the Great Slave Lake. In this vast territory the 'roads', which were at least 150 years old, consisted of tracks beside the rivers along which men, harnessed to their canoes by long ropes, 'tracked' their craft upstream, whilst at the frequent rapids portages had been cut through the woods along which the canoes and their cargoes were manhandled. Only when each lake was reached did the voyageurs sing at their paddles as they made easy progress.

It was a year after setting out from York Factory before Franklin had passed to the north of the last company trading post; a year during which the party had travelled 2,000 miles by canoe, by dog sledge and on snow shoes; during which they had wintered at Fort Cumberland and during which they had overcome countless frustrations. Long since the Orkneymen had been sent home and Canadian voyageurs and Indian hunters had been engaged. Stores had often failed to follow in the company canoes as arranged and members of the party had had to go back hundreds of miles to bring them on so that ammunition would be available to the hunters and pemmican and spirits for the Canadian voyageurs.

Now, in September 1820, whilst the voyageurs built the log houses for Franklin's second winter quarters, Fort Enterprise, on the shores of Winter Lake, and whilst the Indians hunted caribou, both Franklin and Back took separate reconnaissance parties forward to see the Coppermine River down which they planned to travel to the Polar Sea the following spring.

During the winter Franklin met Akaitcho, a chief of the Coppermine Indians who grudgingly permitted some members of his tribe
to accompany the expedition. He feared that the party would be
attacked by the Esquimaux, or would perish in the Polar Sea in
the frail birchbark canoes.

In early June 1821 the expedition finally set out towards the
Coppermine River, dragging two canoes on sledges, two dogs and
four men to each. Mr. Wentzel of the Hudson Bay Company went
with the party as far as the river mouth which was reached in
mid-July. The canoes had been dragged 120 miles over the snow
and navigated 200 miles down the rapid-strewn river. There were
many false alarms of attack by the Esquimaux whom the Indians
greatly feared, but only one small party was encountered and
these, but for one very old man, made off, so that Augustus and
Junius, two Esquimaux whom Franklin had brought all the way
from York Factory to act as interpreters, had little chance to show
their skill.

It was an exciting moment when, still navigating in a labyrinth
of islands, the water was found to be salt to the taste and the party
knew the Polar Sea had been reached. Mr. Wentzel, Akaitcho and
the main body of the Indians were sent back with the strictest
injunctions to hunt and stock up Fort Enterprise for the expedition's return.

The following month was one of arduous but successful exploration and the two frail canoes with their mixed crews of English
surveyors, Canadian voyageurs, Indian hunters and Esquimaux
interpreters navigated eastwards 550 miles along a barren coastline,
upon which it was necessary to land each night to camp, and to
avoid being wrecked when sudden storms arose. There were sufficient caribou onshore for the hunters to supply the camp, and
further east bears became more numerous, providing excellent
steaks and a pleasant change from venison.

At Point Turnagain it was clear that the winter was setting in
and that the caribou were leaving the coast. With only very scanty
supplies of pemmican now remaining, it was necessary to make
for Fort Enterprise.

The canoes returned to the mouth of the Hood River whence

it was planned to return 150 miles overland across the Barren Grounds to Winter Lake.

The large canoes were stripped down and two small canoes for river crossing were constructed. Two men were daily allotted the task of carrying these, whilst the others each carried 90 lb. of instruments and stores.

The party set out on 1st September; one of the voyageurs led the way, beating down the track with his snow shoes, and guided always by one of the surveyors close behind him with a compass. At first musk-oxen and caribou were plentiful, but as the expedition moved towards the heart of the Barren Grounds and the wind rose and heavy snow fell there was no sign of game. Severe hunger overtook the party and soon only 'tripe de roche', a bitter lichen gathered painfully from the frozen rock, was available for food.

A fortnight after setting out, the first river was reached with only one canoe available; the other had been smashed when its porter was repeatedly blown to the ground by the high winds. With the party extremely weak from hunger, crossing the river in relays in one frail craft capable of carrying but three men was an extremely laborious and hazardous task. For over an hour Belanger, one of the Canadians, was marooned on a submerged rock in midstream, on which he had stepped to prevent the canoe capsizing. When eventually hauled to the river bank on a line, he was nearly frozen to death and two men lay beside him to bring back warmth and life to his body.

By the time the second river was reached twelve days later, the second canoe had been left behind on the march by the now utterly dispirited voyageurs, and there was nothing to do but build a raft from willows to be towed backwards and forwards on a rope. Dr. Richardson nearly lost his life in attempting to swim to the further shore with the line. This tedious and terrible crossing, one man at a time, was eventually achieved, and by his reckoning Franklin was able to assure the expedition that Fort Enterprise lay only twenty-five miles distant. Despite a momentary rise in morale, their debilitated state became fully apparent when the men began the march again.

On 7th October Midshipman Hood, quite unable to proceed, remained in the shelter of a thicket of willows with Dr. Richardson and Able Seaman Hepburn to look after him; Midshipman Back and two Canadian voyageurs pushed on ahead for the Fort; whilst Franklin went on with the main body. Junius the Eskimo was already lost for he had failed to return from hunting before the last river crossing.

Soon three of the voyageurs with Franklin, together with Michel, an Iroquois Indian, pleaded to return to the willow thicket, too weary to go on. Only Michel, of the four, ever reached it.

Meanwhile, Franklin and four companions struggled on to the Fort only to find to their utter dismay that not a scrap of meat had been stored within. A bitter wind flapped the shreds of deer skin panels which had formed the window panes, and within a note from Back announced that he and his two Canadians had set out southwards for Fort Providence for supplies. It seemed that neither Wentzel nor Akaitcho had ever expected the expedition to return, for no provisions had been laid in as promised.

Augustus, the remaining Eskimo, and Benoit now set off for Fort Providence as did Franklin but he was too weak to travel and had to turn back to the Fort where Peltier and Samandre lay, both too weak to move. Here Adam, the expedition's interpreter, and Franklin daily brewed a meagre soup from the few deer bones they were able to find round the Fort. Eighteen days passed in this miserable fashion before Dr. Richardson and Able Seaman Hepburn, gaunt and haggard, struggled in with a terrible tale to tell.

In the willow thicket on the trail Hood had rapidly declined and here Michel had returned to join the three Englishmen. Each day the Indian had gone hunting, taking his axe as well as his rifle, and returning without game or an explanation of his doings. Slowly Dr. Richardson and the Able Seaman became aware that Michel must be feeding upon his perished comrades along the trail ahead and even whilst this awful conclusion was dawning upon them they heard a shot from the tent where Michel had been talking to Hood. Michel claimed that Hood had shot himself, but clearly the bullet had entered the back of the Midshipman's head. The three survivors were now in a mortal position.

Michel never permitted the Surgeon and the Able Seaman to be alone together. As they set out along the track after laying

Hood's body among the willows and saying a prayer, Michel dropped behind to load his gun—for what? A hurried discussion between the two Englishmen took place, each offering to undertake the inevitable task. Dr. Richardson shot Michel through the head as he came forward with his loaded rifle in his hands.

Peltier and Samandre died in the Fort and Adam was about to follow them when, nearly a month after Franklin had arrived, three Coppermine Indians, who had been directed by Back, arrived with dried meat and reindeer tongues. And here they sympathetically nursed Adam back to life.

The survivors of the party eventually reached Fort Chipewyan for the winter, proceeding home via York Factory the following summer of 1822, having travelled 5,000 miles to chart 550 miles of the shores of the Polar Sea.

With Parry now as Hydrographer and John Barrow as Secretary, a carefully planned three-prong attack upon the Northwest Passage was developed. In 1824 Parry, leaving Walker in control of the Hydrographic Office, embarked in command of his third expedition; in 1825 Franklin set out undaunted on his second journey to further his exploration of the shores of the Polar Sea; whilst in the same year Beechey in H.M.S. *Blossom* sailed round Cape Horn into the Pacific and northwards for the Bering Strait, whence he hoped to work eastwards along the coast from Icy Cape to join up with Franklin. Both the land party and the men from *Blossom* planned to build cairns along the coast and leave notes for the guidance of Parry, should he break through to the Polar Sea.

The first of the three prongs of the attack then was Captain Parry's expedition, in which he commanded *Hecla* and Commander Hoppner *Fury*, the two sturdy bombs so admirably suited to the work of navigation in ice.

The plan this time was to enter once more the promising Lancaster Sound, but to turn southwards into Prince Regent Inlet whence it was confidently expected that the ships would reach the coast of America in the vicinity of Franklin's recent discoveries.

But the good ice years were gone and it was mid-September before the two vessels fought their way through the young ice into Lancaster Sound, a boat towing from either side of the bows so that their crews could break up the ice as they went. The vessels wintered in Fort Bowen on the east side of Prince Regent Inlet and the following summer crossed to the western side and made their way south through the narrow and treacherous passages between the ice and the rugged shore. Both ships were at one time or another crushed between the ice floes which were drifting southward, or were driven aground by ice floes closing the land.

Eventually *Fury* was so damaged along the keel that she was making water faster than the pumps could remove it, and it became necessary to beach her and heave her down for repairs—a fantastic feat of seamanship to contemplate in these ice-strewn waters.

First a suitable unencumbered beach had to be found, and then some form of harbour built to keep off the southerly drift of ice. The most likely spot appeared to be a shelving beach off which were two grounded icebergs, and between these and the shore the vessels were berthed, *Fury* aground and *Hecla* close seaward of her, just afloat, so that her capstan could be used to heave down the *Fury*.

Hawsers were led from the shore south of the vessels out to the grounded icebergs to secure them lest they should refloat, whilst from the bergs diagonally to the shore to the northwestward further hawsers were rigged, being supported by drums and spars so that they would remain a fathom or so below the surface, and thus form a diverting break against the southgoing ice floes.

Berthed in this perilous harbour, *Fury* was completely destored, much of the cargo being discharged by jackstay to the shore, whilst her topmasts and spars were struck down and secured as outriggers from the ports. Such outriggers are required when heaving down, for from their outboard ends run martingales to the lower mastheads to support the masts against the great strain of heaving the vessel down, which is done by running hawsers from the other side of the lower mastheads to the capstans in the vessel berthed alongside.

Fury was successfully hove down, the icebergs melting and beginning to move inshore even as the operation proceeded. A gale then completely destroyed the ice harbour and *Fury* had to be righted and towed to sea. When the storm passed *Fury* was beached again, but this time no friendly icebergs provided protection and rapidly the ice set in with the ebbing of the summer season. After twenty-five days' struggle, and the season for exploration gone, *Fury* had to be abandoned on the beach which now bears her name and *Hecla*, with both crews embarked, reluctantly returned to England.

Franklin, now a Post Captain, had prepared with the greatest care for his second overland expedition, profiting from his bitter experience of the Barren Grounds and the inhospitable shores of the Polar Sea.

Two special boats were built at Woolwich designed for sailing, rowing or paddling, whilst a third boat, nine feet long, her framework covered with Mackintosh's prepared canvas, was specially constructed so that it might be carried overland for river crossings. This dinghy was named *The Walnut Shell* and on trials 'several ladies fearlessly embarked in it, and were paddled across the Thames in a fresh breeze'.

On this second expedition Franklin determined to take all necessary stores with him, that he and his companions might not again endure the hardship and perils of the previous years; he took 'scientific instruments of all kind, fowling pieces and ammunition, marquees and tents, bedding, clothing, and water-proof dresses, flour, arrow-root, macaroni, portable soup, chocolate, essence of coffee, sugar and tea, not omitting an adequate supply of that essential to all North American travellers—pemmican.'

The expedition left England in February 1825, and with Captain Franklin went again Dr. Richardson and Lieutenant Back with the addition of Admiralty Mate Edward Kendall and a Mr. Thomas Drummond of Forfar as assistant naturalist. Hepburn, the faithful old seaman, was left behind, having been given a quiet billet in Portsmouth Dockyard in return for his valiant services on the first expedition.

Four marines and a dozen naval seamen accompanied the English-built boats, a further two being built in Canada. Less reliance was to be placed on Canadian voyageurs, but Mr. Peter

Dease of the Hudson Bay Company joined the expedition, as did Augustus and a newcomer, Ooligbuck, Eskimaux interpreters from Churchill.

It was a sad day for Franklin when he sailed in a Company ship for New York, for his wife lay dangerously ill, but yet able to urge upon him the need for his departure and hand him a silken Union flag of her own making to carry to the shores of the Polar Sea. She died next day.

The plan was to make northwards and to winter on the Great Bear Lake, and the following summer to travel down the river explored by Mackenzie of the Northwest Company, the same man who had so narrowly missed Vancouver in the North Bentinck Arm. On reaching the Polar Sea Franklin, in charge of one party, planned to explore westwards along the coast, hoping to meet the boats from H.M.S. *Blossom* making eastward, whilst the other party under Dr. Richardson was to coast eastwards to the mouth of the Coppermine River, thus joining up with their previous year's work.

Whilst the main body of the expedition set about building a fort for the winter on Great Bear Lake, Franklin and Back reconnoitred the Mackenzie River and Dr. Richardson the eastern end of the Great Bear Lake to plan his return hence from the Coppermine River. When these parties arrived back they found 'Fort Franklin' complete and snug.

The long winter was passed in the Parry pattern—school, games and preparations for the travels ahead, the officers mingling with the men in these activities. Indians and the few Canadians hunted in the early part of the winter when game was in evidence.

In mid-June the combined parties set out down the Mackenzie. Fourteen men, including Augustus, were to accompany Franklin and Back in *Lion* and *Reliance* to the west, whilst ten men, including Ooligbuck, were to go with Richardson in *Dolphin* and *Union* to the east. On 4th July 1826, in the delta of the Mackenzie River, they separated.

Hardly had Franklin parted company from Richardson when the sight of a mass of tents on the low shore indicated the presence of Eskimaux, so long feared and predicted by the Indians.

The two boats ran under sail towards them, unfortunately

grounding about a mile from the beach. Soon the sea was alive with canoes making rapidly out towards the English boats and pressing closely about them. At first the Eskimaux listened to Augustus as he stood up in the boat and shouted to them that the Englishmen were searching for a deep channel in order that large ships might come to trade with them. But, suddenly, catching sight of the bales of cloth and other stores stowed beneath the thwarts, they could not restrain themselves and by sheer force of numbers, overran the boats, taking all that came to hand. Meanwhile others, wading, dragged the boats across the flats to the shore and there commenced a regular pillage.

Whilst the seamen were having the very buttons cut from their jackets, yet Franklin was determined to avoid the use of muskets and bloodshed. At last the boats escaped from the Eskimaux' clutches to be anchored well offshore, and brave Augustus insisted on landing alone to speak with the 300 or so excited men. He told them that his own tribe in the Churchill district, who had once been similarly devoid of the white man's goods, now received everything needed in abundance, and that unless they returned the stolen goods the white men were unlikely ever to bring trade to these barren shores. It was only the white man's humanity that had prevented them from being slain by musket fire.

The crews watched the gallant little figure, gesticulating to the assembly ashore, and slowly the Eskimaux began to heed his words, collecting the hidden goods and carrying them to the water's edge for return: a bloodless victory brought about by the forbearance of a naval captain and the courage of a simple Eskimo.

Now began the coasting voyage westwards, interrupted daily by fog, gales, rain and ice floes pressing in on the shore, with only occasional glimpses of the Rocky Mountains to the southwest. Franklin was now well on his way, and it would take more than adverse weather to stop this veteran as each day he hoped to see the first of *Blossom's* cairns ahead, which would announce to him the promise of succour, and relieve him of the desperate worry of whether he should press on beyond the point of no return.

Meanwhile Richardson's party in *Dolphin* and *Union* had been coasting eastwards. They, too, had encountered troublesome

Eskimaux whom Ooligbuck had tactfully dealt with, preventing pilfering and bloodshed. Gales they also had in plenty, narrow passages between off-lying islands and the mainland, rock-strewn waters and ice crushing in upon the boats. Finally, before reaching the Coppermine River they had to navigate a strait between a large tract of high land to the north and the mainland on the south. With racing currents, hidden rocks and shifting icefloes, it reminded Dr. Richardson forcibly of Scylla and Charybdis and he was doubtful whether it could be navigated by ships of any size. Clearing the 'Dolphin and Union Strait', he named the cape after the Russian hydrographic surveyor Admiral Krusenstern, who had trained in the Royal Navy and had always worked closely with the British Admiralty.

When Richardson reached the mouth of the Coppermine River, he was on familiar ground and had to leave his heavy boats at the foot of Bloody Falls. From there his party set out on foot overland to the mouth of the Dease River on the Great Bear Lake, where he had reconnoitred the previous year and where a boat would come to convey the party across the lake to Fort Franklin.

Beechey in His Majesty's Ship *Blossom* had set out in January 1825 on his long voyage round the Horn and across the whole Pacific to Bering Strait to play his particular part in the great three-pronged attack. Of course he had a list of many islands to be visited and charted, and many dangers to search for during his long passage. Among his surveyors was young Lieutenant Edward Belcher, of whom we shall hear much in a later chapter, on his first surveying cruise.

The island visits are beautifully described by Captain Beechey in his book *Voyage to the Pacific and Beering's Strait*, for he had carried hydrographic literature yet another step beyond that of Flinders, relegating all his factual position data and nautical directions to appendices in order that he might compile a more readable account. Much space is devoted to descriptions of Pacific Islanders and Eskimaux and the impact of early European and Russian influences upon them.

Whilst Franklin and his men spent the month of December 1825 in their log fort on Great Bear Lake surrounded by a waste of snow and ice, Beechey and his officers passed much of it in the open-sided thatched huts of the Pitcairn Islanders, sheltering from the noonday heat of the tropics.

Although the *Bounty* had been run ashore on Pitcairn Island by the mutineers in 1790, it was not until 1808 that Captain Mayhew Folger in the whaler *Topaz* of Nantucket visited the island. He found the descendants of the mutineers living on the island with John Adams the sole survivor of those who had brought the *Bounty* to Pitcairn. Folger's news reached the Admiralty in 1809 but little notice was taken of it by those who had more pressing matters to deal with.

In 1814 Captain Sir Thomas Staines and Captain Philip Pipon in H.M. Ships *Briton* and *Tagus* were cruising the Pacific in search of Captain David Porter in U.S.S. *Essex*, who was attacking British whalers, when they accidentally came upon Pitcairn Island. They found elderly John Adams presiding so ably over the half-caste descendants of the mutineers that there was no point in carrying him to England for long delayed punishment.

So it was that ten years later Beechey closed the island with the friendliest intentions and perceived a boat coming out to meet the ship manned by old Adams and all the young men of the island. Before they ventured to take hold of the ship, they inquired if they might come on board, and upon permission being granted, they sprang up the side and shook every officer by the hand with undisguised feelings of gratification.

'The activity of the young men outstripped that of old Adams, who was consequently almost the last to greet us. He was in his sixty-fifth year, and was unusually strong and active for his age, notwithstanding the inconvenience of considerable corpulency. He was dressed in a sailor's shirt and trousers and a low-crowned hat, which he instinctively held in his hand until desired to put it on. He still retained his sailor's gait, doffing his hat and smoothing down his bald forehead whenever he was addressed by the officers.'

Ashore, the meeting with the female islanders was equally happy. 'They almost all wore the cloth of the island: their dress consisted of a petticoat, and a mantle loosely thrown over their shoulders and reaching to the ankles. Their stature was rather above the common height; and their limbs, from being accustomed to work and climb hills, had acquired unusual muscularity; but their features and manners were perfectly feminine. Their complexion, though fairer than that of the men, was a dark gipsy hue, but its deep colour was less conspicuous, by being contrasted with dark glossy hair, which hung down over their shoulders in long waving tresses, nicely oiled: in front it was tastefully turned back from the forehead and temples, and was retained in that position by a chaplet of small red or white aromatic blossoms, newly gathered from the flower tree (*Morinda Citrifolia*), or from the tobacco plant: their countenances were lively and good-natured, their eyes dark and animated, and each possessed an enviable row of teeth. Such was the agreeable impression of their first appearance, which was heightened by the wish expressed simultaneously by the whole group, that we were come to stay several days with them. As the sun was going down, we signified our desire to get to the village and to pitch the observatory before dark, and this was no sooner made known, than every instrument and article found a carrier.' Happy surveyors with such assistants!

Like Beechey, we are getting diverted by the delights of Pitcairn Island and we must push on, as he had to do, two days before Christmas, for that distant rendezvous in the Polar Sea.

Visiting Tahiti and the Sandwich Islands, as the Hawaiian Islands were then known, Beechey eventually reached Petropavlovsk where he found despatches informing him of Parry's return to England, but no news about Franklin was good news, hastening Beechey on through Bering Strait to Kotzebue Sound by 25th July, ten days later than he had planned with Franklin more than eighteen months before.

Instructions were painted on the rocks, flour was buried and victuals left for Franklin lest Beechey should miss him along the foggy shore, and the great barge, which had been carried from England for the purpose, was hoisted out and prepared for sea.

Mr. Thomas Elson, the Master, was put in command of the barge and sent northward, his duty being to follow and survey the coastline and to erect beacons on any prominent points, under which bottle messages would be left to guide Franklin.

Blossom sailed northward in support, the complete absence of ice at first tempting Beechey himself to press on in search of the Northwest Passage. But his duty, and also that of Mr. Elson in the barge, was to avoid at all costs becoming fast in the ice, in order that they might retain the mobility so necessary if they were to help Franklin, whose party was now expected daily.

On 17th August, with the sea ice now well in towards the shore, *Blossom* closed the barge off Icy Cape and Mr. William Smyth was transferred to assist Mr. Elson to navigate through the narrow channel, which now existed between ice and rocky coastline.

On 23rd August the barge reached a low point with packed ice on the shore ahead, the sea ice moving in astern, and a great accumulation of Eskimaux showing every indication that they awaited disaster to the barge with certainty and enthusiasm; Mr. Elson thus deemed it prudent to turn back. This, his furthest point, he named Point Barrow after the architect of the great venture which even now all hoped would be crowned with success.

Getting the barge back to Kotzebue Sound was a desperate business, for by now the ice was so close to the shore that the crew had to walk over the rocks 'tracking' the barge by rope, as Franklin's men did their canoes along the rivers of the north.

It was necessary also to placate the Eskimaux, which was difficult when offence could be given by refusing a proffered feast of cold whale's entrails and a bowl of congealed seal's blood.

The 9th September saw the barge again united with *Blossom* in Kotzebue Sound, having added 126 miles of newly surveyed coastline northeastwards from Icy Cape.

Captain Beechey's dilemma was now how long he should stay on in the Sound for, although he continued to expect Franklin's arrival, his ship was not a sturdy bomb to be beset by ice nor did he have sufficient supplies for a winter in the north. Meanwhile Lieutenant Belcher was set to work surveying Chamisso Harbour in a home-made cutter which the carpenter had recently completed for such a purpose from wood he had felled in Tahiti.

Beechey's instructions indicated that he should wait for Franklin until the end of October, but by the 10th of that month a great deterioration of the weather was apparent; the Esquimaux departed for their winter quarters; the migrating birds flew south-ward and the lakes froze over. The Captain then addressed a letter to his officers requesting them for their individual opinions upon the need for departure, and these being unanimously the same as his own, stores and victuals were buried, signs left and the ship sailed away for Bering Strait and a winter in San Francisco. The night of departure was bitterly cold and crisp, giving Beechey the opportunity to observe eighteen sets of lunar distances east and west of the Moon, so that the position of Chamisso Island, upon which much of the work to the north depended, was fixed, an opportunity which had been denied to him all summer.

That was really the end of the great venture for, although Beechey was back at Kotzebue Sound the following summer, and repeated the operation of sending the barge forward, this time with Belcher, it was a useless effort, as by then Franklin was making his way home along the rivers of the north.

Franklin had also experienced an early onset of winter in 1826 which had daily reduced the speed of his advance westward along the shore of the Polar Sea. He could not be certain that *Blossom* had survived all the perils of her long, hazardous voyage around the Horn and across the whole uncharted Pacific. So, reluctantly, with food now only sufficient for him to retrace his steps and no game to be seen, he turned back on 18th August. From Return Reef in longitude 140° 37' W. he travelled back 373 miles along 'the most dreary, miserable and uninteresting portions of sea coast that can perhaps be found in any part of the world.'

Only five days after Franklin had turned back and only 160 miles to the west, Mr. Elson had reached Point Barrow and searched hopefully to the eastward with his glass for any sign of Franklin's party. What a historic meeting this could have been!

CHAPTER ELEVEN

Parry of the Arctic
as Hydrographer

'London, Nov. 20, 1823.

I saw Lord Melville yesterday. To state briefly the *cream* of our communication; he offered me first, and in a very handsome manner, the situation of Hydrographer, stating that the former Hydrographer had not fulfilled the duties of his station satisfactorily and etc. and etc. and that he had kept it open for me. His manner was more than ordinarily kind. I felt it, and thanked him warmly for his goodness in thinking of me, but requested a few days to think of it, being unprepared for the offer, to which he replied, "By all means, there is no sort of hurry". The Northwest Passage was our next subject . . . My verbal communication was, of course, to the same effect, and I closed it, by saying that, *should* another Expedition be determined on, I trusted he would once more accept my services—for that I should not a moment hesitate in declining the other situation, and giving the preference to the more active employment. He said the one need not interfere with the other, or to that effect . . .'

'London, Nov. 26, 1823.

Lord Melville has said and done so handsomely about the Hydrographer's situation, *insisting on keeping it open for me, even during an Expedition*, that I have literally *perforce* accepted it, and shall be appointed probably this day. How I shall get thro' the work, and another equipment, *and* my book, I know not . . .'

Thus wrote Captain Parry, unwilling acceptor of the post of Hydrographer of the Navy, to his brother in 1823. By January 1824 he was very busy equipping his third and last expedition to the North-west which has already been described. And in the year 1827 at his own suggestion, and whilst still Hydrographer, he led an expedition by way of Spitzbergen across the Arctic ice using sledge-boats in an attempt to reach the Pole. Although he intended to use reindeer to pull the sledge-boats this proved impracticable and the task devolved upon the sailors, who pulled the sledges by night and rested by day. They averaged about twelve miles daily for thirty-five days from the edge of the ice, where they were landed, to 82° 45′ N. when the journey had to be abandoned. By now the ice was drifting southward at about the same speed as the party was advancing, so that while the men rested by day they drifted back the dozen or so miles they had gained in the night.

Only fifteen miles further advance would have earned them the Government bounty for reaching 83° N., but this proved beyond the powers of the expedition, and Parry and his men had to be content with the cold comfort that they had penetrated further towards the Pole than man had done before.

To follow Captain Parry on his great voyages gives us no idea of the devotion he gave to the Hydrographic Office. He never forgot the cares of his office, although for a great deal of the time First Secretary Croker did his utmost to reduce the status and value of the work the Office was doing.

It will be recalled that by the time Hurd died in office Admiralty Charts were on sale to the Merchant Fleet and that chart supplies to His Majesty's ships were organised according to the stations on which the vessels were employed and to which they were sent in prepared boxes.

It seems clear, however, that Hurd's failing health, evident from his correspondence towards the end, had deprived him of his earlier drive, and that the office records, then comprising some thousands of documents, were neither in order nor properly listed at the time of his death.

It must be said in Croker's favour, therefore, that within a few days of Hurd's death at the end of April 1823 he appointed

Lieutenant Alexander Becher to complete the catalogue of published charts and to make a comprehensive index of all charts,
plans and other papers which Becher described as 'lying in pro-
miscuous heaps and filthy with dirt'. This task was to take him
three years to complete, burdened as he was with other duties
concerned with the supply of charts to agents and to the Fleet.

When, therefore, in November 1823 Captain Parry took up his
duties as Hydrographer, he found Lieutenant Becher an invaluable
Naval Assistant (a title which he eventually assumed) whom he
could leave to watch the naval side of the work when he was absent
in northern seas, whilst John Walker, now many years in office,
dealt with the civil side of affairs. Becher had learnt his surveying
with Captain Owen on the Great Lakes, had served under Captain
Bartholomew during *Leven's* first surveying voyage and later as
'Hydrographic Officer' in H.M.S. *Conway* under Captain Basil
Hall on the west coast of South America. So he had plenty of sea
experience to which he added during the next forty years an
unrivalled knowledge of work in the office itself—forty years which
I certainly do not envy him, but to whom our Office must be long
indebted, for he set the pattern for naval assistants, posts which
exist to this day and ensure that the nautical eye is still cast over
every chart compiled for the use of the mariner.

Whilst Parry was absent in the Northwest in 1824–25, John
Walker battled as well as he could against the efforts of Croker to
reduce the establishment of the office. Croker was particularly
against the employment of naval officers in drawing their fair
charts in the office, and by calling for a weekly report on their
progress he drove both Captain Peter Heywood and Captain
Smyth from their tables, the latter taking with him all his Mediterranean material.

Back from his third expedition Parry devoted the year 1826 to
office matters and himself engaged in the long struggle with
Croker, in particular to get Becher's term of office extended, for
the three years allotted for catalogue and index work had now
expired.

There was in the Office a great mass of Remark Books which
had been steadily accumulating since about 1760. Many were of

little value, but there were also voluminous Remark Books sent in
by enlightened officers. It was Parry's plan to prepare from these
books published Sailing Directions for the use of the Fleet, and
for sale to the public; further, he believed that Becher was a very
suitable man to index the Remark Books in preparation for the
work of compiling the Sailing Directions. 'Indexing Remark Books
is so much in the ordinary course of the Hydrographic Department
work that I see no reason for Mr. Becher to be specially retained
for it, while unless some further explanation be offered I cannot
sanction any compilation of Sailing Directions.' Thus replied
Croker.

However, Becher was eventually retained, and Joseph Dessiou
and John Roe were appointed to write Sailing Directions in February 1828. *The West Indies Directory, Vol. I* was published in 1829,
only a month or so before Parry left the Office, the first of a series
which today comprises over seventy volumes covering the world.

Becher took charge of the office during Parry's absence in 1827
on the polar expedition, and during that absence an event took
place which temporarily put Croker in the shade and gave the
Hydrographic Office a fillip. The Office of Lord High Admiral
was revived after many years in abeyance and was conferred upon
His Royal Highness the Duke of Clarence, later to become William
IV, the 'Sailor King'. His interest in nautical affairs extended
particularly to matters of charting.

The Lord High Admiral, after a look at the office, ordered the
immediate engagement of six extra draughtsmen; he permitted
those officers who had been suspended in their chart drawing to
return to their desks; he laid down that officers of the Hydrographic Office were to be exclusively under the Hydrographer's
orders; he directed that a clerk was to be engaged for chart supplies
duties so that Becher could apply his full attention to the publication of Sailing Directions.

The Lord High Admiral also sent a circular to all surveyors
setting out in detail the scales to be used for various types of
surveys—for general, coastal and harbour charts, the scale increasing for each of these types. The circular went on, 'You will in
future transmit the rough charts also, showing the whole of the

triangulation, and giving so explicit an account of your mode of proceeding and of determining the several bases, as may enable His Royal Highness to judge of the degree of confidence that may be placed in the accuracy of your several surveys.'

During this brief, rosy period the Hydrographer was able to increase his naval assistants to four by stating, 'The slowness with which our hydrographic materials are rendered available by publication arises entirely, I conceive, from the small number of individuals employed in this Office, for it so happens, although I believe unintentionally, that almost in proportion as the surveying work has increased (as it has done since the Peace) so has this establishment been diminished; there being three individuals less belonging to it, at this time than in the year 1823!'

One of the new naval assistants, Lieutenant William Sheringham, when placed in charge of the supply of charts to agents, reached the conclusion that the Admiralty charts were only used by the agents to improve their own charts for sale. He proposed one agent only, under more strict surveillance, and this agency was taken over by R. B. Bate, 21 Poultry, London, whose name became synonymous with Admiralty Charts, as did that of Potter of the Minories many years later.

Parry's period as Hydrographer is marked by considerable scientific effort at sea which he encouraged both as Hydrographer and as expedition leader.

Captain Sabine had accompanied Parry on his first Arctic voyage, where he had made pendulum experiments as well as celestial and magnetic observations at the observatory built ashore on the ice. In 1822, having returned to England, Sabine was fortunate in being able, with the aid of his naval friends, to procure the use of H.M.S. *Pheasant*, Commander Clavering, to visit places both on the African and American coasts as well as some Caribbean Islands so that he might extend his pendulum experiments.

On return to England from the *Pheasant* voyage Sir John Barrow's presence as Second Secretary to the Admiralty ensured that Sabine's further request for a ship to go north was gratified. *Griper*, well-tried in Parry's first voyage, was allotted to the task with Clavering, now a collaborator with Sabine, again in command.

This voyage went in 1822 to Spitzbergen and thence across to Greenland for further pendulum experiments ashore at each place where it was possible to land the equipment, for only on a stable platform ashore was this work, of course, possible.

When the coast of Greenland was reached Clavering pushed *Griper* on through the barrier of ice until forced to turn back at 75° North. At each point where Sabine landed with the pendulum he took with him a young Lieutenant, Henry Foster who, with Becher, had served in *Conway* in South America, where he had carried out pendulum experiments under the guidance of his enlightened Captain, Basil Hall.

It later came about that Parry, looking for an astronomer for his third voyage to the Northwest, selected Foster, and during the first winter at Port Bowen he made such successful observations both for magnetism and refraction, as well as with the pendulum, that his results in due course gained for him the Copley Medal of the Royal Society and advanced him to the rank of Commander on the same day.

The pendulum measurements consisted of determining at each observation spot the exact length of a pendulum which makes one swing per second. The pendulum was found to be longer towards the poles, indicating an apparently greater pull of gravity. The results of Sabine's work from H.M. ships combined with eight French readings gave a length of about 39 in. at the equator with an increase of 0.2 in. at the poles.

The centrifugal force at the equator, which acts against the pull of gravity, could be calculated, for the radius of the Earth was known. This force, when converted into a decrease in pendulum length, more than accounted for the difference between pendulum lengths computed for equator and pole. This left a greater mass attraction at the equator than at the pole, and from the difference of the two the ellipticity of the Earth was calculated. Sabine found that the North/South axis was 1/289.1 shorter than the equatorial axis.

This was a relatively crude and early figure, but immediately opened the way to better world charting. With gradually improving instrumentation gravity is still being measured with pendulums today to learn more about the shape of the earth and the anomalies within. By the recent development of a seaborne gravimeter, which substitutes for the pendulum an elegant spring balance, mounted on a gyro-stabilised platform, it is now possible to measure gravity over that two thirds of the earth's surface previously denied to us for this purpose. These instruments are carried in Her Majesty's surveying ships; geophysical work at sea has always been among their tasks.

During much of Parry's period as Hydrographer the Royal Society had been considering an approach to the Admiralty with a view to launching a world scientific cruise, and had been in communication with a number of scientists and naval officers, as well as the Hydrographer himself, as to the extent and type of the observations to be made on such a voyage.

One of those in whom the Royal Society Committee placed their faith was a Captain Basil Hall, the enlightened man who had commanded *Conway* in South America when both Becher and Foster had served with him and absorbed his enthusiasm.

Basil Hall was an Edinburgh Scot, whose father had been President of the Royal Society of Edinburgh. Although never a surveying officer, he was noted for the excellence of his Remark Books, and was a supporter of Parry in his efforts to publish Sailing Directions. Not only was he intensely interested in the Marine Sciences, but he wrote with interest of his travels, during which he commanded *Lyra* on a voyage with Lord Amherst's mission to China. His *Fragments of Voyages & Travels* are delightful and amusing essays on life at sea in the early nineteenth century.

Basil Hall's proposals for the expedition were published in the *Edinburgh New Philosophical Journal* in 1826 and here are suggestions along the lines of the appendices he had published for his own voyages in *Lyra* and *Conway*—observations of longitude at salient points, magnetic variation observations, wind and current observations, measurement of tides and tidal streams, height measurement of coastal mountains, details of nautical supplies obtainable at foreign ports and more observations for the length of a second pendulum so that a true Figure of the Earth might be finally established.

Hall advocated that many such observations were required by the same observer with several pendulums at many different situations along similar parallels of latitude, for he believed there might be anomalies around the world at the same latitude.

And the man to command the expedition? Basil Hall plumped for Henry Foster without a moment's hesitation.

With the general introduction of the chronometer at sea many lists had been published giving the positions of all the major ports of call throughout the world. But even lists published in the same country varied, not to mention those published by different countries. Parry was in correspondence with France, Denmark and Spain on this matter for each had a Hydrographer, France having had a Hydrographic Office since 1720, Denmark since 1784 and Spain since 1800. The longitudes were based on varying numbers of observations of differing accuracy, and sometimes so much effort had been put into finding the longitude that the comparatively simple latitudes were wrongly computed. The situation was chaotic and James Horsburgh, the Hydrographer to the East India Company, joined with Captain Parry in preparing a list of the places around the world they wished to see fixed by the expedition.

The Lord High Admiral was pleased with the proposals, and once a vessel had been chosen Commander Foster was placed in command. The scope of the expedition was world-wide, the supply of special instruments comprehensive, the detailed planning under Foster extensive—all was on a large scale except the vessel herself—*Chanticleer*, built as long ago as 1804, a ten-gun brig now carrying but two guns, 237 tons, with a complement of fifty-seven men all told.

By the time she sailed from Portsmouth at the end of April 1828, it appears to have been decided that *Chanticleer* should return after the plan of the Atlantic had been completed, although the reasons for this are not clear, unless the vastness of the task for so small a vessel had now become apparent. Sailing via the Canaries and Cape Verde Islands, thence down the coast of South America to Staten Island east of Cape Horn, Commander Foster made the most southerly pendulum observation up to that time, at Deception Island in the South Shetlands. This island he aptly named, for the deep harbour consists of the crater of an ancient volcano, and only on the southeast are the sides of the crater sufficiently eroded to admit a vessel through the narrow entrance, which was found only when the hope of locating a harbour had been nearly abandoned. As *Chanticleer* sailed in through the narrow entrance a dreary and gloomy waste opened out around the circular harbour, a waste covered with innumerable penguins, the noise of which the men likened to the distant bleating of folded flocks of sheep on the Downs at home.

Although it had been easy enough to enter, efforts to leave this desolate harbour after two months of pendulum observations became extremely tedious. Each day when attempts were made to unmoor the small ship fierce gales would sweep down from the high crater sides and necessitated letting go the anchors which had just been so laboriously weighed. The water was deep, the holding ground poor, adding to the danger; but after a week *Chanticleer* reached the entrance to find light contrary winds. All boats were lowered, with a will to be free of this dreary place, and the vessel was towed clear at last.

In 1826 Admiralty surveys were begun in South America, commencing with Magellan Strait whither Captain Parry had despatched Captain Phillip Parker King, recently returned from Australian surveys, in *Adventure* together with Commander Pringle Stokes in a small barque of 235 tons named *Beagle*, whose name later became historic.

Captain Foster had met Captain King when their vessels had earlier been in company in Monte Video and King, aware of the inadequacy of *Chanticleer's* storerooms, had suggested a meeting which now came about on Good Friday, 1828, in the Bay of St. Francis in the mountainous Hermite Island near Cape Horn. *Chanticleer's* officers and men had been on short rations for some months and many luxuries were made available to them by Captain King and his men. Among these were tins of Donkin's preserved meats which had now found a secure place in vessels sailing from England for extended voyages. It enabled *Chanticleer's* crew, wrote the surgeon, 'to have a joint of mutton cooked in London, to eat fresh and good at Cape Horn, which is more than entered the minds of the men formerly.'

On Sunday, 24th May, *Chanticleer* weighed for her run to the Cape of Good Hope. As she passed *Adventure*, still at anchor, the crews exchanged three hearty cheers as these two surveying ships parted in this remote and lonely cove.

There now followed a good run to the Cape where Foster was able to conduct his pendulum experiments and rate his chronometers in the pleasant surroundings of the recently established Cape Observatory, and in the delightful company of Dr. Fallows, the Astronomer.

Meanwhile the *Chanticleer's* surgeon, Dr. William Webster, to whom we must turn for an account of the voyage, fell in love with the Cape and its people as did nearly every sailor calling there in those days. Every account of a voyage, however salty, pauses for a chapter to tell of the beauty of the countryside, the neatness of the town, the hospitality of the English townsman and the Boer of the veld, Green Point Races, balls, picnics, expeditions on Table Mountain, ostrich hunts, nights at the theatre, the fine dresses of the women, the excellence of the wine and even the happiness and contentment of the slaves.

Leaving the Cape, pendulum stations were made at St. Helena, Ascension, Fernando de Noronha, Maranhão, Para, Trinidad and finally Porto Bello on the Isthmus of Darien.

Meridian distances had been carried by the ship's chronometers from the Cape to each of these places, and now the proposal was to carry a further distance across the isthmus to Panama to provide a point of departure in the Pacific. A chain of meridian distances right around the world was a requirement dear to the Hydrographer's heart, for such a closure would do much to clear up the many discrepancies in the published lists.

The method of making the time transfer over the isthmus was to be achieved by rocket firing, for however the timepiece was carried across the isthmus to Panama it was certain that the unstable motion of a canoe and the irregular movements of a mule on a stony track would upset the steady rate of the clock, housed as it had been for so long in a sling from the deckhead onboard.

If therefore it was possible to fire rockets at a high point on the peninsula, then those in the ship or on the shore on the Atlantic side could take the time of firing with carefully rated chronometers, whilst the person who had proceeded to Panama would also take the time of the rockets using the watch he had taken with him, and thus obtain a time check before using the watch for longitude observations at Panama.

The best way to cross the peninsula was to take a canoe up the Chagres River four or five days to Cruces, whence there was a rocky road running twenty miles to Panama.

Mr. Fox, with a chronometer, was left at Porto Bello, as also was Lieutenant Williams with a party of twelve seamen. Whilst Mr. Fox established himself near the shore, Lieutenant Williams and his party made their way for six days through the thick jungle and across the many streams that lay between Porto Bello and Cerro Algoroba (1,341 feet) which had been selected as the rocket site.

Meanwhile the ship sailed along the coast to anchor in Navy Bay about thirty miles southwestward and close to the mouth of the Chagres River where Captain Foster at once set out up river by canoe.

This first attempt was a failure for, although Williams' party reached the mountain top, cleared the site and fired the rockets on a clear night, neither Mr. Fox at Porto Bello nor Captain Foster at Panama saw a thing. This information was very disappointing to Williams when he reached Porto Bello after considerable privations brought about by constant damp and heat, overgrown jungle trails and above all the leeches, which worked themselves unnoticed inside the men's clothes and even their boots.

Early in Williams' journey some of his men had become querulous under these conditions, and it became necessary for him to curb this tendency at once. The party happened to be short of rum owing to a leaky calabash, so Williams called the men together and explained that as rum was now short they should agree that if any man grumbled on the march his ration should go to the general stock. From then on a man had only to offer the hint of a complaint for the others to shout out 'Do you grumble?' which the complainant would at once vigorously deny.

Mr. Fox had the launch and, together with Williams and his party, they returned to the ship in Navy Bay to find Captain Foster preparing for a second attempt.

This time the Captain accompanied Lieutenant Williams' party up the Chagres River to Gorgona where he was instructed to fire his rockets from Mount Caravella behind this village. Meanwhile the Captain and one other pushed on by canoe to Cruces and by road to Panama. This time success was achieved; both the Captain in Panama and Lieutenant Horatio Austin in the ship saw and timed the rockets.

On completion of his observations at Panama Captain Foster set out on his return journey reaching Cruces on the morning of 5th February; here he boarded a canoe with Peter Veitch, his servant, and Mr. Fox and Mr. Kay, two young officers from the ship.

All day the canoe made good speed downstream. The Chagres was a beautiful river running clear over rocks and pebbles and bordered by wide savannahs, studded with massive bongo trees at the riverside. The Captain was pleased with the success of the expedition, which would return now direct to England. He lay with his companions on the palm mats beneath the awning of the canoe happily engaged in cheerful conversation.

About 5.00 p.m., just after the canoe had safely negotiated a small rapid, Captain Foster announced his intention of going aft for a word with the native steersman. As he climbed out from beneath the after end of the awning, with one foot on the gunwale, he inadvertently leant upon it. It gave way and in a moment the Captain was in the river.

Mr. Fox and Peter Veitch went overboard at once into the swiftly flowing rivers to aid their Captain, but he never came to the surface, and it was only with considerable difficulty that his would-be rescuers regained the canoe.

Night was almost upon them and there was no chance for a search so that at dawn next day they reached *Chanticleer*, under way off the river mouth and impatient to be homeward bound.

Austin, the First Lieutenant and now in command, despatched parties in the ship's boats up the river to search for the body, which was found three days later by Williams caught in the roots of a tree at the river bank and half devoured by turkey buzzards.

The body had been molested by natives—the pockets cut out of the suit, the note book and watch gone: Britain had lost her leading field astronomer and his last unusual meridian distance could never be computed.

His officers and men buried his mutilated body at the foot of a bongo tree by the river to which they nailed a board inscribed with a seaman's knife: 'Commander H. Foster, His Majesty's Ship *Chanticleer*, drowned in Chagres River Feb. 5th 1831.'

It was not to Parry, under whose direction as Hydrographer the expedition had set out three years before, that Lieutenant Austin carried the sad news, but to Captain Francis Beaufort who had been Hydrographer since May 1829.

The Duke of Clarence had vigorously pursued his duties as Lord High Admiral. He was deeply interested in the training of officers, the welfare of the men; and with Barrow's assistance he carried out vigorous inspections of the home dockyards. But he felt that existing rules and regulations restricted his high office, and this so frustrated him that he resigned as Lord High Admiral in 1828—a victim of 'red tape'. The bright period the Hydrographic Office had enjoyed under the Lord High Admiral was at an end.

Parry found himself once again as he described it 'A Director of a Chart Depot for the Admiralty, rather than a guide and originator of Maritime Surveys'—galling indeed for one who considered the whole vast Arctic as his own to explore and chart as he chose.

Parry had recently been knighted, yet he resigned his post with the Admiralty for the post of Commissioner of the Australian Agricultural Company, a task in the new continent he felt would be more fitting for his energy and which would be less trammelled by political interference.

Although Parry now passes from the hydrographic scene at the early age of thirty-eight years, he subsequently played a leading role in the introduction of steam vessels when he served at the

Admiralty as Comptroller of Steam Machinery, and it was during his time in that office that the screw propeller was introduced into the Navy. Later still in his life he, with other senior naval officers, championed the simple seaman's cause.

His long confinement with seamen in his ships in the Arctic, together with his leadership of them in many a desperate situation, and his faith in the constant help of The Lord in every tribulation, placed Parry in a unique position to be in the van of those who, in the first half of the nineteenth century, recognised the sailor as a human being worthy of his country's thanks and consideration.

This was a period during which 'The Royal National Institution for the Preservation of Life from Shipwreck' was formed with its many lifeboats and rocket stations around our shores; 'The Shipwrecked Fishermen and Mariners Royal Benevolent Society' was established for the relief of widows and orphans of those lost at sea; 'Sailors' Orphans Schools' were opened; 'The British and Foreign Sailors Society' had as its object the religious, intellectual and social elevation of seamen; and in many British ports the first 'Seamen's Homes' were built, where sailors could find a good cheap lodging secure from the dockside crimps who lived by deceiving sailors, and robbing them during their first hectic nights onshore after paying off.

All these causes had Parry's support and during his period as Captain Superintendent at Haslar Hospital, which commenced in 1847, and later as Lieutenant Governor of Greenwich Hospital, he found time to inform seamen at crowded public meetings of the benefits of the many institutions now established for their betterment and to urge upon them the need to improve their moral and religious character in order to live up to their new-found position in society. Parry was promoted to Rear Admiral in June 1852.

Although Parry is the only Hydrographer in our story to lay down the task prematurely, his services both to the improvement of seamen and their ships placed all his successors at the Hydrographic Office in his debt.

CHAPTER TWELVE

Magellan Strait

The early years of the nineteenth century saw the Spanish South American colonies taking advantage of their mother country's preoccupation in Europe to gain their independence, and at the end of the Napoleonic Wars it was Britain, with her unchallenged Navy, who was able to move into these former Spanish colonies, until now closed to her.

President Monroe's famous doctrine of 1823 inferred that the United States would resist further European colonisation in South America; Britain, however, was not seeking colonies but friendship and trade, desiring to exploit the mineral and mining potential of these countries and to export to them the ever increasing flow of goods that resulted from the Industrial Revolution.

Guided by Foreign Secretary Canning, Britain began to recognise the various South American Republics and soon British money was being extensively invested there.

As always, trade needs ships and ships need charts, and the Spanish had only recently begun releasing charts of their American colonies for use by others. Consequently in 1826 a hydrographic expedition left England to make a survey of the coasts of the peninsula of South America from the River Plate southwards, through Magellan Strait, and northwards on the west to the island of Chiloe—a formidable task which was to take five years and resulted in rendering the west coast of South America easily accessible to the trading vessels of Europe.

A glance at the men and the ships which set out on this

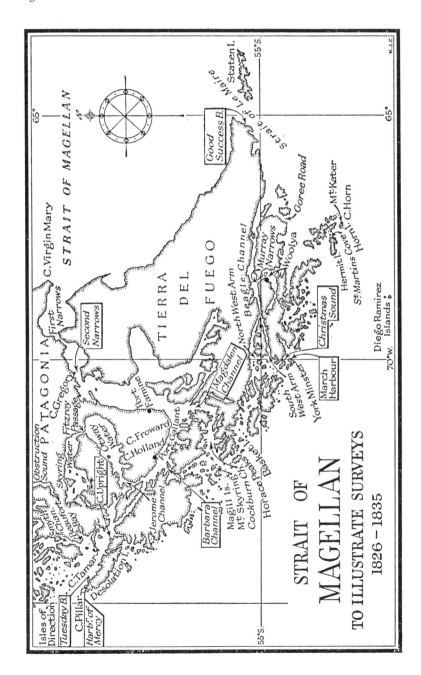

Isles of Direction
Tuesday B.
C.Pillar
Harb.r of Mercy
Smyth Chan.
Beaufort Bay
C.Tamar.
Desolation I.
Obstruction Sound
Skyring Water
Fitzroy Passage
Jerome Channel
C.Upright
Otway Water
Barbara Channel
Magill Is.
Mt.Skyring Ch.
Cockburn Ch.
C.Holland
C.Froward
Port Gallant
Porte Famine
Horace Peak
Basket
South West Arm
York Minster
March Harbour
Christmas Sound
Magdalen Channel
North West Arm
Beagle Channel
Murray Narrows
Woolya
Goree Road
Mt.Kater
Hermit I.
St.Martins Cove
C.Horn
Horn I.
Diego Ramirez
Islands
Good Success B.
Strait Le Maire
Staten I.
TIERRA DEL FUEGO
PATAGONIA
C.Virgin Mary
First Narrows
C.Gregory
Second Narrows
STRAIT OF MAGELLAN
N
65°
65°
70°W.
55°S.
55°S.
K.J.C.

STRAIT OF MAGELLAN
TO ILLUSTRATE SURVEYS
1826–1835

expedition to South American waters tells us something of the surveying which had been going on in other parts of the world.

Since 1813, when Lieutenant Smyth had seized the opportunity to survey Sicilian waters with his gunboats, he had been employed continuously in the Mediterranean. In 1817 he had been given the sloop *Aid* for work in the Adriatic, and in 1821 the *Adventure*, a roomy ship of about 500 tons, in which he delineated the north coast of Africa from the mouth of the Nile to the Strait of Gibraltar.

In 1824 'Mediterranean' Smyth came home to pay off *Adventure* and to draw his charts, by which time he had made a great name for himself as a surveyor, not only in England but in many parts of Southern Europe and North Africa, where he had worked with eminent scholars and cartographers. It was said that when he was working in Egypt Mehemet Ali offered him Cleopatra's Needle as a gift to King George IV, but Smyth could not spare the time from his surveys to embark the massive monument.

Adventure was the ideal ship for the South American expedition; she was capacious, she carried no guns and had been well adapted by Smyth for surveying. Sailing on this venture were two of the many young officers who had learnt their trade from Smyth in the Mediterranean: Lieutenant Thomas Graves, now appointed mate and assistant surveyor in *Adventure*, and William Skyring, as Lieutenant and assistant surveyor in the tender *Beagle*.

To command *Adventure* and the expedition Captain Phillip Parker King was chosen. He was born on Norfolk Island, the son of Captain Gidley Philip King, who had been Governor of New South Wales in the days of Flinders' voyage in *Investigator*. Captain P. P. King remembered how, when he was a boy of ten, Flinders came sunburnt and unshaven into the Governor's House on his return from Wreck Reef. He was unaware then that he himself would complete the great Australian survey that Flinders had begun, but undoubtedly his boyish enthusiasm for adventure was heightened by the tales Flinders had to tell at the parental table at Port Jackson.

P. P. King had been sent out to Australia by Hydrographer Hurd in 1817 to complete the unfinished work on the coasts of Australia that Flinders was forced to abandon when *Investigator* became unseaworthy in the Gulf of Carpentaria. Those surveys King had steadily pursued, first in the cutter *Mermaid* and then in the sloop *Bathurst*, both vessels provided by the Colonial Department, whom the Admiralty had persuaded to finance the voyages.

King had sailed *Bathurst* home to England in 1822, and he had prepared his dozen Australian fair charts and written the narrative of his surveys by 1825, when he was ready for this new command.

In command of the tender *Beagle* was Captain Pringle Stokes, a fine seaman but without practical surveying experience. He had recently been studying mathematics in Edinburgh to suit him for his task.

Before setting out Captain King studied the few existing charts of the area available to him. Foremost among these was the one in Hawkesworth's Voyages. This chart incorporated additions by Wallis (*Dolphin*, 1767), Carteret (*Swallow*, 1767), Byron (1765) and Bougainville (*le Boudeuse*, 1766). Cordova's chart was not available outside Spain, although a written report of an early voyage through the Strait by the Spaniard Sarmiento (who had attempted to form a colony in the Strait in 1585) was much used by King.

Another that King probably studied was Narborough's chart of 1670, which can be seen in the British Library. It is a sort of 'road-map' of Magellan Strait, made for a seaman wishing to make the direct passage from Cape Virgin Mary in the east to the Isles of Direction, which guide the mariner into the Strait from the Pacific; a workmanlike document, it ignores to a great extent the countless channels and fjord-like arms of the sea, which deviate from the Strait. It does, however, carry much valuable incidental information, including a drawing of the natives, male and female, 'who come aboard of ye ship poore and naked'; there is a factual illustration of a guanaco on the north side of the First and Second Narrows where these valuable suppliers of meat were to be found; supplies of fresh water are shown; it describes the 'good planes' of Patagonia contrasting so violently with the 'land of Desolation all craggie peeks on which are perpetuall snow hills, which is Tierra del Fuego.' Good anchorages are shown, including, of course, 'Port Famin' on the coast of Patagonia, where 'good riding and good fishing' referred to the quality of the anchorage and the availability of fresh supplies rather than to the recreational possibilities; and where every vessel passing through the Strait paused for water and rest despite its forbidding name.

Port Famine had become for the Magellan Strait what Point Venus had become for Tahiti and Port Jackson for New South Wales—the accepted port of call for navigators, who added to the careful observations which were steadily accumulating for such key places and making them suitable points of departure for surveys.

It was Captain King's plan to tackle the most difficult part of his survey first whilst his crews were fresh and enthusiastic, and thus the summer of 1827 found the expedition at Port Famine.

From here King sent Stokes westward in *Beagle* to survey the entrance to the Strait from the Pacific and to work eastwards from Cape Pillar; the decked-in boat *Hope*, with Lieutenant John Wickham in charge, was sent to examine the channels running eastwards into Tierra del Fuego; the ships' boats were to work locally across the Strait.

It was soon apparent to all that the bad name which this part of the world had acquired on account of its weather was fully justified. Many days of high winds, rain and mist were punctuated infrequently—even now in summer time—by a few fine clear days. The extreme foulness of the weather was brought home to the *Adventure* when, only a month after operations began, Lieutenant Ainsworth was lost with two of his crew when high winds overtook him in the gig whilst crossing the Strait to Port Famine. John Corkhill, the excellent Captain's coxswain, was one of the men drowned with Ainsworth: he had volunteered for this detached survey.

Meanwhile *Beagle* too had been experiencing the weather. After rounding Cape Froward she commenced the long beat to the westward; it took her thirty-one tacks in heavy squally weather before she came to anchor under Cape Holland ten miles westward.

By the end of January *Beagle* was at Cape Upright and feeling the long swell of the Pacific beneath her. A typical day's sailing which resulted only in a return to the anchorage she had left in the morning is thus described by Captain Stokes in his journal:

'The hands were turned up at daylight "up anchor"; but the heavy squalls that came off the high land of the harbour rendered it too hazardous to weigh, until a temporary lull enabled us to make sail, and re-commence beating to the westward against a dead foul wind, much rain, hard squalls and a turbulent cross sea.

'The squalls became more frequent and more violent after noon; but they gave, in daylight, sufficient warning, being preceded by dark clouds gradually expanding upwards, until their upper line attained the altitude of about fifty degrees; then came heavy rain, and perhaps hail; immediately after followed the squall in all its fury, and generally lasted fifteen or twenty minutes.

'In working to windward we frequently extended our "boards" to the south shore (not without risk considering the state of the weather), and with the hope of making out Tuesday Bay, or some anchorage thereabout; but the coast was covered with so thick a mist that not a single point, mentioned by preceding navigators, could be recognised.

'About seven in the evening we were assailed by a squall, which burst upon the ship with fury far surpassing all that preceded it; had not sail been shortened in time, not a stick would have been left standing, or she must have capsized. As it was, the squall hove her so much over on her broadside, that the boat which was hanging at the starboard quarter was washed away. I then stood over to the north shore, to look for anchorage under the lee of a cape, about three leagues to the north-west of Cape Tamar. On closing it, the weather became so thick that at times we could scarcely see two ships' lengths ahead.

'These circumstances were not favourable to the exploration of unknown bays, and to think of passing such a night as was in prospect, under sails in the Strait would have been a desperate risk; I was obliged therefore to yield the hard-gained advantage of this day's beat, and run for the anchorage whence we had started in the morning.'

It took *Beagle* thirty days from Port Famine to reach the Harbour of Mercy, so aptly named, lying close under the lee of Cape Pillar. Here Stokes met his first Fuegians. He found them listless and dirty, with lank black hair; they had low foreheads, prominent noses with wide nostrils, and large mouths filled with teeth of a dirty brown colour. Their scant beards and eyebrows had been plucked with mussel shell tweezers. For protection both men and women wore but a sealskin thrown cape-like about their shoulders. They had no domestic animals, appeared to exist largely upon shellfish and seal blubber, and when onboard the *Beagle* ate avidly everything offered, but more particularly relished the tallow with which the bases of the sounding leads were armed in order to discover the nature of the seabed, notwithstanding that much sand remained embedded from a recent cast. The Fuegians' habitations were but an arbour of sticks covered with a rough thatch of grass and sealskins, within which the family squatted round warming their private parts before a smoking fire of damp driftwood.

Many of *Beagle's* men were to see Captain Stokes' successor attempt to bring the benefits of European civilisation to these unlikely recipients.

Beagle joined *Adventure* in March at Port Famine when much progress had been made in surveying the main Strait. Both vessels returned to Monte Video in April 1827, and here King purchased the *Adelaide* schooner and placed Lieutenant Graves in command to augment the surveys.

On the north side of the Strait, between the First and Second Narrows and under the lee of Cape Gregory, the expedition had first met the inhabitants of the open rolling plains of Patagonia. Although they found them smaller than the giants described by earlier voyagers, yet these Patagonians were far superior to the Fuegians who inhabited the dank and gloomy forests of the southern and western shores of the Strait.

The Patagonians had their uses, for, mounted on their horses, they hunted the guanaco which grazed on the rolling plains, and these provided excellent meat supplies for the expedition whenever they called at Cape Gregory. A woman was the commanding personality here at Cape Gregory, and when *Adventure* called again in January 1828 Maria embraced Captain King lovingly, her ochreous painted red face close to his.

Maria loved to drink and feigned illness until rum was produced, when she would at once settle down to get steadily tipsy with her fellows, laughing, crying, screaming and bellowing till sleep mercifully overtook them. The next morning she would again be seen, riding down towards the shore on her white horse, looking this time almost as ill as she had claimed to be.

Back at Port Famine in March 1828 it was King's plan to send *Beagle* to explore and survey the west coast from Cape Pillar northwards to 47° South and for *Adelaide* to continue work within the Strait. Meanwhile *Adventure*, acting as the base ship, would remain at Port Famine, perhaps for a year, in order to obtain a comprehensive meteorological record of these waters.

The southern portion of the west coast of South America is fronted by a complex archipelago, the western shores of these islands being exposed to the constant pounding of the great seas which build up across the vast fetch of the southern ocean. It was *Beagle's* task to coast these exposed shores, delineating them as she went northwards. The weather became increasingly vile as she passed the Gulf of Trinidad of Sarmiento, and reached shelter at last at Port Santa Barbara at the northern end of Isla Campana, where the accounts of Byron and Bulkeley had led Stokes to expect it. They had been wrecked in these parts from the *Wager* on Anson's voyage round the world, and here, over eighty years later, Stokes found an old worm-eaten beam from the vessel.

Beagle was now on the south side of the vast Gulf of Peñas which she proceeded to explore, finding good shelter at Port Otway on the northern shore but not on the eastern side, where bad weather detained the ship for the first ten days of June 1828 in a foul anchorage among the Hazard Islands with three anchors down and topmast struck. 'Nothing could be more dreary,' wrote Stokes 'than the scene around us. The lofty, bleak and barren heights that surround the inhospitable shores of this inlet were covered, even low down their sides, with dense clouds upon which the fierce squalls that assailed us beat, without causing any change: they seemed as immovable as the mountains where they rested.

Around us, and some of them distant no more than two thirds of a cable's length, were rocky inlets, lashed by a tremendous surf, and, as if to complete the dreariness and utter desolation of the scene, even birds seemed to shun its neighbourhood. The weather was that in which the soul of man dies in him!'

And this is exactly what was happening to poor Stokes. He was worn out by the weather, the work and the worry of every night and day.

A misfortune overtook him as he sailed from this 'horrid' place, as he describes it, which finally broke his spirit. *Beagle* had one really good boat, an excellent yawl in which Skyring had gone away countless times to sound, coastline, land for observations and climb the distant peaks. This boat had been used for weighing one of the ship's three anchors, and once the other two were weighed Stokes headed for the open sea where he attempted to hoist the yawl, but here the waves were too high and the yawl was stove in alongside and lost.

Mr. Benjamin Bynoe, the surgeon, now insisted on fourteen days' cessation of surveying and a rest for captain and crew, an unusual and brave proposal to put to a surveying captain. Stokes acquiesced but it was during the fourteen endless days of inactivity and rain at Port Otway that his soul finally died. Skyring was in command in all but name as the vessel sailed southward, now in fine light easterly weather. And as Skyring filled in details of the coastline he had missed on the way north the captain remained listless in his cabin.

Scurvy had broken out in *Adventure* despite fresh meat, wild celery, fish and the regular airing and drying of the messdecks. And this, combined with the general listlessness of his crew, decided King reluctantly to abandon his year's meteorological records. He announced that he would sail when *Beagle* rejoined him, and every eye on deck was turned towards the south across the ruffled waters of the Strait. *Beagle's* arrival was greeted by three spontaneous cheers, but as she passed close under *Adventure's* stern to anchor Skyring shouted across that Captain Stokes was confined to his bunk and could not wait upon Captain King.

King went over to see him, and although he shuddered at every mention of another surveying cruise, Stokes seemed determined to obtain provisions from *Adventure* and set out again; but on the day the ship was ready word came by boat to *Adventure* that Stokes had shot himself. He lasted twelve days under Mr. Bynoe's care but he died in a delirium, his mind imagining that *Beagle* was driving on to a lee shore, for the last and fatal time.

Adventure, *Beagle* with Skyring in well-deserved command, and *Adelaide* now sailed in company for the River Plate, where they arrived at the end of September. King met Foster in Monte Video and arranged to meet *Chanticleer* later at Staten Island or Cape Horn.

The vessels sailed on to Rio de Janeiro for stores in October and here soon arrived the Commander-in-Chief, Sir Robert Otway, in his flagship *Ganges*. He ordered *Beagle* to be hove down and repaired, and made an appointment which, violently unpopular both with Captain King and the surveying assistants, led directly over the years to Darwin's great opportunity and *Beagle's* lasting fame: he appointed his Flag Lieutenant, Robert FitzRoy, to be Commander in *Beagle* instead of the much deserving Skyring.

Having joined *Beagle*, FitzRoy arranged that Midshipman Batholomew Sulivan, who had been with him in *Thetis*, should be appointed to his new command, where Lort Stokes (no relation to the former Commander) was already serving as Midshipman.

The ship was anchored off Hospital Island, Rio de Janeiro, where she had been hove down and where the rigging was being remade ashore. The First Lieutenant wanted all hands ashore for this work; they lived in tents, and one night he sent the two Midshipmen and Kirke, the mate, onboard with their hammocks with orders to sleep aboard as duty watch, relieving the quartermaster and sending him, with the watch, onshore.

The quartermaster's farewell warning as he left for the shore was not to go aft as 'the ghost was there'. This was the ghost of poor Commander Stokes, which haunted the ship. The carpenter was one of many who had seen it but declared that he would never disclose to mortal man how ghastly the sight had been.

As soon as the three young men were settled for the night the poop cabin door began to slam in the wind. This fixed, sleep was interrupted by Stokes, 'I hear the sound of breathing very loud ahead'. All three listened, and sure enough they heard heavy breathing, and soon footsteps on the deck above. 'The ghost, it's coming down below!' Sulivan slipped from his hammock behind the companion ladder, and presently appeared first one naked foot and then the other on the steps. Sulivan seized both the bare ankles and a voice above roared out, 'Oh! the ghost! it's got me!' It was one of the men who had drunk too much and gone to sleep in the heads, thus missing the boat ashore.

Adventure sailed from Rio on 27th December 1828 leaving *Beagle* to follow when her repairs were complete. At the end of January *Beagle* was inside Lobos Island in the entrance to the River Plate catching up with *Adventure* which had just been sighted over Goritte Island when a furious pampero struck.

Sulivan had dysentery and lay in a cot in the poop-cabin. Several times *Beagle* was on her beam ends and at length the water inside the ship rose nearly to the cot, and the Midshipman struggled into his trousers and crawled out on deck. Here he took a stance on the almost horizontal mizzen mast. Two men had already been blown right out of the rigging and drowned. Captain FitzRoy was standing on one of the uprights of the poop rail and holding on to another.

The vessel was so much on her beam ends that the topsail yards were blown up to the masthead, the man who had been on the weather yard-arm escaping to the cap of the mast.

The ship was standing straight for the rocks and breakers of Lobos Island when both anchors were let go and she came up to the wind and held fast. The water was so shallow that the ship's bottom touched the flukes of one of the anchors as she passed. It was all over in twenty minutes, but *Beagle* had sustained more damage to her boats in this short time off the Plate than during all her voyaging in the South. Fortunately the Commander-in-Chief arrived in *Ganges* next day and put his carpenters, sailmakers and seamen to work to repair his former Flag Lieutenant's battered vessel.

FitzRoy transferred Sulivan to *Ganges* in view of his forthcoming examination for Lieutenant, but he did not forget this useful young officer.

On 1st March 1829, the Squadron was at last away south. This year the plans were for *Beagle* to pass through the Magellan Strait, detaching *Adelaide* with Graves and Skyring to explore the Magdalen and Barbara Channels, outlets to the Pacific from the Strait towards the southwest. *Adventure* was to go direct to Staten Island for her rendezvous with *Chanticleer* and then to Valparaiso so that King could inform the Chilean Government of the work of the squadron, and to embark provisions for *Beagle* and *Adelaide* which would rendezvous at Chiloe Island.

At New Year's Harbour, Staten Island, King found a note from Foster saying that he had gone to St. Martin's Cove on Hermite Island close behind Cape Horn, and here in this 'disused cove' King met him on 16th April, the meeting referred to in the previous chapter.

Whilst Foster carried on his laborious pendulum experiments ashore and while the crews transferred provisions from the bulky *Adventure* to the tiny *Chanticleer*, King charted the coves about the islands and climbed the mountains for theodolite observations and barometer height records. He was accompanied by Lieutenant Kendall of *Chanticleer* who had travelled with Franklin to the Polar Sea.

Both theodolites and barometers were cumbersome in the thick vegetation and on the rocky screes of the steep mountain sides. 'We had ascended but little way, when the unfortunate theodolite escaped from my coxswain, rolled down the ravine and was much damaged. On the descent great care had to be taken to avoid the barometers suffering the same fate. However unimportant we might think bruises and scratches, a broken barometer would have been a serious accident.' In such phrases did King describe the ascents.

The night before *Chanticleer* sailed Foster dined at King's table and there told of his presentiment that he would not survive his present voyage: it was a sad farewell despite the cheers of the ships' companies.

Adventure sailed to seaward of the coastal archipelago and reached Valparaiso on 22nd June where she embarked provisions for the squadron, whilst the Captain travelled with Lieutenant Wickham to Santiago, the capital of Chile, ninety miles away.

Here King waited upon General Pinto, Director of the Chilean Government, to describe the purpose of the voyage with a view to preventing suspicion or interruption of the work in Chilean waters.

Director Pinto received King with the greatest politeness. 'He entered into the particulars of our past voyage with much interest, assuring me that every facility should be afforded, and every assistance rendered, whenever it might be required; and in this assurance we never found ourselves deceived. I make this observation with the more pleasure, as it was very unusual in our communications with the authorities of those governments we had previously visited, to find the objects of our voyage considered in the least interesting.'

On 26th August 1829, *Adventure* came to anchor off San Carlos in the island of Chiloe, where *Beagle* awaited her and *Adelaide* was daily expected. Mr. Williams, the English harbourmaster, was helpful and the Chilean Governor kind. 'I established myself at a house in the town, obtained by his (Governor's) kindness; and there fixed my portable observatory, and set up an azimuth-altitude instrument,' wrote King of a true surveyor's home from home.

Beagle's new Commander had learnt his job fast and the report he now made to Captain King completely vindicated the Commander-in-Chief's appointment. FitzRoy had certainly been busy during the last five months.

After passing Port Famine FitzRoy had detached Graves with Skyring and the surgeon, Bynoe, as volunteers, in *Adelaide* to go down the Magdalen Channel while he sailed on through Magellan Strait to Port Gallant. Here he left Lieutenant Kemp in charge of the ship and went off for a month's survey voyage in the cutter and whaler with young Stokes and a dozen men.

Knowing that it would rain every day, they took with them little water but plenty of dry provisions. Each member of the crew had his clothes covered with canvas to keep out the wet and wore 'southwesters' on their heads. Each man of the party had a blanket with a hole for his head and a drawstring to wear poncho fashion.

They set off up the Jerome Channel and four days later entered a vast inland sea with damp forest-clad shores on the western side and dry plains typical of Patagonia on the east. FitzRoy named it Otway Water in honour of his benefactor, the Commander-in-Chief. They crossed this and, passing northwestwards through FitzRoy Passage, entered a second vast sea lake—Skyring Water.

Each night the boat was beached and camp pitched, fires were lit, often with the greatest difficulty on the damp ground, supper was made, a sing-song often followed and then the men lay down to rest with one of their number on guard against native prowlers. Sometimes the crews would have been rowing for ten hours or so and sleep came quickly.

Each peak of eminence on the shore was scaled and rounds of theodolite angles and compass bearings were taken to keep the plot going. As the boats pulled or sailed on, keeping as steady a course or speed as they could, the bowman used the leadline to record the depths on each leg of the journey and thus fill in the picture.

The month's trip ended in a sodden camp, from which a dog had stolen their last piece of pork; the Commander shared with his men the only razor to smarten themselves before returning to the *Beagle* on the morrow.

All was shipshape at Port Gallant; only *Adelaide* was awaited. 'I never was fully aware of the comfort of a bed until this night. Not even a frost-bitten foot could prevent me from sleeping soundly for the first time during many nights,' wrote FitzRoy.

On the shortest day of the year Skyring and Graves returned to Port Gallant having navigated down the Magdalen Channel, westwards along the Cockburn Channel and out to the Magill Islands. Here a party of six under Skyring in freezing conditions scaled precipitous Mount Skyring (3,000 feet), from which they had a great expansive view of the islands and the Adelaide Passage through which they would sail on to the Barbara Channel, which could be seen curving away to the northwestward; to the south-westward they gazed across the open sea. As the Barbara Channel subsequently led them back to Magellan Strait they had established two new outlets to the Pacific.

They built a cairn on the summit of Mount Skyring under which they buried a bottle containing a list of the six who had gained the summit—'Please leave this document and build the pile, under which it is placed, at least six feet higher', it read. On 24th February 1981 Commander Roberts of the Chilean Survey Ship *Piloto Pardo* flew two helicopters to the summit of Mount Skyring with a party of seamen to search for the message. Although the bottle was broken and the list of those building the cairn missing, a number of medals and coins and other small items were recovered, including one medal on which could be clearly read 'HMS *Adventure* and *Beagle* 1828'. The items are now in the Martin Gusinde Archaeological and Historical Museum in Puerto Williams.

FitzRoy would have been carrying out his instructions if he had now sailed direct for Chiloe Island, but that was not his way. He instructed *Adelaide* to see if an inside passage existed from Beaufort Bay northwards behind the coastal archipelago to the Gulf of Trinidad, whilst he himself sailed northwards on the seawards side. Success here enabled Skyring and Graves to honour their old Mediterranean chief by naming the Smyth Channel.

Beagle sailed again from San Carlos in November, *Adelaide* and *Adventure* in December, the former having as a replacement for her mainmast the town's fine flagstaff.

All three vessels were on their last lap of the great southern survey, and Captain King, assessing how much each could do, issued instructions and ordered a rendezvous at Rio de Janeiro in June 1830.

Adventure had left her chronometers at Valparaiso to be cleaned by Mr. Roskell, the agent there for Messrs. Roskell, chronometer makers of Liverpool. She returned now to collect these and to run a final 'chronometer chain' from Valparaiso, Concepción, Port Famine to Monte Video, thus connecting the longitudes of each. Port Famine had been used during the survey to extend chronometric longitudes to many points within the area and thus every one of these would now be connected to the well-established positions at Monte Video and Valparaiso.

Adelaide was to enter the Gulf of Peñas in the archipelago and sail down the Mesier Channel which, it was believed, would emerge in the Gulf of Trinidad, whence her northward route should be followed down to Beaufort Bay. Every one of the fjord-like channels leading eastward towards the Cordilleras was to be explored with the hope of finding a channel through the mountains to FitzRoy's Skyring Water.

Skyring was confined to bed for at least a month during the cruises which successfully passed through the Mesier Channel. The surgeon believed his illness due to fatigue and sitting too long while constructing charts in his poky cabin.

But by the time the most promising channel was entered Skyring was on deck again. This was Sarmiento's 'Ancón Sin Salida', which despite its name gave encouragement as it serpentined many miles first eastward and then to the south.

The schooner was navigated through two dangerous narrows before a base was measured and Skyring and Kirke triangulated their way forward in the boats along each side of the winding fjord. Round every bend a new and encouraging reach lay ahead, and now and again from a high point open water could be seen beyond the next headland.

It was exciting work as the laying down of the observed triangles on the fieldboards indicated a steady approach towards the northern shore of Skyring Water, but it was a bitter moment when Obstruction Sound ended abruptly at the foot of a range of lofty hills, beyond which, only five miles or so distant, lay the inland sea.

To *Beagle* was assigned the survey of the seaward coasts of Tierra del Fuego from Cape Pillar, round the Horn to the Strait of Lemaire, as broken, desolate, remote and sea-battered a coastline as the world has to offer.

Commencing at Cape Pillar FitzRoy worked his way along, carrying forward the work by taking angles from the peaks ashore and from ship stations at sea, distances between them being carefully measured by the patent log towed astern from the vessel.

At last, ascending Mount Skyring, with 'his usual companion, a theodolite' he obtained a most satisfactory round of angles including 'most of the remarkable peaks, islands and capes, within a range of 40 miles'. There were loose stones about the summit of the mountain in which were iron pyrites which rendered Kater's fine compass quite useless; but FitzRoy had established a white post on the shore near the ship from which he had obtained the true astronomical bearing of Skyring's massive cairn on the summit. So, by including now the white post in his round of angles, all the work was correctly orientated, and a good connection with Skyring's work in the Barbara Channel established.

Now commenced the next leg of the survey to close on Foster's well-established position at St. Martin's Cove behind Cape Horn. The familiar routine went on, boat expeditions leaving to explore the labyrinths of islands from the ship, anchored in well determined positions.

Whilst *Beagle* lay uneasily at anchor beneath the Horace Peaks, from which descended in profusion furious williwaws, the Captain felt some anxiety for Mr. Murray, the Master, who was away for a week with a whaler's crew.

At three in the morning of the 5th February FitzRoy was called to be informed that the coxswain and two of the whaler's crew had arrived alongside in an incredible sea-going basket, in which they had been navigating for thirty-six hours. They had a sad tale to tell.

At night whilst the Master and his whaler's crew had been resting on a remote island, their boat, safely moored in a sheltered cove, had been stolen by Fuegians. The coracle had been constructed, under the direction of the Master, from small boughs, lined with canvas from the tent and caulked with clay. It was a precarious craft but proved sufficient to carry the news to the ship.

FitzRoy himself took charge of the second whaler and sailed at once to 'Basket Island', and after relieving the stranded crew set off in search of the thieves.

A cut-down oar here, a piece of rope there and the odd bottle or other piece of equipment found upon the beaches left a trail which FitzRoy followed in search of the stolen boat. There were brushes with the Fuegians, much chasing of smoke from fires and landing to search abandoned wigwams, but the boat was never found, and the search ended with FitzRoy in possession of three Fuegian children but nothing else.

The stolen whaler had been an excellent boat, built by Mr. May the carpenter whilst at San Carlos. There was nothing to be done but for him to build another from a fine spar which *Adventure* had obtained at Valparaiso and which had been transferred to *Beagle* at Chiloe.

To seek a sheltered anchorage where the Carpenter and his assistants could work ashore on the building of the boat, FitzRoy made for Christmas Sound, where Cook had anchored in his *Resolution*, and to which his aptly named towering rocks of York Minster were a visible guide. Here a snug cove was found, where the first half of March was spent in March Harbour building the boat, whilst the other whaler and the cutter divided their time between surveying expeditions, and the keeping of pilfering Fuegians at a distance from the boat-building operations.

During this period the boat parties returned two of the three Fuegian children to their tribe and captured without difficulty two young men, 'York Minster' and 'Boat Memory', who joined the eight-year old 'Fuegian Basket' onboard *Beagle*.

On 22nd April *Beagle* had reached Horn Island and FitzRoy climbed from the shores of the cove which had been occupied by *Chanticleer* to Mount Kater to close his observations. From here the final leg of his survey lay northwards to the Strait of Lemaire.

Mr. Murray, the Master, was instrumental in discovering the eastern end of the long, straight Beagle Channel, which almost certainly led westward to the Pacific—but there was no time to confirm this; and later he surveyed the coast on the western side of the Strait of Lemaire and Good Success Bay, a useful harbour of refuge for vessels encountering foul winds in these straits.

One day in the Murray Narrows, which permit access to Beagle Channel from the southeast, FitzRoy handed to a member of the crew of a native canoe a large shining mother-of-pearl button for which he received in exchange a young boy who seemed delighted with his new position. It was when he got back to the ship that FitzRoy realised that 'Jemmy Button', as the men now called him, was of the 'Yapoo' tribe and had little in common with the other three Fuegians onboard. The latter indicated that they were often at war with the 'Yapoo', which made it clear to FitzRoy that he could not now land his three Fuegians from the west among the Yapoo, and their territory lay many a mile to windward. He decided, there and then, to take all four Fuegians to England, and there to teach them English, religion and husbandry, with the object of returning them at some future date to Tierra del Fuego, where they might form a nucleus of civilisation around which a better life for the Fuegians would develop.

Thus it was that on 2nd August, when *Beagle* rejoined *Adventure* at Rio de Janeiro, she had onboard the four Fuegians, who had been singularly unmoved by the civilised bustle of Monte Video, and now awaited their arrival in England with little outward interest or enthusiasm.

Both vessels reached Plymouth Sound on 14th October 1830 to pay off.

King and FitzRoy supervised the drawing of the charts and wrote their Sailing Directions. What had the expedition achieved?

The navigation from Atlantic to Pacific could now be clearly described: two escape routes from the southern part of the Magellan Strait direct to the Pacific Ocean had been charted, enabling westbound vessels encountering northwest winds to make their way more quickly to the open sea; an inshore route had been found on the west coast from the Gulf of Peñas direct to the Magellan Strait for small vessels using the prevailing northwest winds; the rugged coasts around Cape Horn had been charted, as had the Strait of Lemaire; and the remote and dangerous Diego Ramirez Islands had been fixed where they lay, far out to the southwest of Cape Horn.

One thing the surveyors could not do was to control the violent westerly winds which, for the next 100 years, were to make the successful rounding of Cape Horn a feat of dogged seamanship, exemplifying man's struggle against the elements.

CHAPTER THIRTEEN

High Noon: Beaufort as
Hydrographer

With the advent of peace in 1815 Britain commenced her long, steady policy of maintaining the freedom and the safety of the seas. These were the tasks of the Royal Navy, and their successful achievement ensured that the Pax Britannica lasted for nearly a century.

There were two great hazards at sea at the beginning of the long peace: piracy was rife and curtailed the freedom of the seas, whilst the relatively few existing charts were completely inadequate for safe navigation. The Royal Navy set about removing the pirates and making the charts.

The nation's excitement had been aroused by Captain Parry's expeditions in search of the Northwest Passage and the North Pole, but such ventures had only improved the safety at sea for a small number of whalers. What was required were more expeditions of the type from which King and FitzRoy had just returned, resulting in improved charts and Sailing Directions for vessels engaged in trade with the South American Republics.

Admiralty charts had been on sale to the merchant fleets of the world since 1821. Hurd had put this proposal forward in an effort to gain better salaries for his staff, but five years later chart sales were a part of Britain's aim of providing freedom and safety on the seas for all. Such a policy appeared to suit Britain in her search for raw materials for her growing factories, and markets for the resulting products.

The year 1829 was more than ripe for an expansion of charting to meet the growing demands of trade, and it was indeed fortunate that John Barrow, the Second Secretary at the Admiralty, selected Captain Francis Beaufort as the new Hydrographer of the Navy. It had been Barrow who had chosen Beaufort, and his ship the *Fredericksteen*, many years before, out of the whole Mediterranean Fleet, to be sent to survey Karamania. Now Barrow had been asked by Lord Melville to choose between him and Captain Peter Heywood, last survivor from the *Bounty* mutiny.

When Beaufort took over the chair in May 1829 he was fifty-five years old, the age at which, today, the Hydrographer of the Navy retires. He remained in office for twenty-six active years.

He found in the Office the works of Flinders in Australia, Smyth in the Mediterranean, King in South America and Owen in Africa; but plotted on a map of the world these surveys left a great void which Beaufort was determined to fill. Turning to home waters he considered the few surveys available totally inadequate for the safety of shipping. He set about planning how all this work could be achieved.

The day after taking office there began to flow from his pen a copious stream of letters to the surveyors at sea urging zeal, counselling care and commending achievement. Few at first, surveyors in the field steadily increased in numbers as he scattered them across the globe, each furnished with a clear and concise set of instructions for the conduct of their surveys. Within a few years FitzRoy had returned to South America; Belcher and Kellett to the west coast of the same continent; Vidal, Henry Denham, Skyring and William Arlett went out to complete the surveys of the West Coast of Africa northwards from the Gambia; Francis Blackwood and Owen Stanley were on the Northeast Coast of Australia and in New Guinea; Sulivan surveyed the Falkland Isles; Lort Stokes and Byron Drury carried out the first survey of New Zealand since Cook's day; William Bate surveyed the Palawan Channel; Richard Collinson was in China; Richard Owen with Edward Barnett was in the Caribbean; Bayfield was still working on his great survey of the St. Lawrence; Graves returned to the Greek Archipelago with Thomas Spratt; William Hewett, in the

Fairy, was making the first comprehensive survey of the North Sea; and Frederick Beechey was working in the Irish Sea while his young brother Richard was also working in Ireland. George Thomas, Henry Otter and William Sheringham were generally employed in Home Waters.

These were some of the world-wide operations which Beaufort directed; they make the task of writing Britain's surveying story at sea a very complex one. Rupert Gould, who attempted such a history in the 1920s, gave up at this stage, admitting that with the advent of Beaufort the canvas became too vast for him to cover. 'There are masses of facts and figures available,' wrote Gould, 'but to get them into any order, chronological, historical or even alphabetical, is like trying to unscramble a scrambled egg.' I intend to attempt the unscrambling by dealing with Francis Beaufort first, the man and his administration over the twenty-six years from 1829, and then, in subsequent chapters, try to impart the spirit of this great age of hydrography by a number of smaller pictures of the more outstanding surveyors who worked so faithfully for the Hydrographer.

As a young man Beaufort fell from a boat when securing alongside his ship in Portsmouth Harbour and, like many a young sailor in those days, he could not swim, so he began to drown. Shipmates came to his assistance within a few minutes. Back onboard, he 'underwent the usual vulgar process of emptying the water by letting my head downwards, then bleeding, chafing and even administering gin'.

But during the brief period while he was in the water and almost succumbed the principal events of his short, youthful life had appeared clearly before him, each act being accompanied by a consciousness of right and wrong. When he was Hydrographer, many years later, Lady Lavinia Spencer asked for details of his thoughts on this occasion, for she had scientific friends who were studying facts relative to the human mind while struggling with death.

Already, at the age of twenty, those drowning thoughts must have had plenty to range over. He had been born the second son of the Rector of Navan in County Meath who had made an excellent map of Ireland. He had entered the Navy as a volunteer at the age of thirteen, and, under Captain Lestock Wilson, had surveyed in the East Indiaman *Vansittart* in the East Indies, where this vessel was wrecked. At the time of his near drowning he was newly back from service with Lord Howe at the Battle of the Glorious First of June. Later he had again fought the French and the Spaniards, had been wounded more than once, had convoyed vessels across the oceans of the world, chased pirates in Greek waters and surveyed on the south coast of Turkey and in the River Plate.

Beaufort was a small, kindly but utterly determined man, who, some time after he became Hydrographer, married his second wife Honora, a sister of Maria Edgeworth, the novelist. She had made a pleasant home for him at 7, Gloucester Place. From here, after three hours' work before breakfast, he set out each day for the Admiralty where he arrived on the stroke of nine, and there laboured at his desk for eight hours. His first wife Alicia, daughter of his early Commander, Lestock Wilson, had died in 1835.

Beaufort's name is known to every seaman, for his scale for measuring the force of the wind by eye is still in world-wide use today. When employed as Hydrographer to the East India Company Dalrymple had prepared a pamphlet entitled *'Instructions to Captains'* which encouraged masters of Indiamen to record geographical and meteorological data in the course of their voyages; whilst to facilitate the recording of wind strengths he set down a numbered scale of 1 to 12.

When young Commander Beaufort was about to sail in command of H.M.S. *Woolwich* in 1806 to convoy sixteen Indiamen home from the East Dalrymple, then Hydrographer of the Navy, supplied him with copies of his many charts and his papers, including the windscale which Beaufort copied into his private journal. FitzRoy had been persuaded to use the windscale in *Beagle* by 1831; in 1837 it was introduced into the Surveying Service by Hydrographer's order whilst the Board of Admiralty, at Beaufort's request, brought it into general use in the Navy the following year.

Beaufort latterly had a great contemporary in the United States, Matthew Fontaine Maury, U.S.N., who had been in charge of the Navy's Depot of Charts and Instruments since 1842. He, like

Beaufort, had studied meteorology and ocean currents during his first years at sea, and once settled ashore he had published his famous *Wind and Current Charts*, which enabled shipmasters who used these charts intelligently to shorten long sea passages by many days.

Maury was instrumental in arranging the first international meteorological conference in Brussels in 1853, the year before Beaufort's retirement. One of the United Kingdom delegates was Captain Frederick Beechey, who by this date served as the first professional naval officer in the Maritime Department of the Board of Trade, a post held by a surveying officer until a few years ago.

The conference resulted in a number of nations adopting a standard type of weather reporting log and Beaufort's Scale was unanimously approved for international use.

On return from this conference Beechey was able to persuade the Board of Trade to set up a Meteorological Department of which Captain FitzRoy, long back from his wanderings, became the first Director.

The Beaufort Scale was related to the amount of canvas each type of vessel could expect to carry in the wind force prevailing. In later years 'sea' and 'shore' criteria were introduced to assess the steps of the Beaufort Scale using the appearance of the surface of the sea or the drift of chimney smoke to gauge the wind force, but basically the scale has stood the test of time. 'Force 12 on the Beaufort Scale' ('a hurricane such that no canvas could withstand') is still a phrase to chill the marrow of a seafarer no matter how well-found his ship.

When Beaufort became Hydrographer there was no method whereby charts, once sold, could be kept corrected for new information, short of printing a new chart.

'There are no charts of any part of the world so accurate and no directions so perfect as not to furnish frequent occasion for revision and amendment.' So wrote Beaufort on the title page of the *Nautical Magazine* which, subsidised by the Admiralty and the Mercantile Marine Fund, was first published in 1832 under the direction of the Hydrographer and edited by Becher, his naval assistant.

Part of the 'Address to the Public' on page 1 of the first number read: 'The principal feature of the work will consist of the particulars of those hidden maritime dangers which are too often fatal to ships . . . Much information, of a nature highly valuable to mariners, is scattered about, destitute of any systematic arrangement by which it can be made available to them; but the pages of the *Nautical Magazine* will hereafter become the receptacle, in which it will be preserved for their reference.'

The *Nautical Magazine* performed the services of *Notices to Mariners* until November 1834, when these latter were established and appeared as official publications over the Hydrographer's signature. By 1835 the *Nautical Magazine* had discontinued its section on Hydrography to give greater emphasis to reports of interesting voyages, feats of navigation and *Nautical Miscellany*, which last remains a lively feature of the magazine today. *Notices to Mariners*, correcting the charts, published daily and averaging 4,000 a year, the weekly editions of which make up a bulky, if unwelcome, mail for the navigating officer after many days at sea, are yet another reminder of Beaufort and his works that lives on.

Whereas Maury was the leading figure in promoting international co-operation in the field of meteorology, Beaufort gave similar attention to co-operation in recording the rise and fall of the tides.

The study of tides had not reached an advanced state when Beaufort took over the Hydrographer's chair, although Mr. Dessiou, previously engaged in writing Sailing Directions, was by 1830 in the office working on tidal matters. Using times of high water which had been recorded over a complete lunar period Dessiou was able, with the assistance of a Mr. Ross, to compile information sufficient for the publication of the first *Admiralty Tide Tables* in 1833. This was a mere pamphlet giving the times of high water at Plymouth, Portsmouth, Ramsgate, Sheerness and London.

An understanding of tidal theory was required before the *Admiralty Tide Tables* could be expanded, so Beaufort began co-operation with Dr. William Whewell, later to become Professor and Master of Trinity College, Cambridge. Whewell, of course, required observations to use as his data, and in 1834 the Hydrographer arranged with Captain William Bowles, Comptroller-General of the Coast Guard Service, for a period of tidal readings to be made at all points along the coast where officers of that Service were stationed. All Coastguard Stations were brought into this scheme the following summer, and this in turn gave impetus to a truly international effort in 1835 when, with permission of Their Lordships, Beaufort sought and obtained co-operation in the recording of tides on both sides of the North Sea, the Channel and, with the United States coming in, both sides of the North Atlantic.

Whewell now had ample material to work on so that the reliability, the coverage and stature of the *Admiralty Tide Tables* began to grow towards their present standard.

The consecutive times of high water at each recording point along a coastline showed Whewell that the tidal wave moved steadily forward and, assuming that this wave moved somewhat similarly offshore, he drew on a chart of the North Sea co-tidal lines from the surrounding coast. These lines were designed to join all points at which high water occurred at the same instant and they were numbered 0 to 11 indicating the number of hours after the time of the Moon's transit at Greenwich at which high water occurred.

The pattern of the co-tidal lines, when projected into the centre of the North Sea where, of course, there were no recorded times for high water, indicated to Whewell that the sea was oscillating like water in a basin, high on one side when low on the other but with a point in the middle which does not change depth. This theory was put to the test by Beaufort who sent out Captain Hewett in *Fairy* to search near the spot where Whewell expected to find his 'amphidromic point'. *Fairy's* boat, securely anchored over the flat bed of the North Sea, found at the second position occupied that she was indeed very near the point, for in twenty-four hours there was no change in sounding by leadline.

Despite this practical proof, Whewell's theory was not generally accepted in the world of science for nearly 100 years. But the theory was sound, and today the modern editions of Admiralty co-tidal charts of the North Sea, enhanced as they are with

observations in recent years from a wide variety of offshore positions, confirm Whewell's argument. The co-tidal and co-range lines
are little changed, simply refined with thirty-minute time intervals
and height ranges in metres.

Beaufort was a scientist of those days; he had been a Fellow of
the Geological Society since 1808, the Royal Society since 1814,
the Astronomical Society since 1820 and had been a prime mover
with John Barrow in forming the Royal Geographical Society in
1830. The Hydrographic Office assumed a scientific character and
the Hydrographer became the link which connected the Admiralty
with scientific bodies at home and in Europe and America.

In 1831 a Scientific Branch of the Admiralty was formed containing the Hydrographic Office, the Royal Observatory at Greenwich, the Cape Observatory, and the Nautical Almanac and
Chronometer Offices, the estimates for these establishments being
prepared by the Hydrographer. The Chronometer Office was later
absorbed by the Nautical Almanac Office. In 1831 the Board of
Visitors to the Royal Observatory, headed by the President of the
Royal Society, chose Lieutenant Becher as their Secretary.

By inspecting the first estimates prepared for the Hydrographic
Department in 1831 (a total of £9,746), one is able to see what a
puny staff Beaufort had to assist him. John Walker, who had been
in the office since Dalrymple's day, died that year and was succeeded as Assistant Hydrographer by his second son Michael, his
third son Thomas being one of four draughtsmen. There were
three naval assistants—Becher, Barnett and Dessiou.

When the drawings had been prepared by the draughtsmen they
were sent for engraving on copper to Messrs. Walker of Castle
Street, Holborn, a firm run by John, the eldest, and Charles, the
youngest of old Walker's four sons. John also worked with Horsburgh, Dalrymple's successor as Hydrographer to the East India
Company, and in turn succeeded Horsburgh in 1836.

Once the plates were engraved they were delivered to the
basement of the Admiralty building whence they were still carried
three floors up to the copper press when printing of the charts was

required. It is not clear if one or two copper printers were employed, but there is a record of a new press being installed, still
on the top floor, in 1836 when a Mr. Crofton Croker took charge
of the printing.

With such a small staff it was inevitable that Beaufort himself
spent a great deal of time inspecting and perfecting every new
chart. Resulting from this individual treatment standard symbols
soon developed and by 1835 the first sheet of *Abbreviations used in
Admiralty Charts* was published and the Admiralty Chart assumed
the character which it maintained until 1967 when the metre
replaced the fathom and four-colour printing of charts was
adopted. The datum of Low Water Spring Tides was finally
adopted so that every chart in the future showed the least water
a mariner could expect; compasses on charts were shown as true
roses with a magnetic north arrowhead; abbreviations to describe
the nature of the bottom, so important to a vessel in search of
anchorage, were standardised; stipples to denote drying sand and
mud banks were introduced; fathom-line symbols were adopted:
and the underlining of 'drying soundings' to show the height of
sand or mud uncovered at low water was introduced.

The numbers of new charts published each year steadily increased from a total of 19 in 1830, Beaufort's first full year in office,
to 130 in 1855, the year of his retirement.

Lieutenant Frederick Bullock had commanded a small paddle
vessel, *Echo*, whilst surveying the River Thames in 1827–28 but
such ships did not come easily to the Surveying Service. In 1837,
the year of the young Queen's accession, Parry, back from Australia, took over as Comptroller of Steam Machinery at the Admiralty, and Beaufort could feel he had 'a friend at court'.

During Parry's ten years in the post the screw propeller was
introduced, but it was the small paddlers that revolutionised survey
work when six, led by *Shearwater* under the command of Captain
John Washington, were appropriated for surveying in 1841 around
the shores of the United Kingdom.

These steamers took over from a motley collection of hired
boats, largely unsuitable, which had been used at home for ten
years. For the first time surveyors could run ship sounding-lines in

the direction they deemed best in a systematic manner; they could work in calm as well as windy weather; and they could leave or return to harbour as they wished. The standard of work at home rose appreciably until in 1848 came a bitter blow when all six steamers were withdrawn by the Admiralty for famine relief work on the western coasts of Scotland and Ireland. It was back to the inconveniences and unreliability of the hired boat.

This was followed in 1851 by another blow—the going had been too good. A sudden cut of £10,000 in the Hydrographer's vote of £70,000 meant the curtailing of surveys abroad. Beaufort's complaint to the Secretary of the Admiralty concluded: 'I will not trifle with your time by repeating here any hackneyed truisms about the comparative expense to the country in the cost of surveys or in the loss of ships and cargoes, but I will just entreat you to weigh the small sum you propose to save against the large amount of mischief which may be the result.'

In 1853 an attempt was made to get back the use of the six paddlers, but the false economy of the hired boats was to continue, which resulted in the resignation of Captains Bullock, Sheringham, George Frazer and Robinson for lack of suitable appointments.

Nor were efforts to increase the office staff successful and towards the end of his tenure Beaufort believed that the French, Danish, Russian and United States Hydrographic Departments, to whom he had been showing the way, were beginning to overtake him. It was useless for him to point out to those holding the purse strings that charts were the life-blood of the world's greatest maritime nation. 'The natural tendency of men is to undervalue what they cannot understand,' said he.

But he had plenty to hold his attention. He issued in 1850 the first edition of the *General Instructions to Hydrographic Surveyors*, a book which, now in its sixteenth edition, sets out procedures to be followed in every form of survey and oceanographic work and how the records should be rendered. With others, the Hydrographer influenced Their Lordships to publish in 1849 the first edition of *The Admiralty Manual of Scientific Enquiry* which consisted of chapters, written by leading scientists of the day, detailing how seafarers, by careful observing and recording, could add to scientific knowledge.

The advent of iron ships had added to the importance of determining more accurately the deviation of the steering compasses and Beaufort formed a committee to study the matter. This resulted in the establishment in 1842 of a new Compass Branch, closely associated with the Hydrographic Office, which organised the regular and frequent inspection and swinging of the compasses in the Fleet.

In 1846 a Harbour and Railway Department was established within the Hydrographic Office, which, until transferred to the Board of Trade in 1862, placed upon the Hydrographer the responsibility of ensuring that any new bridge or railway should not interfere with existing harbours, rivers or navigable waters. As always, Beaufort took these duties seriously and even opposed the laying of the railway track along the seashore near Dawlish because 'of the indifference of promoters of railway schemes to the rights or convenience of others'. Some will wish that he had been successful.

Beaufort's knowledge of all things nautical resulted in his being widely consulted. His sound advice on pilotage, harbours of refuge, siting of lighthouses, lifesaving rockets and countless maritime matters added daily to the high standing of his office; he was even consulted on behalf of Her Majesty who wished to know where she could land to reach Osborne without passing through the inquisitive crowds at Cowes.

In March 1854 he wrote to Captain Bayfield, 'being eighty years old, as deaf as a post, with failing eyes and shaking hands, and above all, with memory clean gone, it would be too silly to remain here till some broad hint reached me from higher quarters.' But in that month the war with Russia broke out and Their Lordships would not let him go for a further nine months.

Despite the economies of his later years Beaufort left surveyors working in every ocean and, on the shelves, a series of 2,000 charts covering every sea; 140,000 copies of these were printed in his last year of office for sale or issue to the Fleet, which was largely deployed in the Black Sea and the Baltic, piloted by surveying officers in the war against Russia.

Beaufort set the pattern during this high noon for hydrography which we have followed for 150 years, maintaining our position in the very forefront of the world's chartmakers.

CHAPTER FOURTEEN

The Voyage of the *Beagle*

Poor 'Boat Memory' died in the Naval Hospital in Plymouth, whither all four of FitzRoy's Fuegians had been sent for their smallpox inoculations. The three that survived this ordeal had been boarded for a year with the Revd. William Wilson of Walthamstow. Here they were taught English and religious knowledge, carpentry and simple agriculture, enjoyed the company of neighbours, and on one great occasion were taken to London for an audience of King William IV and Queen Adelaide, the latter putting one of her own bonnets on the head of Fuegian Basket.

FitzRoy had imagined that some suitable ship would, sooner or later, be sent to complete the South American surveys, for the whole coastline from the River Plate southwards to Port Desire was yet to be completed, as also was the northeast side of Tierra del Fuego and the western part of the Beagle Channel. The exposed western side of the Chonos Archipelago was still to be mapped, whilst to the north the long coasts of Chile and Peru awaited the chartmaker.

However, as the months of 1831 rolled by there was no plan forthcoming for resuming the work. FitzRoy became increasingly anxious about his three young Fuegians, for he had faithfully promised that they would return to their homeland, and he fervently hoped that they would form the first small nucleus of civilisation in Tierra del Fuego. He dreamt of a prosperous Christian settlement, supplying meat and vegetables to seafarers increasingly following the newly charted channels from the Atlantic to the Pacific.

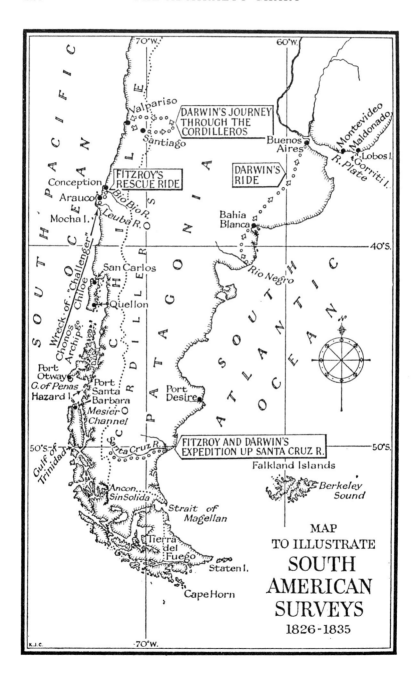

MAP
TO ILLUSTRATE
SOUTH
AMERICAN
SURVEYS
1826-1835

FitzRoy at last, seeing no move by Their Lordships, chartered a Bristol vessel at his own expense to carry the Fuegians back to their distant homeland. He planned to sail in this ship himself and to take two missionaries to be established in Tierra del Fuego. This chartering had hardly been arranged when the Admiralty decided to resume the South American surveys, and *Beagle* began fitting out again at Plymouth, FitzRoy being appointed to command.

It was Beaufort's wish that *Beagle*, on completion of her South American surveys, should return across the Pacific running a chain of meridian distances, closing a massive longitude traverse of twenty-four hours westwards right round the world, and to include a great majority of the now well-established stations.

She was to carry longitude by time, using chronometers first to Madeira, Tenerife and Cape Verde, all well-established positions by now, and then to Fernando de Noronha, twice checked for longitude by Foster in *Chanticleer*. It was essential to an accurate traverse that the intervals between stations be kept as nearly equal in time as possible, so that the rates of the chronometers could have the same influence throughout. Accordingly it was planned to sail on to Bahia, Rio de Janeiro, and to the River Plate; Port Desire, Port Famine and other fixed stations in the area of recent surveys would be included on the run through to the established position at Valparaiso. Thence, the Hydrographer directed *Beagle* should cross the Pacific via Galapagos Islands, to the best of all established positions at Point Venus, Tahiti, then to the Bay of Islands, New Zealand and on to Port Jackson. Hobart and King George Sound were to be the stepping stones to Cocos-Keeling Islands which, as well as being a convenient chronometer rating stop, would enable a sounding investigation to be made of a typical coral atoll situated far out in the ocean. Mauritius would be visited on the way to the well-established position at Cape Observatory; thence the voyage was to be directed in equal steps back through the Atlantic to close the great traverse at the starting point, where it would be seen how many seconds had been lost or gained after three or four years of careful rating around the world.

Permission was obtained from the Admiralty for the three young Fuegians to sail in *Beagle*, together with a Mr. Richard Matthews, a missionary who was prepared to take up residence with them in their inhospitable homeland.

Lieutenant John Wickham was appointed First Lieutenant and Lieutenant Sulivan again joined *Beagle* at FitzRoy's request. FitzRoy, musing over his earlier voyage in the South, realised how useful it would be to carry with him a competent naturalist; he wrote to Beaufort asking if a suitable young gentleman could be found to share his own cabin, who could collect specimens and record the natural history of the land and sea about the vessel during her voyage. Beaufort found such a young man, Charles Darwin, aged twenty-three, the son of a doctor practising in Shrewsbury. However, he was an enthusiastic geologist and naturalist and would enjoy this unique opportunity before settling down as a country parson.

Darwin's father was opposed to the voyage as a waste of his son's time, but his uncle, Josiah Wedgwood, was so enthusiastic that the father was persuaded. Charles travelled to Plymouth; a note of commendation from Beaufort preceding him left it to FitzRoy to engage him or not. FitzRoy was only twenty-six years old, so that the two men who were to live so closely together were of an age. They took to each other at once—of this we have written evidence from both sides—and a great voyage was launched.

The Dockyard at Plymouth received high praise from FitzRoy for the fitting out of the *Beagle*; she was complete in every detail and awaiting fair winds by the autumn of 1831. This was not achieved without hard work on the part of the officers.

A ball was held onshore on the eve of sailing to which Lieutenant Sulivan hoped to take the eldest daughter of Admiral Young. He lay down for a brief 'caulk', after a day spent in making numerous last minute arrangements onboard, and he was so exhausted that when he was shaken for tea by the steward he went, walking in his sleep, to the wardroom clad in his nightshirt and nightcap and carrying his duckgun. He placed his gun in the corner, took tea, and shouldering the gun again marched off back to bed to the great amusement of his mess-mates. It was dawn on sailing day when he awoke to find he had quite missed the ball. Fortunately for his future marriage a southwest gale was blowing and a delay in sailing enabled him to make his peace with Miss Young before departing two days after Christmas.

The officers and men soon found that their young Commander had developed into an extremely 'taut hand'. He was devoted to his duty and to the proper conduct of his vessel, which he ensured by his eagle eye and sharp temper. It was not often that he failed to find fault with the morning watch when he first came on deck, and it was a well-chastened officer of the watch who handed over to his relief in the forenoon.

On 26th July 1832, *Beagle* anchored off Monte Video and for the next two years she was employed in her surveys of South America. It was clear to FitzRoy that he would never complete this programme without the aid of other vessels, and *Beagle's* voyage is unique in the way her commander bought or chartered local boats and small ships with his own funds to further the work.

The first of these chartered craft were two small schooners, *Paz* and *Liebre*, owned by a Mr. Harris of Rio Negro. He accompanied Lieutenant Wickham as local pilot during the eight months or so in which the latter charted the coast from Port Desire northwards to the Plate, including detailed surveys of the Rio Negro, Bahía Blanca and the intricate reef-studded shores between them.

FitzRoy hurried south to establish his Fuegians. Westerly gales beyond the Horn prevented *Beagle* working westward to the vicinity of York Minster, the massive cape whence came the Fuegian of that name; but this young man now readily agreed to be landed in the territory of Jemmy Button's tribe. Fuegian Basket was daily becoming more attached to York Minster who guarded her as his wife, scowling when parted from her or when she was addressed by another. So it was decided that all three were to be landed together with Mr. Matthews, and on Jemmy's advice Woollya was chosen as the site of the little settlement. Here a good landing beach was backed by an open stretch of undulating ground, rare enough in these parts so thickly clothed in dark and gloomy woodland.

Woollya lay on the west side of the Murray Narrows. The ship was anchored in Goree Road and the journey onward made by boats. The yawl and three whaleboats were loaded with building material, tools, crockery, cooking utensils and the many household gifts received by the three Fuegians during their long sojourn in England; a mouth-watering cargo indeed in the eyes of the wild inhabitants of this lonely land.

A party of sailors went ashore from the boats at Woollya and commenced building three houses before native canoes began to arrive; once the first had come there were soon over 100 Fuegians, men, women and children, including Jemmy's mother and brothers, milling round the sailors as they worked, and admiring the clothes of the now supercilious York Minster and his companions. A boundary line had to be marked in the sand beyond which native onlookers were not to advance.

With the houses erected, the gardens dug and sown and Matthews and his three Fuegians established ashore, FitzRoy decided to leave them for a few days to settle in. Meanwhile he explored by boat the western end of the Beagle Channel to its union with the open sea by the Northwest and Southwest Arms.

Anxiously did he return to find a considerable concourse of Fuegians encamped about the newly established little settlement, trampling over the seedbeds and invading the privacy of the houses. Matthews had experienced a very difficult time; tools and food supplies were constantly being stolen, only those items buried beneath the floor of the hut or hidden above the rafters were safe. Night or day natives were always in his house cajoling, pleading and threatening with sticks and stones in their efforts to obtain food, tools or clothing.

It was impossible to hold any kind of consultation amongst this covetous throng. Matthews entered the yawl which was pulled some yards from the beach so that a quiet discussion of the future could be held with FitzRoy, whilst the Fuegians, obviously awaiting the outcome with avid interest, squatted on the shore, 'Like a pack of hounds awaiting the unearthing of a fox.'

It was clear that Matthews' life was threatened, that the three young Fuegians were daily reverting to type, and already preferred life in the makeshift wigwams to the well-built houses provided for them; and with *Beagle* now bound for the Falkland Islands it was reluctantly decided to withdraw Matthews; yet FitzRoy still hoped that the three would establish themselves as a civilised core among their savage kinsfolk. It was a bitter moment for the Commander and brought to an end his long cherished dream of bringing Christianity and civilised living to Tierra del Fuego.

England had occupied the Falklands with a handful of settlers as long ago as 1766 when MacBride in H.M.S. *Jason* had made the earliest charts of the islands. This desolate land had later been contested by France, Britain and Spain and later still by the United Provinces of the Rio de la Plata.

With the emerging importance of the Magellan Strait and the consequent increasing use of the Falklands by merchant vessels and whalers proceeding to and from the Pacific, England had decided to reassert her claim and H.M.S. *Clio* (Captain John Onslow) had visited Berkeley Sound in January 1833 to rehoist the colours.

Beagle arrived in the Falklands on 1st March 1833, to find a local Irishman doing his duty. (He had been requested by *Clio's* captain to 'hoist the flag up and down when vessels arrived and every Sunday.') FitzRoy in assessing the work to be done to carry out his instructions for charting these extensive islands came to the conclusion that yet another vessel would be required. Mr. William Low, a well-known whaler skipper, had just arrived in the islands in his sealing schooner *Unicorn*, his holds empty after a disastrous season. FitzRoy's wish to purchase this vessel was 'unconquerable': 'A fitter vessel I could hardly have met with, one hundred and seventy tons burthen, oak built, and copper fastened throughout, very roomy, a good sailor, extremely handy, and a first-rate seaboat.' He bought her, after survey by Mr. May the carpenter, for £1,300, renamed her *Adventure* 'to keep up old associations' and despatched her to Maldonado in the River Plate to be fitted out for survey work.

When *Adventure* was ready Wickham was given command and after paying off *Paz* and *Liebre*, their task completed, *Adventure* went to the Falklands. *Beagle* sailed to survey the northeast coast of Tierra del Fuego. Completing this, FitzRoy re-visited Woollya to find the settlement utterly abandoned and only a few turnips running to seed in the garden. This time *Beagle* was anchored off the settlement and as the canoes closed in it was seen that one native, with matted, dishevelled hair and a blanket about his middle, was vaguely familiar; it was Jemmy Button, emaciated but happy with a young wife who passed almost as a beauty in these parts.

Jemmy dined onboard with the Captain for whom he had brought a fine sea-otter skin; he seemed quite content with his lot and had no desire to leave his homeland again. He told how York Minster with Fuegian Basket had, early one morning while Jemmy slept, set off in a large canoe for his tribal land in the west, taking with him every one of Jemmy's civilised possessions.

Apart from a report received by Captain Sulivan, when extending the surveys of the Falklands in H.M.S. *Philomel* in 1842, that a native woman speaking good English had recently spent some nights aboard a whaler in the western part of the Magellan Strait, no word was heard again of FitzRoy's three protégés, except for Jemmy Button many years later, which is another story, but now he had shaken hands all round and left *Beagle* for the last time. A thin curl of smoke from his farewell signal fire could be seen far astern as *Beagle* stood into the open sea.

In March 1834 *Beagle* was back in the Falklands for a rendezvous with Wickham in *Adventure*. FitzRoy found a tense but more settled situation ashore. H.M.S. *Challenger* (Captain Michael Seymour) had visited Berkeley Sound in September 1833 to find that Mr. Dickson, the Irishman left in charge of the colours, had been murdered, together with about six other settlers, by a party of gauchos and Indians who had fled with all the horses to the boggy and bleak interior. Before sailing for Chile Captain Seymour had put ashore Lieutenant Henry Smith and four seamen volunteers with a small party of marines to rule over a community of fugitives from justice and murderers.

In July 1834 *Beagle* and *Adventure* were at Valparaiso and the surveying officers took up accommodation ashore for the drawing of the charts resulting from two strenuous years' work. Throughout these years FitzRoy had never relaxed, taking over the watch on deck when the seas were high, leading arduous expeditions ashore, checking every computation, constantly alert for the onset of foul weather when at anchor, anxious when boats were away from the ship and ever aware that his task was so great that he might never achieve it. He was worn and thin, and as the surgeon, Bynoe, saw the daily decline he was reminded of the fateful ending of Stokes that he had witnessed in this same cabin five years before.

It needed only the arrival of mails from England, and a letter from the Admiralty declining to reimburse FitzRoy for the chartering and purchase of vessels, to bring him to utter desperation, for these had cost him £3,000 and he was now beset by personal financial difficulties. He would have to sell the *Adventure*, the grand little schooner for which he had such great plans both on the west coast of South America and in the Pacific. He fell into the deepest gloom, resigned his command and placed Wickham in the post, for he believed his mind was becoming deranged.

Dr. Bynoe was very attentive, and once the charts had all been completed and despatched to England and the painful selling of the *Adventure* accomplished, he was able to persuade FitzRoy to take over command again to resume work in November. Chiloe Island was surveyed southwards to its extremity Quellon, 'The extreme point of South American Christendom'. *Beagle* surveyed the seaward side, whilst Sulivan with the yawl and a whaler made his way down the eastern side. Both the ship and the boat party spent Christmas 1834 in their own fashion. 'Strong gales set in . . . and kept us prisoners several days. This Christmas was unlike the last: it was a sombre period. The wind blew heavily; all looked dismal around us; our prospects for the future were sadly altered; and our immediate task was the survey of another Tierra del Fuego, a place swampy with rain, tormented by storms, without interest even of population: for hitherto we had neither found traces, nor heard the voice of natives.' From the east coast Sulivan wrote home,

'It rained every day but one for six weeks, and most of the days never ceased raining, but by great good luck we have not had one person unwell. I shall amuse you with a few stories. For instance, our foraging on a small island inhabited by Indians, on Christmas morning, from nine to twelve, in a heavy gale of wind and tremendous rain, before we could get eggs enough to make our plum-pudding or a sheep to eat. However, we got into the Padre's house attached to the church, as our tents, clothes, and blankets were wet through, and by 4 p.m. had one side of the sheep roasted, another side boiled, twelve pounds of English fresh roast beef heated, and two immense plum- puddings made. No bad quantum for twelve men! It would have amused you if you could have seen us in a dirty room with a tremendous fire in the middle, and all our blankets and clothes hung round the top on lines, getting smoked as well as dry, while all hands were busily employed for four hours killing a sheep, picking raisins, beating eggs, mixing puddings which were so large that, in spite of two thirds of the party being west-countrymen, we had enough for supper also. However we passed a pleasant day in spite of wind and weather, and it was a holiday to us, as we could only afford to knock off work when it rained too hard constantly to be able to move, which happened on Christmas Day and New Year's Day. Every other day for eight weeks we were hard at work.'

As the survey moved back towards the north along the coast of Chile FitzRoy's spirits rose again, and, by first borrowing and then purchasing a small 35-ton vessel, *Constitucion*, and detaching Sulivan in her, he completed the survey of the coast of Chile. In September 1835 Mr. Usborne, Master's Assistant, was placed in command of *Constitucion* with a volunteer crew to survey the whole coast of Peru, with orders on completion to sell the vessel and make their own way home to England. *Beagle* herself set out for the Galapagos, borne rapidly thither on the Humboldt Current.

Before following *Beagle* across the Pacific it is worth recalling a remarkable exploit by FitzRoy which had nothing to do with surveying but illustrates the energy and determination of *Beagle's* Captain in coming to the rescue of a shipwrecked crew of one of His Majesty's Ships.

Beagle lay at Valparaiso on 16th June in company with H.M.S. *Blonde*, wearing the broad pennant of Commodore Mason, when news was received that H.M.S. *Challenger* lay wrecked on an inaccessible coast northeast of the island of Mocha. FitzRoy, leaving Wickham in command of *Beagle*, hastened onboard *Blonde* to offer assistance in what would be a difficult rescue. *Blonde* left for the Bay of Concepción at once, whence FitzRoy was to go on south by land to the scene of the wreck and reconnoitre the possibility of bringing *Blonde* into the dangerous coast to effect the rescue. Ashore in Concepción urgency was added to FitzRoy's task by news that *Challenger's* crew had entered the Leuba River, near Morguilla, in boats and there were encamped; the situation was made the more desperate by information that a large body of the ferocious Arauco Indians were making towards the camp with evil intent.

FitzRoy quickly arranged horses, provisions, a native guide and two companions, Mr. Fuller and Mr. Vogelborg, the latter a German with considerable knowledge of the Indians.

Dawn found the party at the first river, the Bio Bio, which had overflowed its banks so that it was necessary to ride the 200 yards across the shallows where with spur, whip and voice the horses were persuaded to leap over the gunwhale into the ferry boat. On the far bank the horses had to be similarly spurred to leap into the water. Then the party set off at full gallop for some miles until a steep range of hills was reached over which the horses had to be led. Some miles of good going along the seashore followed before ascending the heights of Colcura. Here it is as well to take FitzRoy's own excellent account of the ride.

'Perched on a height overlooking the sea, and directly above a snug little anchorage, is the hamlet called Colcura; and thither we hastened, inattentive to the complaints of our guide (who was likewise guardian of the horses), and trusting to Vogelborg's recollection of the road. Riding into a sort of field entrenchment at the top of Colcura hill, we were accosted by a sly-looking, sharp-visaged character, whose party-coloured jacket appeared to show that its owner held some

office of a military nature, but whether that of corporal or
higher, I could not determine until I heard him say he could
give us a good meal, and that he had three fine horses near
the house: when at once styling him "gobernador" I rebuked
myself for having thought ill of his physiognomy, and proceeded to unsaddle. Disappointed, however, by a scanty bad
meal, we thought to regain our tempers upon the backs of
our host's horses; but not an animal had he sent for; nor, to
our further vexation, could any inducement tempt him to
lend one of those fine horses, which, he still said, were close
by. The Indians, he declared, were expected daily; he knew
not the moment he might have to fly for his life; on no
condition would he lend a horse: no, not if a fleet of ships
were wrecked, and I were to offer him an ounce of gold for
each mile that his horse should carry me.

'Saddling our own steeds and quitting the thin-faced dis-
penser of tough hens and sour apples, we set off at a gallop,
leaving the lazy guide whom we brought from Talcahuano,
to return there with the two worst animals (it was fortunate
indeed we had brought with us a spare one), and in two
hours we reached the foot of Villagran; that hill so famed in
Araucanian story. Being a natural barrier, it was a spot often
chosen by the Araucanians, at which either to lie in ambush
for the Spaniards, or openly oppose them.

'We ascended the heights by winding narrow paths, up
which our horses were led, in order to spare them as much
as possible, and met a small party of Chilians, on their way
from the wreck of *Challenger* towards Concepción, from
whom we heard that the wreck had been abandoned, and
that the officers and crew were entrenched in a secure
position, on the height of Tucapel Viejo, close to the mouth
of the River Leuba. We were also told that the Indians
increased in number daily, and that great fears of their
hostility were entertained.

'Descending the hill, we reached Chivilingo, a village near
a small river which runs through a "hacienda" belonging to
the Santa Maria family. We called at the door of their large

barn-like dwelling, to ask if horses could be spared. The mistress of the house happened to be at home, having lately arrived from Concepción; and directly she heard my story she ordered every horse to be put in requisition; but, unfortunately, two only were within reach, one of which was lame. All the others had been sent to grass at a distance. After acknowledging her kindness, and paying her "major-domo" for the hire of the horse, we pushed on with that one and two of the least jaded of our own animals.'

They negotiated the Carampangue river on balsa rafts upon which the horses stood precariously as they were poled across.

'The last few miles had been slowly accomplished by dint of whip and spur; but from the river to Arauco was a long league over unknown ground, in the dark, and while rain fell fast. Heavily we toiled along, uncertain of our way, and expecting each minute to be bogged; our horses, however, improved as we neared their anticipated resting place, and almost tried to canter as lights appeared twinkling within an open gateway in the low wall of Arauco. We asked for the house of the "Commandante" and were directed to a rancho rather higher and larger than the rest. Without a question we were received, and told to make the house our own. That we were wet and tired, was a sufficient introduction to the hospitable Chilian.'

The Commandante had been assisting at the wreck and an armchair of European style, a gift to him from Captain Seymour, looked oddly out of place in the barnlike ranch-house. He supplied fresh horses and a guide next day and urged speed in view of the impending attack by the Indians. The party rode on in the pouring rain across the swampy ground.

'We passed over no hills of any consequence as to height, though generally we were ascending or descending. An inshore circuit was taken, to avoid crossing three rivers, which, near the sea, are difficult to pass; and having lost our way (notwithstanding the alleged excellence of our guide), a native,

almost Indian, was easily prevailed upon to run by the side
of our horses until he put us into the right track. Before
running through the bushes, he carefully tucked up his loose
trousers as high as possible; thinking, I suppose, that his skin
was less likely to be torn than the trousers; and thus
bare-footed and bare-legged he ran before us for several
miles with the greatest of ease. At the cottage from which
he came, a very good horse, in excellent condition, and well
cleaned, was standing in a yard. I asked the owner to let me
hire or buy him, but he would consent to neither; alleging
that, in the Indian country, his life depended on having a
good horse close to hand. Three thousand Indians had assembled, he told me, and were expected to make an attack
upon the Chilian frontier; but on what particular part was
quite uncertain. They had heard of the wreck, and were
actually going to the place to plunder the crew, when accidentally met and driven back by Colipi, with his friendly
tribe.

'After our running guide had left us, though put into the
right track, we were soon at a loss again; so numerous were
the tracks of horses and cattle in this rich pasture land. The
professed guide whom we had brought from Arauco, was
more useful in recovering half-tired horses, than from knowing the way; no sooner did he get upon a horse, which one
of my party could not persuade to go out of a walk, than he
started off at full gallop, exulting in his skill. Perhaps his secret
lay in a sharp pair of iron spurs; for the thick skin and coarse
hair of horses, so roughly kept as these, is proof against
ordinary spurs, used with humanity.

'Going very much by chance, often losing our way, and
often taking a cast round to look for the most frequented
track, we at last arrived at Quiapo, a hamlet consisting of
five huts only, just in sight of one another on neighbouring
hills.

'Riding up to the nearest hut, we tempted a young man
who occupied it, to sally forth in the rain in search of fresh
horses. This exertion was caused by the sure stimulant—

money. We might have talked of the wreck, and the Indians, until that day month, without exciting our acquaintance to move; but the touch of dollars at once overcame the apathy with which he listened to our first request for food and horses. His wife told us to kill a fowl, if we could, for there was nothing else to be had; so forth we sallied, and as each understood that the permission applied to himself, great was the confusion among the poultry. To the dismay of our hostess, we soon reappeared, each with a fowl; but a certain silver talisman quickly hushed her scolding, and set her cooking. Meanwhile the rancho was ornamented with our wet clothes hanging about to be dried; but rain came through the roof in so many places that our trouble was useless. Dripping wet, having been soaked since morning, and of course cold, we could not go near the fire, because of smoke; so with a long pole we poked a hole through the thatch, which let the smoke out, and then closing round the fire, we surprised the good woman by our attack upon her half-roasted fowls.

'Before our host returned with horses it was evening. He would have detained us till next morning, could his arguments have availed, but finding that with or without him, on we were resolved to go, he set out at a good pace towards Leuba. Less rain and wind encouraged hopes of a fine night, so we trotted or galloped along while daylight lasted, but as the night grew dark rain again poured down: and, obliged then to go slowly, we followed one another as close as possible, placing the guide in front with a white poncho. While in the open country we got on pretty well, but after two hours easy work, we found that the track was taking us through thick woods. My first intimation of the change was being nearly knocked off my horse by the bough of a tree, so pitchy dark was the night; and after this I kept my head on the horse's neck, trusting to his eyes entirely, for I could see nothing. That our guide could find the way has been a matter of astonishment to me ever since: he never failed once. Some of the defiles through which he led were knee-deep in clayey mud, so stiff that the horses could hardly move. Often we were set fast in such places, obliged to get off, and feel for the track—knee-deep, and up to our elbows in mud—for it was upon hands and knees that we went, oftener than upon our legs. Our guide knew we were in the right track, but each of us was obliged to seek safe footing for himself and his horse, in the defiles among steep ravines and streams, swelled by heavy rains. Passing these streams was dangerous, and there only did the guide hang back. At one brook which seemed by the noise, to be deep and large, he refused to cross, saying his horse would not go on, and that we could not get over in the dark. However, Vogelborg was not to be stopped. Leaving his own horse stuck fast in a slough, he scrambled through, hauling my horse after him by the bridle. Holding by my horse's long tail, and driving him on, I scrambled after: Vogelborg then went back, and with the guide brought the others over. At last we emerged from the wood and from the horrible ravines. Another hour brought our small party to an Indian settlement, near the river Leuba; and as we rode by the huts, our guide talked to those within at the utmost pitch of his voice, as if determined no one should be ignorant of his adventure . . . we were approaching the banks of the Leuba as fast as our tired horses could drag their hoofs through deep, loose sand, when a solitary light moving on the dark side of the opposite high land, showed the place where our countrymen were anxiously waiting for assistance: we had heard that their encampment was under Tucapel Heights, and close to the river's mouth.

'As soon as we arrived at the water side, I hailed as loudly as I could call, but no answer was returned. Again I hailed "Challengers a-hoy," and a faint "hallo" repaid us for every difficulty. "Send a boat!" I called. "Aye, Aye!" echoed from the hills. Lights appeared directly coming down from the hill: a little boat came across the river, and very soon we embarked in *Challenger's* dinghy, the only boat saved. The Master and one man were in her, from whom we heard that all the party were well, and that they had not yet been molested by the natives.

'Captain Seymour was at the landing place. Old friends, meeting under such circumstances, can say but little. Hastening to the encampment, where all had turned out to hear the welcome news of assistance being at hand, we made their hearts rejoice by saying that the *Blonde* was at Talcahuano, and coming to their relief.'

Having summed up the situation, noted the conspicuous high land in the vicinity, sketched the river mouth and searched the offing by eye for dangers, FitzRoy set out along the arduous return route to Talcahuano to pilot the *Blonde* to the Leuba entrance. Apart from two men drowned whilst first quitting the wreck, all the Challengers were safely embarked in *Blonde* twelve days later, just as the daily sick list began to mount and increasing numbers of Indians were gathering vulture-like about the encampment. Captain FitzRoy's desperate ride, sixty miles each way as the crow flies, through rugged country, had not been in vain.

At sea, despite seasickness which often confined him in his hammock, Darwin continued to make his regular observations of the fish, the plankton, the pelagic animals and the birds; but it was onshore in South America that Darwin found his greatest treasures and pleasures. He accepted the opportunities, freely offered by FitzRoy, to sail with the detached surveying parties and such boat cruises he particularly relished when they were commanded by Lieutenant Sulivan, for he was a keen observer of nature and a very competent botanist. Here is Sulivan's description of such an expedition:

'On August 29th I left in the yawl with a mate and ten men. We started from the ship at 1 p.m. with a strong breeze but a favourable tide, and we beat up to Punta Alta in time to have everything landed, the tents rigged, and the pot under way before sunset. Tea is a great luxury in cruises of this kind. We always boiled a large boiler holding four gallons full every morning for breakfast, and the same for supper, and we never had any left, and, as there were only twelve of us, we must have drunk one eighth of a gallon each meal, or five and a half pints a day. The same pot full of mess made of salt pork, fresh beef and venison, and biscuit was also emptied for dinner, and meat also of some kind both for breakfast and supper. Such hardships are hard to put up with, the idea of being among mudbanks in a boat with only two pounds of meat, two thirds of a gallon of tea, one pound of bread, and a quarter of a pint of rum each per day is dreadful!!!

'In the evening we got all ready for beginning work at daylight, and then part went on board the boat to sleep. On the 30th we began at 6 a.m. and had finished our work by breakfast time, but waited for Darwin to examine the beach at low water for fossil remains of animals, which are very plentiful. Besides getting some he had seen before, he this morning found the teeth of animals six times as large as those of any animal now known in this country, also the head of one about the size of a horse, with the teeth quite perfect and totally different from any now known, and just at low-water mark he found the remains of another about six feet long, nearly perfect, all embedded in solid rock. We started at low water for the settlement, leaving two hands digging out the bones.

'After supper we all went on board, and moored the boat head and stern about four yards from the bushes, to ensure her grounding in the centre where the mud was quite soft. The evening looked very gloomy, with heavy thunder and lightning; but we were quite snug under an awning, which we filled as much as possible with tobacco smoke, to drive away the mosquitoes and sandflies which were very trouble-some. By filling the upper part of the awning with smoke, we kept them all out. I never in my life, I think, laughed in the way I did for about three hours at the stories they were all telling in turns. We had among the men two or three excellent hands for keeping every one alive, and tonight they performed their part to perfection. Such hands are invaluable in a cruise of that kind, particularly if the work is very hard, as they keep the men's spirits up in a most surprising manner. I think I never in my life saw people more happy than all our party were; they were in roars of laughter from morning till night, and up to all kinds of amusements when on shore, except when I brought them to an anchor occasionally to prevent their shaking the ground (near my instruments) and then they would find something amusing in that; and when men in those spirits are happy and comfortable, it is astonishing how much they make work fly.'

Darwin also took the opportunity of leaving *Beagle* at one anchorage and travelling overland to meet her at another, and thus did he explore the arid gravelly plains of Patagonia and the lush level pampas about the estuary of the River Plate. He rode 600 miles from Rio Negro, via Bahía Blanca to Buenos Aires, accompanied only by one or two gauchos. He met General Rosas of the Republic of Buenos Aires who was waging a war of annihilation against the Indians, who, in turn, were quite ruthless in destroying small parties of travellers such as Darwin's should they encounter them. The General gave permission for the English naturalist to use the relays of horses available at the military 'postas' which had been established along the army's lines of communication, and thus made Darwin's remarkable journey possible.

From his first night in the open Darwin came to love the life.

'About two leagues beyond this curious tree we halted for the night; at this instant an unfortunate cow was spied by the lynx-eyed Gauchos, who set off in full chase, and in a few minutes dragged her in with their lazos, and slaughtered her. We here had the four necessaries of life "en el campo"— pasture for the horses, water (only a muddy puddle), meat and firewood. The Gauchos were in high spirits at finding all these luxuries; and we soon set to work at the poor cow. This was the first night which I passed under the open sky, with the gear of the recado for my bed. There is high enjoyment in the independence of the Gaucho life—to be able at any moment to pull up your horse, and say, "Here we will pass the night." The death-like stillness of the plain, the dogs keeping watch, the gipsy-group of Gauchos making their beds round the fire, have left in my mind the strongly-marked picture of this first night, which will never be forgotten.'

Darwin accompanied FitzRoy on a memorable expedition up the Santa Cruz River when the party penetrated 140 miles towards the foot of the great white-capped range of the Cordillera and to within sixty miles of the nearest arm of the Pacific. Later, from Valparaiso, Darwin travelled eastwards via Santiago and right over the Cordillera by the Portillo Pass to Mendoza on the arid plains below, returning through the Uspallata Pass. The smooth-worn shingle of the Patagonian plains and the evidence of shells even at 14,000 feet, above the Portillo Pass, enabled Darwin to see how the whole continent had been uplifted from beneath the bed of the sea, and led him to state 'that not even the wind that blows is so unstable, as the level of the crust of the earth'.

The Galapagos Islands, volcanic and of recent origin, provided for Darwin the ideal laboratory for the study of the theory of evolution which had begun now to form in his mind. The islands, separated by deep water and strong currents, teemed with aboriginal creatures, new birds, new reptiles, new molluscs, new insects and new plants, each species having different evolving characteristics on each island. The giant marine and terrestrial lizards, the huge tortoises and the widely differing finches fascinated Darwin as he noted their individual differences when he landed excitedly on each island of the group.

Tahiti, New Zealand and Australia were of interest to Darwin, of course, but it was probably when visiting the atolls of Cocos-Keeling that he derived the greatest enjoyment on the homeward journey. It was Beaufort who had instructed FitzRoy to make a survey of these fascinating structures, with their long narrow, palm-clad strands encircling a shallow lagoon and with a startling increase of depths without.

Darwin had seen clear evidence of massive uplift in the South American continent and here in the Indian Ocean he saw a great subsidence as a solution to the mystery of coral atolls. If a great range of mountains or a chain of islands slowly sank beneath the surface of the sea atolls would be formed. Corals, which grow as a fringe around a tropical island, grow vigorously outward towards the open sea but tend to die when not so exposed, and when clogged with sediment close to the shore. Nor can corals grow at greater depths than about thirty fathoms, so that as the last peak of an island sank beneath the sea an area of dead coral sediment would remain to form the floor of a shallow lagoon, whilst the perimeter, coral exposed to the open sea, would ever build upwards on a platform of dead and sinking coral. Detritus thrown up by the waves would form substance enough for the colonisation, by drifting coconuts and other seeds, to form the long, often man-inhabited, strands of which the islands of Cocos-Keeling were typical.

The meridian traverse ended at Greenwich where *Beagle* arrived in November 1836. Her chronometers should have recorded a world circling traverse of twenty-four hours: in fact they exceeded this by thirty-three seconds. It was perhaps unfortunate that the most interested guest to witness the completion of the traverse, the Astronomer Royal, was not received onboard as well as he might have been. So many people came off to visit the ship that the Captain had given orders that only respectable-looking people were to be admitted by the accommodation ladder; others were to enter by the gangway to which they had to ascend by means of three-inch wide steps projecting from the ship's hull.

Sulivan, who was on watch, was surprised when a plainly-dressed man and a very pretty woman, who had surmounted the gangway, asked to be shown to the Captain. It was the Astronomer Royal with his wife. The sentry was questioned as to why these people had been directed from the accommodation ladder. 'They did not look respectable, Sir,' said he.

Of the excellent work of the missionaries which they had witnessed amongst the smiling Tahitians and the ferocious Maoris both Darwin and FitzRoy were appreciative, for both were religious men. But by the time the expedition reached England Darwin was no longer set on a career as a parson; his theories of the origin and evolution of man and animals, which were to shake the very foundations of the Church, were already forming in his mind. Whereas Darwin saw the shells and sea-washed pebbles of the plains of Patagonia as evidence of the instability of the earth's crust, FitzRoy believed that these resulted from the Great Flood of Genesis; FitzRoy could visualise no 'improvement' of Man since creation and believed that there were no separate beginnings of savage races but that all were direct descendants of Adam and Eve.

Despite occasional quarrels onboard, inevitable when two strong-minded men are closely confined in a single cabin for years, the two had got on well during the voyage; later they drifted apart as Darwin's thoughts on evolution were made public and his book of the voyage far outstripped FitzRoy's and became itself *The Voyage of the Beagle*. But Darwin never forgot the opportunities FitzRoy had given him during his years in *Beagle* and to which he owed the very foundations of his own success. He followed FitzRoy's subsequent unhappy career with sympathy as the latter stood as Conservative M.P. for Durham in 1841, not without an unfortunate assault upon a rival in Pall Mall; as Governor of New Zealand for five years from 1843, quitting the post at the request of the settlers who found him too sympathetic to both Maoris and missionaries; as Superintendent of the Meteorological Office from 1854 until he took his own life ten years later, a victim to overwork and an unreasonable disappointment that the storms his office forecast sometimes failed to materialise.

Only three years before his death FitzRoy spoke out strongly against Darwin's publication of *The Origin of Species* at the Oxford meeting of the British Association.

But this bitterness must be overlooked, and the complementary value of the two men's relationship in the *Beagle* recognised for what it achieved. FitzRoy's charts opened up the South American continent to European trade and Darwin's *Voyage of the Beagle* and *The Origin of Species* opened men's minds to the creation of the universe.

CHAPTER FIFTEEN

Belcher

During almost the whole of Beaufort's reign as Hydrographer there served at sea a most turbulent surveying captain, Edward Belcher. He had enjoyed an active life in the Navy since 1812, when he went to sea at the age of thirteen. He has already featured in this story as a young Lieutenant with Beechey in *Blossom* when he was placed in charge of the barge on the shores of the Polar Sea. He got his first surveying command in 1830, the *Aetna* continuing the survey of the West Coast of Africa.

Belcher was active, intelligent, inventive, bombastic, querulous, warlike and forthright. He quarrelled with his seniors and abused his juniors. In three and a half years in *Aetna* he court-martialled the majority of his officers, whom he thought formed a 'ring' against him. He himself was also court-martialled and acquitted, although Their Lordships were loth to give him a further command.

There are in the Hydrographic Office many files of complaining letters to Beaufort, his chief, and among the records of 'out letters' many soothing, cajoling and sometimes downright rough letters from Beaufort to Belcher in many a far-flung field. Beaufort recognised Belcher's value as a surveyor and he it was who persuaded Their Lordships, against their own judgement, to give him another foreign command. And so it was that Belcher, to the delight of the engineer, left the paddler *Lightning* surveying in the Irish Sea, for *Sulphur* on the West Coast of America.

Beechey, in command of *Sulphur*, had gone sick and had come

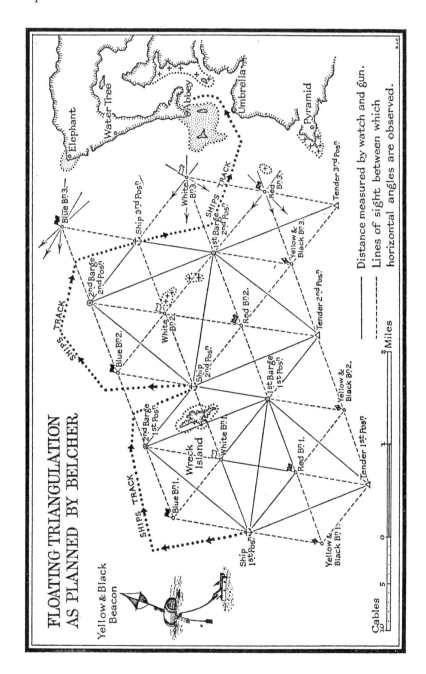

FLOATING TRIANGULATION
AS PLANNED BY BELCHER.

home before Belcher arrived at Panama. Here he took over from
Lieutenant Henry Kellett, temporarily in command, who returned
to *Starling*, *Sulphur's* tender. Belcher soon accused Lieutenant Richard Collinson of 'tampering with the Ship's Company' and sent
him under a cloud to England. 'What a bundle of discord Beechey
has left me.' Belcher was back in form.

At this time every young surveying officer had to learn his trade
from his elders, taking what tit-bits of professional knowledge might
be thrown his way, and every Captain had his own ideas. Belcher
gives Beechey no credit for teaching him in *Blossom* and, in fact,
claims to be self-taught in command of *Aetna*, where he wrote a
surveying manual which was published in 1835 shortly before he
left to join *Sulphur*.

A *Treatise on Nautical Surveying: containing an outline of the Duties
of the Naval Surveyor, with cases applied to Naval Evolutions and
Miscellaneous Rules and Tables useful for the Seaman or Traveller*, as
its title implies, attempts too much and is difficult to follow. Not
content with laying down how surveyors should go about their
business, Belcher introduces grandiose plans whereby a number of
ships of the line combine to employ themselves usefully in surveying whilst blockading an enemy port; he devised cunning methods
whereby a traveller with no form of instrument may, by lying
down, gauge the heights of buildings; and advises how all manner
of military intelligence should be gathered by the surveyor, even
to the extent of finding an excuse to turn out the local soldiery
that their military capability may be ascertained. Belcher was
obsessed with war and saw surveying as an associated activity.

With patience, somewhere amongst these diverse instructions
may be found a description of the instruments currently in use by
surveyors; a detailed explanation of the conduct of an offshore
survey; and instructions for making a harbour plan. The latter is
unhappily complicated for the beginner, as one side of the harbour
is presumed to be occupied by an enemy, making the planning of
triangulation complex, and necessitating the fixing of the enemy's
guns and assessing their arcs of fire.

The sextant, for surveying, had finally come to stay. 'Only
Masters still use the Azimuth Compass. In a survey ship instantly

the sextant is in request; even the pleasures of the table are forgotten. Astronomical pursuits, surveying etc. have a peculiar attraction. Let but one moderate draught be taken fairly tested, a species of intoxication follows, scientific mania ensues. Example only is wanting, and if that happen to be the principal (Captain or Lieutenant) the contagion rapidly spreads—it becomes the fashion.'

The sextant was used ashore in conjunction with the mercury artificial horizon, for taking equal altitudes of the Sun, a.m. and p.m., to rate the chronometers that they might be used as accurate recorders of longitude. The sextant was similarly used with the artificial horizon to observe the Sun's meridian altitude for latitude. At sea the sextant was used with the sea horizon to a lower standard of accuracy, and in the boats it was used horizontally with the station pointers to fix when sounding.

Belcher claimed to have improved the station pointer by the introduction of the small cut-away semi-circle at the centre to mark the boat's position with a pencil point; previously a pricker had been fitted to the station pointers for this purpose, which Belcher found unsatisfactory because it tore the paper on the field-boards.

Onboard, the sextant and the ship's compass were used with the Sun to obtain a true bearing between one floating mark and another; ashore the theodolite and an azimuth compass were used to obtain the same with greater accuracy.

At sea bases were measured by the firing of a gun, ashore by the use of chains or rods.

Belcher describes with the use of a diagram, reproduced here in a simplified form, the plan for carrying out an imaginary survey off the African coast. The ship is approaching a natural harbour with off-lying reefs. It is necessary to commence the survey some thirty miles to seaward, the ship working her way shorewards, always in surveyed water, until she can enter the harbour, with boats ahead of her, to make the detailed chart of the anchorage.

The resources available to the surveyor are first of all the sturdy converted bomb *Aetna*, of 376 tons, and a tender, *Raven*, a 100-ton cutter. *Aetna* carries two 5-ton barges, decked in and hulls coppered; two 25-foot cutters; one 32-foot whaleboat and two 25-foot gigs. *Raven* carries two gigs. All are in service. Four floating beacons carrying a mast and topmark twenty-two feet above the water are constructed using 60-gallon casks and are moored with anchors devised by Belcher using three 56-lb. pigs of ballast for each.

The ship, the tender and the two barges are capable of remaining in anchored positions for as many days as required, whilst the beacons can, of course, be left moored as long as necessary. Signals from the masts of the vessels, from the gaffed topsails of the barges, and the topmarks of the beacons can be seen for five miles. The ship, her tender and even the barges are capable of firing guns for the timing of base measurement by a distant observer with a spyglass and a good watch.

The four vessels mentioned above, together with the four beacons, are used to locate and mark fixed stations in the survey, ideally set out in a pattern of equilateral triangles. New stations are occupied by boats running the log distance of five miles from an existing station to a position subtending an angle of approximately sixty degrees between two existing stations. Once moored in these approximate postions the exact angles of each triangle are observed in the vessels or from boats lying to the beacons; many of the sides are measured by gun and watch as shown in firm lines in the diagram.

The boats, with two leadsmen in the headsheets relieving one another, and largely under sail, sound the area within each triangle fixing by sextant and station pointers using the floating fixed marks. If sailing or pulling direct from one mark to another the coxswain keeps himself directly between them by using Roper's sounding machine, a sort of 'seebackrescope' in which both objects can be viewed and kept in line, whilst distance is obtained from the towed log.

As the areas are covered to the satisfaction of the Captain and shoal areas examined, the ship, tender and barges move to their second assigned positions, the ship moving forward in sounded water. Each move has to be carefully planned that nothing may be lost: Belcher sees a similarity to chess.

It would be tedious to describe the many moves planned for the morrow by the Captain each night. He wrote orders and drew a diagram for the officer in charge of each boat. The failure of one to take an angle, maintain a position or time a gun as ordered, would jeopardise the whole day's complicated plan.

Here are Belcher's written orders for Lieutenant 'K' in charge of the First Cutter on the first day of the survey.

'You will proceed with the red beacon S45E by compass, in company with the tender, (both using pat. log.,) and place the beacon on that bearing five miles (not less) from the ship. Moor the beacon securely with the tide, and assist in laying out warps to enable the tender to approach within a few feet of it. The ship will (when the tender denotes she is ready) fire three guns. Note the beats minutely. The tender will then fire (possibly the barges.) Take angles to all objects in position. During the time the tender is employed in mooring in position, employ yourself in sounding out the space as noted by the elongated dots in the subjoined diagram. (The yellow/blue beacon will be placed by first barge.) *Vide* diagram for boats orders.

'On tender mooring, you will return to the beacon, and take a new round of angles to all objects. After this, endeavour to work out the small dotted lines of soundings (obtaining angles at yellow/blue beacon). The lines will bring you on a wind, on your southern legs, and steering about E.N.E. on the northern; tide in favour by the time you leave yellow/blue beacon; return by sunset.'   E.B.

There were eight sets of boat's orders to be made out each night, after the present day's work had been plotted and progress assessed.

By the time ship, tender, barges and beacons had occupied three positions each, the ship herself was able to make port and the harbour survey commenced in the face of an imaginary enemy.

So far the latitude and longitude had been carried forward by plane trigonometry through the network of triangles from the position obtained when the ship first anchored. Now, onshore, with artificial horizon, a patient and careful observing routine, a higher quality position was obtained and carried through the shore triangulation from the observation spot to stations along the shoreline.

From these stations the floating beacons, still in their final positions, were fixed by theodolite intersections and the whole floating network readjusted for latitude, longitude, azimuth and scale. Belcher regarded the whole as a plane chart—there is no talk of projections when dealing with larger-scale surveys, and the adjustment is effected by redrawing in ink the meridians and parallels which up to this stage had remained in pencil.

'The soundings,' writes Belcher,

> 'being the *most important part* of the plan to the *seaman*, too much nicety cannot be observed in following out the *particular lines on tangents of the coast*, or two headlands, or conspicuous objects, in line. Eventually these may become the leading marks for avoiding dangers; and strange it is, that in almost every intricate channel, nature has so placed her objects, that it might almost be imagined they were designed for such a purpose.
>
> 'It is not to be imagined that this duty is to be left, as a matter of course, to assistants. Judicious lines of sounding, particularly in closing Sailing Directions, should be taken by the *principal*, and wherever any discrepancy in the work leads him to doubt, that doubt should be resolved by *himself*. Few will find fault, with the land within; but should an unlucky dependence on labours of others ground one of His Majesty's ships, or even a merchantman, no excuse, however perfect, will save his character.'

For the reduction of soundings to low water datum, efforts were made with poles to measure the spring and neap ranges at the port. Subsequently the times of high and low water were observed daily and the officer in charge of the tidal work hoisted flags in the vessel every hour after or before high water so that officers in the boats could subtract from their soundings a proportion of the range according to the tables of Murdoch MacKenzie.

Belcher advises on sounding marks: 'In erecting and making marks, the lime bag will be found of importance; and a very simple method of marking a spot is to wet the place, and *cast* powdered lime *at it*. It is more convenient, economical, and the mark lasts longer.' Until recently hardly a surveyor has sailed without his sack of lime; it was the curse of the seaman in charge of the survey store as this insidious stuff seeped into every bin and locker. The use of fluorescent material slowly broke down the agelong cult of whitewash.

'Although it may be imagined,' concludes Belcher, 'that the daily duties of the surveyor are arduous enough, yet his interest appears to receive fresh impetus as day closes and the stars begin to show; and he will probably be found watching their motions until dawn warns him, that some little repose is necessary to perform properly the duties of the ensuing day.'

For five years *Sulphur*, with Belcher in command, and with her tender *Starling* under Kellett, was employed on the west coasts of Central and Northern America, working clockwise with the seasons as Vancouver had done long before, to Monterey, San Francisco and the Sandwich Islands in the winter, to start in the spring in the Northwest. Eventually the time came to sail across the Pacific for home. Belcher visited the Marquesas, Tahiti, Raratonga, Tonga and the Fijis, where *Sulphur* broke the pintles of her rudder, grounding on a reef. The United States Exploring Expedition under Captain Wilkes was present in the Fijis, and a meeting between Wilkes and Belcher provided new pintles from Wilkes' ship, *Peacock*, which was well provided. Wilkes found the stout dark Englishman a secretive and prickly fellow who evaded his request for information on the Northwest coast of America, and would not exchange magnetic data obtained by both men observing at the same station in the Fijis.

Belcher sailed on through the New Hebrides (Vanuatu), where the missionary Williams had so recently been murdered at Malakula, and where he found a number of Samoan missionaries of Williams' London Mission Society miserably awaiting a similar fate; on to New Guinea, Amboina and eventually to Singapore on 16th October 1840, where an official letter from Their Lordships ordering him to China awaited him.

Since 1820 the Chinese and the British had been at loggerheads over opium. There were a number of British merchants resident in Canton who had, with the aid of bribeworthy Chinese officials, been importing opium from India despite a Chinese Government ban. In 1837 Lin, the Governor of Canton, took a stronger line and began confiscating opium found in British ships and warehouses in Canton.

To deal with him in Canton was Captain Charles Elliot, R.N., Chief Superintendent of British Trade in China, and singularly ineffectual he proved to be.

In May 1838 Elliot sent a fast clipper from the Canton River to Suez to convey the news to England that British merchants were being molested and that the Chinese appeared to be preparing for war.

Meanwhile the uncertainty in Canton and congestion in Portuguese Macao resulted in the anchorage between Hong Kong and the mainland becoming the rendezvous for British shipping in China, and English merchants set up modest establishments on Hong Kong Island.

In reply to Elliot's pleas Commodore Sir James Brewer arrived in the mouth of the Canton River with substantial sea and land forces in June 1840, and Elliot announced a blockade of Canton.

Belcher was at last being called to survey in war, but after five years away from home, and with the usual discord among his officers, he hardly knew whether 'pleasure or disappointment prevailed'.

The purser, his clerk and Midshipman Nicholson were constantly drunk at sea, and on one occasion after drinking all night with the Gunner the latter fell overboard and had to be rescued. Belcher believed the purser to be the ringleader, had him courtmartialled at Singapore and dismissed the service, leaving Mr. Curtis, a religious maniac, as his chief annoyance.

'I suspect we shall be quite in time for *anything* like active operations.' He wrote to Beaufort from Singapore, 'We are preparing for a new voyage after *five years* absence.'

'I am *very nearly* in the state which I was twice reduced by *Aetna* labours and unless the *smell of earth* during my sojourn here recovers me I shall be little fitted to do justice to your kind and too flattering anticipations. However, you know I can occasionally rally,' and so he did when he joined Brewer's squadron in the mouth of the Canton River in mid-December, despite a cold reception from the Commodore, who seemed to be unaware of how a survey ship could assist. He displayed towards Belcher 'extraordinary neglect of the courtesies of life', which hurt his pride, having come hotfoot from Singapore expecting to be hailed as the saviour of the situation.

Belcher received no orders, 'But it never can happen that those who are not competent to act themselves can give orders to surveyors!' So he set to work in businesslike fashion on his own to survey the approaches to the twin forts of Chuenpee in the east and Tycocktow on the west side of the entrance to the Canton River.

On 7th January 1841, Captain Elliot finally decided that Canton should be attacked and the river fleet under Captain Sir Humphrey Fleming Senhouse sailed upstream. The advance upon Canton is a story of brilliant combined operations as each set of forts was attacked and overwhelmed. But after every success Elliot acceded to the Chinese request for an armistice, during which the enemy consolidated their remaining fortifications.

The first attack overwhelmed the forts of Chuenpee and Tycocktow, first by bombardment from the ships and then by storming by the marines. Belcher in *Nemesis*, a steamer with a brilliant Master, Hall, in command, piloted her past the forts and into Anson Bay behind Chuenpee where she caused the greatest destruction with Congreve rockets to a fleet of war junks anchored there.

With Belcher piloting, the fleet moved up to the forts either side of the Boca Tigris, and known as the Bogue forts, when the first armistice was agreed. This ceded Hong Kong to Britain in perpetuity and trade was to be resumed with China.

Sulphur sailed to Hong Kong where Belcher was first to hoist the Union flag and the survey of the new colony commenced. Belcher's chart shows 'Matheson's Stores & Wharf', 'Happy Valley' and 'Sulphur Channel', all still familiar names to those who know Hong Kong. Then back to surveying the Bogue 'whilst all around are idle and enjoying themselves'.

But not for long, for the Chinese were still arming and a successful British attack on the Bogue forts was launched on 20th February during which the Chinese Admiral Kwan was killed, and part of the British squadron moved on up to the Second Bar near Whampoa Island, where a floating boom barred the way and a second armistice was agreed.

On 7th March the third British attack took place and Belcher was just in time to be in the forefront again, at least according to his own spirited account '. . . on reaching the gate [of Howqua's Folly], found some people at the embrasures. As they did not attend to my gestures to open the gates, my boat's crew in a few seconds pitched me through the embrasure, when the Chinese vacated at double quick time by the opposite one. A shot soon opened the gates, the union was substituted for their hieroglyphics, and Lieutenant Kellet, of the *Starling*, was left as acting governor.' The *smell of earth*, or was it gunpowder, had certainly recovered him.

By now the Sulphurs had completely won the confidence of Captain Senhouse by their pre-attack surveys, their skilful piloting and their spirited action in the consequent engagements: '*Sulphur's* services are indispensable at the points of future attack,' said he.

After this third armistice the merchants returned to Canton, but not for long, and Elliot warned them to leave again in May as the Chinese were once more preparing for war. A mob gutted the British factories as *Nemesis* led the squadron upstream once again.

It was necessary to find a place where troops could be landed advantageously to take the city of Canton and to Belcher was assigned this reconnaissance. This he carried out with armed boats from *Sulphur* and *Starling*. He decided that a position off Tsingpoo well above the city of Canton seemed a likely place from which to take the defences from the rear. On his way upstream he captured and sent back to the squadron large numbers of tea-boats for use in landing the troops upon his selected beach. He also captured a number of junks. Finding a junk with her masthead gear still rove he had himself hoisted, with his sextant, 100 feet to the masthead. From here he made a careful appraisal of the whole of the enemy's positions, taking sufficient angles for the compiling of an accurate view. Unfortunately he had forgotten that he had ordered the junks to be burnt, and a cry from below informed him that his junk was well on fire. He had to be most hastily lowered to the burning deck, and was but 100 yards away when she blew up with a great explosion and sank. Happily her mast remained standing above the water to mark the beach Belcher had selected for the landing.

He dropped downstream to the squadron, reaching the *Blenheim* at half-past eleven that night to find Captain Senhouse sitting in his easy chair. 'Well, Captain Belcher,' said he, 'I thought I was right in sitting up for you.' Plans for the morrow were laid, despite the doubts of Captain Elliot and the English traders from Canton, who claimed they had seen the river below Tsingpoo dry right across. But Belcher was sure of his soundings, and although *Sulphur* touched as she led the way up past Canton to Tsingpoo, the landings were a complete success. The city was within the grasp of our soldiers when Captain Elliot made his last truce with the Chinese Governor.

Back at Macao Belcher was instructed to prepare *Sulphur* for her passage home. Lieutenant Collinson had been sent out, to Belcher's fury, by Beaufort as surveying officer to the Fleet. He had avoided Belcher although he was living with Kellett onboard *Starling*, which vessel was now to remain on the China coast.

Belcher was suffering from an abscess on the liver; with the excitement of action over, his letters to Beaufort reverted to their gloomy tone: 'No crow quill pens for years. Paper all damaged.' 'My tracing of Bogue has been spoilt by mice and my tracing man has been ordered not to confine himself to the table but take plenty of exercise in the fresh air.'

'How do you reconcile to your *conscience* keeping Kellett and myself without our rank when we so much *require* it at the present moment when youngsters who have been mids under me will be claiming superiority!!' So had he written to Beaufort at the commencement of the operations, but in May 1841 he got his post captaincy and gathered a C.B. before he sailed for home in November of the same year.

The year 1842 saw the end of the war with China and the resultant opening of a number of ports on the China coast to British trade. Collinson and Kellett had done great work in piloting the Fleet. Sounding ahead in their vessels *Plover* and *Starling* they had guided a naval squadron 200 miles up the hitherto uncharted Yangtze-Kiang.

Sir Edward Belcher, who was knighted in early 1843, was given command of *Samarang* to proceed to the China coast to survey the ports laid open by the treaty. A last-minute despatch put aboard at Falmouth ordered him to visit Sarawak, in Borneo, to communicate with a Mr. Brooke who had established himself there; and also to examine a reported seam of coal at Brunei with a view to its use by Her Majesty's steamers.

On leaving Singapore, *Samarang* encountered some difficulty in finding the entrance to the Sarawak River, but by capturing a fearful native in a canoe and introducing him to a blackboard and chalk the way was found.

Since Stamford Raffles had established a trading post at Singapore, commerce with Borneo and the Eastern Archipelago was feasible. China had long held the monopoly in this trade but vessels from Borneo were now bringing produce to Singapore and returning with British goods, now increasingly available.

Mr. James Brooke, an adventurous man, had sailed from England in his yacht *Royalist*, arriving in Sarawak at the moment when the local Rajah, Muda Hassim, was being attacked by his enemies and had assisted him to overthrow them, largely by the use of a cannon landed from the ship. In return for his friendship Muda Hassim ceded to Mr. Brooke the vast territory of Sarawak, and the famous dynasty of English rajahs was founded.

In the preceding centuries Malays had driven the indigenous Dyaks inland from the coasts of Borneo, and settling there they had set up as traders or pirates as opportunity offered. It was the pirates of Borneo who represented the greatest threat to expanding British trade, and the Royal Navy was currently engaged in reducing their activities.

With antimony and gold mines thriving in the hinterland, Rajah Brooke was as anxious as anyone to keep the coasts of Borneo and the sea lane to Singapore free from piracy, and thus he gave a warm welcome to every man-of-war that dropped anchor in the Sarawak River.

Leaving Kuching *Samarang* grounded on a ridge of rocks in the river about a mile below the town, with shallow water to port and six fathoms close to starboard. The obvious and immediate danger was that the ship would heel over and capsize. Despite a swarm of hornets, the 16-in. coasting cable was secured to trees ashore and held by double runner purchases from the mastheads to the deck, where they were hauled taut. As the tide rose, it was found that the list of 22° prevented the discs on the endless pump chain, which raised the water, from entering the hollowed trunks that formed the 'wells'. Water gushed into the holds as the ship heeled to 45°. Here she held in a perilous position whilst instruments and chronometers were moved by boat in a heavy downpour to Mr. Brooke's residence.

All but Belcher now believed that *Samarang* was a total loss, and, if Marryat is to be credited, none of the officers nor men would be sorry, for their Captain had made his usual hell onboard.

However, the Captain was a seaman and, despatching Mr. Hooper, the purser, to Singapore in *Royalist* for man-of-war assistance, he set his men to work despite the fever and diarrhoea from which many were suffering.

Rajah Brooke had built 'atap' huts for the accommodation of the officers and men, had provided food and set the Dyaks to work upstream felling timber and floating the logs down to the *Samarang*. Three of the largest of these were rigged in the following manner from the starboard bulwarks: one to form sheerlegs with the foremast, the other pair as sheerlegs on their own, the heads of both sets being connected by a stout spar. Two very sturdy trees were next selected and laid across the ship, using tackles from the heads of the sheers to place them in position. These were lashed with half of their lengths extending to starboard, and beneath them a great raft of logs was built and secured. From the ends of these two massive outriggers to the head of the sheers were rigged powerful tackles and all hauled taut.

All hatches and openings were made watertight, the chain pumps were fitted with leading boards to direct the discs into the trunks, and the next tide confidently awaited.

As the water rose the raft exerted an increasing effort beneath the giant outriggers which cracked and groaned ominously but did not give. At the same time the pumps were manned, and men on deck hauled together on the purchases which led to the mastheads and the coasting cable leading from the mastheads to the shore. The righting movement was enormous whilst water diminished in the holds. The cry came—'She's moving'—from an officer set to watch a plumb line affixed to the fore cabin bulkhead. The work, commenced at 9.00 p.m., was crowned with success when, at 1.00 a.m. the vessel, filled with stinking mud, was hauled off to anchor in safety.

The visit to Brunei, which followed as soon as the ship was habitable, resulted in the discovery of only a few baskets of coal in which Belcher showed little interest. This was a disappointment to the Sultan who had prepared a superb curry for the occasion of the visit, served from a vast ornate chamber pot set in the centre of the table.

Arrived at Hong Kong in September 1843, Belcher was refused permission by the Commander-in-Chief to survey the open ports of the mainland. No doubt he knew something of Belcher's turbulent ways and considered Lieutenant William Bate, with his small vessel, *Young Hebe*, better suited to the diplomatic task of charting the ports of China so recently and so reluctantly opened to British trade. Bate had been wounded during the attack on Canton described earlier, and after joining Collinson who taught him surveying, he spent many valuable years charting the coast of China. He was killed by a single musket ball fired from the city wall as he was measuring its height with his sextant during the capture of Canton on 29th December 1857, during the second war with China. He was mourned by every British consul and merchant on the coast.

But back to Belcher and the *Samarang*, whose sailing was delayed until he had apologised for his boorish behaviour towards the Commander-in-Chief. The next three years he devoted to surveys of the islands of the eastern seas, visiting places as widely separated as Japan and Celebes and surveying an extensive part of the coast of northeast Borneo. He also found time for the warlike and political activities he so loved.

He joined, with his boats, expeditions mounted by Captain

Keppel of H.M.S. *Dido* against pirate lairs on the Borneo rivers; searched for an English woman said to be enslaved in Borneo; accompanied a naval squadron to Brunei to arrange the cession of the island of Labuan to the Queen; recovered shipwrecked Lascars held to ransom in eastern Borneo; signed treaties of friendship with the Sultans of Gunong, Tabor and Bulungan and had one glorious battle of his own with supposed Illanon pirates when they came upon him at his observations upon a reef in the Molucca Passage.

This last resulted in Sir Edward receiving £10,000 bounty for the officers and men of *Samarang*, by decision of the Admiralty Court in respect of the death of 350 pirates and the destruction of their vessels which Belcher claimed. This was granted despite the fact that a strong protest was received from the Dutch Government, in whose territory the affair took place, claiming that these were not pirates but a force maintained to combat them, and that they had flown the Dutch flag—a fact Belcher did not deny; he said that it was so dirty that he did not accept it as the Dutch colours.

They hurled spears at Belcher, which fell close to his instruments, but he kept them at bay by ordering his gig's crew to fire above their heads. He could not afford to lose his precious observations and waited patiently until he had obtained his afternoon equal altitude sights before 'retaliating for this piece of treachery'. A battle then raged, off and on, for twenty-four hours between *Samarang's* gig and barge and a dozen prahus manned by scarlet clad 'pirates' capering on a platform above the rowers. The barge's cannon did devastating work with grape shot, and the affair only ended when Sir Edward was struck and thrown overboard by a ball from the pirate chief's cannon when Belcher himself was in the very act of firing a Congreve rocket at the chief.

But the Hydrographer cared for none of these things:

'Your last letter,' wrote he to Belcher, 'is really all Hebrew to me; Ransoms and dollars; queens; treaties and negotiations? What have I to do with these awful things; they far transcend my limited chart-making facilities, however well suited they may be to Admiralty Lords, to Commanders-in-Chief, to Governors of Colonies and to you; and with them, my very good friend, you must arrange your diplomatic enterprises, and to them you must look for applause. Fortunately the Board have not sent your despatches upstairs, nor asked for my opinions which I beg leave to reserve for affairs of soundings, angles, and other humble things of that kind. That you have been doing good service to your country I will not deny, but the harvest I look for at your hands does not stretch beyond the reach of a deep-sea line and all the credit I crave for you, and through you for myself, must be won in the Kingdoms of science and reaped in hydrographic fields. As I have no late drawings from you I have no critical remarks to offer. I am sorry to see the name Japan in your letter till what you had begun to the southward was finished.'

If Beaufort thought Sir Edward surveyed too little, his officers and men thought it too much. He kept them long hours in the boats, whilst they never knew from one day till the next where they were to be. They made their arrangements for a happy Christmas in Manila, but Belcher took the ship off at a moment's notice to spend that period surveying a remote and cheerless bay. On boat expeditions the Captain's boat was well provisioned with delicacies whilst ship's biscuit and salt beef were the only comestibles in the others.

There were occasions, however, when the officers had their own back on their Captain. Young Marryat was returning from an up-river search for pirates; the river was so narrow that the bowman was hauling the boat through the overhanging bushes with a boathook, when he stuck it into what appeared to be a hanging ball of moss. It was a nest of hornets, to which the man left the boathook hanging, as the boat was carried forward by the current. The Captain's boat was not far behind, and hailing him, Marryat requested the boathook be collected as they passed. The captain's bowman wresting it from its hanging position brought down the whole hornets' nest. 'The insects appeared to have knowledge of the service, for they served out their stings in the same proportion as the prize money is divided; the Captain came in for his full share.'

At last, after three and a half years, the end of the ordeal was suddenly and unexpectedly in sight. Marryat describes the receipt of the news:

'*Royalist* at last arrived: she had but few letters but, valuable and dear to us as letters always were, she brought intelligence that made every heart, except one, beat with delight. Was it possible? Yes, it was true—true! We were *ordered home*. Oh, the delight, the frantic joy, which was diffused through the whole ship. To have witnessed the scene we should have been considered as mad. Every one embracing one another, shaking hands, animosities reconciled at once, all heart-burnings forgotten: we would have hugged everything we met—dogs, monkeys, pigs—except the Captain. All our sufferings and privations were forgotten in the general ecstasy, and, although thousands of leagues were still to be run before we could arrive at the desired goal, and months must pass away, time and space were for the time annihilated, and, in our rapture, we fancied and we spoke as if we were within reach of our kindred and our homes. Could it be the *Samarang* that we were on board of?—the same ship that we were in not one hour ago?—the silent, melancholy vessel, now all hands laughing, screaming, huzzaing, dancing, and polkaing up and down the decks like maniacs? And when the excitement was a little over, and we became more rational, why were we ordered home? was the first surmise. We had been sent out on a seven years expedition, and we had not yet been out four. The surveys were not half finished. Was it the row that the Captain had with the Admiral [The Commander-in Chief at Hong Kong], and the reports of many officers who had quitted the ship? We made up our minds at last that it must have been upon the representations of the Admiral to the Admiralty that we had been ordered home. There could be no other reason. We drank his health in nine times nine.'

CHAPTER SIXTEEN

Home Waters

What has been called Beaufort's 'Grand Survey of the British Isles' was his successful attempt to rechart practically the whole of the coasts and inshore waters of these islands during his twenty-six years of office.

To see the overall picture of this grand survey it is necessary to examine briefly the work of about a dozen naval surveyors who were placed in charge around our shores by Beaufort, and whose broad areas of activity are shown on the accompanying diagram.

George Thomas has already been mentioned. He made his first survey for the Admiralty in the Schelde in 1809. From 1811 for the next thirty-five years Thomas was employed almost continuously in the English Channel, the Approaches to the Thames, the North Sea, the east coasts of England and Scotland and the Orkneys and Shetlands. There are nearly fifty surveys by Thomas in the archives of the Hydrographic Office. His old vessel *Investigator*, of which he was the sole commander for twenty-five years, lasted until 1835 when, being completely worn out, she was replaced by the brig *Mastiff*, new back from the Mediterranean.

Thomas' surveys were performed with tremendous care, and such an over-attention to detail that he occasionally received a rebuke from Beaufort for the slow progress of the work. The gallant old Master died onboard his vessel in the autumn of 1846, on his way south for his winter lie-up at Woolwich after another rough and blustery season in the Orkneys. Despite his devotion during twenty such seasons, he never achieved promotion, although he

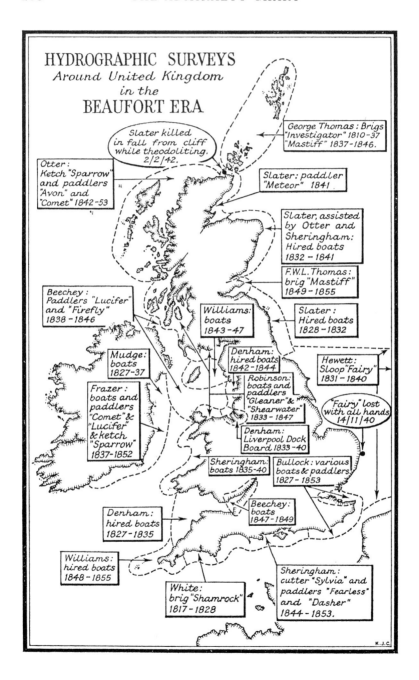

HYDROGRAPHIC SURVEYS
Around United Kingdom
in the
BEAUFORT ERA

Slater killed in fall from cliff while theodoliting. 2/2/42.

George Thomas : Brigs "Investigator" 1810-37 "Mastiff" 1837-1846.

Otter : Ketch "Sparrow" and paddlers "Avon" and "Comet" 1842-53

Slater: paddler "Meteor" 1841

Slater, assisted by Otter and Sheringham: Hired boats 1832-1841

F.W.L.Thomas: brig "Mastiff" 1849-1855

Beechey : Paddlers "Lucifer" and "Firefly" 1838-1846

Williams: boats 1843-47

Slater : Hired boats 1828-1832

Mudge: boats 1827-37

Denham: hired boats 1842-1844

Hewett: Sloop "Fairy" 1831-1840

Frazer: boats and paddlers "Comet" & "Lucifer" & ketch "Sparrow" 1837-1852

Robinson: boats and paddlers "Gleaner" & "Shearwater" 1833-1847

"Fairy" lost with all hands 14/11/40

Denham: Liverpool Dock Board 1833-40

Sheringham: boats 1835-40

Bullock: various boats & paddlers 1827-1853

Denham: hired boats 1827-1835

Beechey: boats 1847-1849

Williams: hired boats 1848-1855

White: brig "Shamrock" 1817-1828

Sheringham: cutter "Sylvia" and paddlers "Fearless" and "Dasher" 1844-1853.

K.J.C.

was successful in the case of his son, who was promoted Lieutenant in 1841 after application had been made by the father through Beaufort:

> Sir,
>
> I beg leave to communicate to you that having served *thirty* years as Maritime Surveyor under the Hydrographical Department, during which period my services have been called into requisition on several important occasions, led me to apply to my Lords Commissioners of the Admiralty for promotion, considering that the arduous duties performed, and my long services entitled me to a claim upon them; but it appearing by their Lordships letter of 27th December 1837, that the door of promotion is for ever shut against me and that I must remain the remainder of my life the Junior Officer of my class as far as pay is concerned; I most humbly implore you to urge my claims in favour of my son, Mr. Fred. Wm. Leopd. Thomas; he has served thirteen years in the *Investigator* and *Mastiff* under my command, the latter four years as Assistant Surveyor, and has passed examination for a Lieutenant in Her Majesty's Navy five years.
>
> I have the honour to be, Sir,
> Your very humble Servant,
> Geo. Thomas, *Master Commanding.*

Young Thomas took over the survey of the Orkneys on his father's death, and on their completion was employed in the Firth of Forth. He retired a Captain in 1864.

A pupil of Smyth's in the Mediterranean, Commander Michael Slater, was employed from 1829 to 1842 on the northeast coast of England and southern Scotland, and then on the coast of Scotland from the River Tay to Thurso Bay. Here, on 2nd February 1842, his career ended; he inadvertently fell to his death from the cliffs of Holbourn Head whilst making a theodolite station. His assistant, Lieutenant Henry Otter, took over the work, at first in hired boats but later, as a Commander in 1844, he was given the ketch *Sparrow*, and in 1847 the paddler *Avon*, as he worked westwards around

Cape Wrath and southward along the intricate, gale-swept, rock-bound coasts of the west of Scotland.

Commander William Hewett had been working off the east coast of England in Parry's time but in 1830, under Beaufort, his great labour in the North Sea really began when he commissioned a sister ship to *Beagle*, the bark *Fairy*.

Hewett's survey embraced the whole southern portion of the North Sea to the Dutch coast including the Dogger Bank, four chronometers being supplied to carry longitude. Hewett's tidal work with Whewell has already been described, and for a description of the outstanding chart published as a result of his surveys we can go to Admiral Sir Archibald Day, a former Hydrographer of the Navy, who describes it thus: 'A notable chart was No. 1406, March 21st 1842, *The North Sea from Dover to Calais and Orfordness to Scheveningen* by Hewett in the *Fairy* 1831–40 with the banks and soundings within two or three leagues of the coasts of France, Belgium and the Netherlands adapted from the surveys of Beautemps-Beaupré and Ryk. It used a datum of Low Water Ordinary Spring Tides and gave notes of the tidal rise in various parts of the chart. An immense number of soundings was shown and their pattern indicates how the lines of soundings were parallel or starred . . . There were two vertical cross sections of the seabed, below a horizontal low water datum line, between England and the Continent.'

Hewett did not live to see this chart. When the surveying season of 1840 ended *Fairy*, about to return to Woolwich for the lie-up, was ordered to call briefly at Yarmouth so that Hewett could report on a new dredging invention. She sailed northwards from the vicinity of Orfordness on a bright clear day with falling barometer, but as dusk fell clouds began to gather, the wind rose rapidly and the great gale of 13th/14th November was upon her; *Fairy* never reached port.

She was a well found ship and at first no particular anxiety was felt for her. But on 20th November *The Times* gave news that a fishing smack arriving in Yarmouth had reported that during the gale of the night of 13th November her men had seen a three-masted vessel founder, and had heard the heart-rending cries of her crew. The dreadful state of the weather had prevented any assistance being given.

Beaufort, knowing Hewett as a fine seaman, refused to believe this report and even wrote to Norway, believing that *Fairy* could have run for shelter there. A reward for her discovery was offered. On 10th February came a definite report that the wreck of the *Fairy* had been found off Lowestoft, and the Hydrographer was forced to admit a terrible loss to his service. There were no survivors and the Royal Navy voluntarily raised a massive fund for the widows and children.

Even Belcher admired Hewett and wrote to Beaufort from China : 'Have just heard of the loss of poor Hewett—a very steady hard-working fellow not to be *replaced* by any of the feather bed crew about Charing Cross. You can fill his vacancy but you will not get one to stand North Sea work as he did, although he was *said* to be too much in port I know what the weather is around Great Britain and he must be very fond of ducking who keeps his vessels on the move.' How delightfully does Belcher's phrase still describe for those of us at sea our brethren holding posts in Whitehall.

Captain Frederick Beechey was employed in the Irish Sea in paddlers. He was a better seaman than he was a poet; when moved to publish a tribute to his brother officer in the United Service Journal of March 1841, two verses of a long ode ran as follows:

'Twas not to combat Britain's foes,
She left her native shore;
To aid no work of death she goes,
Nor deadly missiles bore;
But labouring to promote the cause
Of science, gain a world's applause.

How fares it with that gallant bark,
How speed her jovial crew?
Along the waters drear and dark,
While fearfully it blew,
Was heard a wild heart-rending cry,
And groans and shrieks of agony.

Beechey became the expert on the Irish Sea and the communications between England and Ireland. He advised on rail and shipping routes between London and Dublin; he designed improvements for Holyhead and other harbours on both sides of the Irish Sea; and he advised on the postal service between Scotland and Northern Ireland.

Beechey also surveyed the River Severn from Worcester to Minehead, during which he overcame the difficulties imposed by the racing tidal streams that have tried the skill of his successors equipped with speedy motor boats.

All the navigable rivers were charted in the Beaufort era, not least the Thames, where Commander Frederick Bullock started the survey at London Bridge almost as soon as Beaufort took office. Tying in his own riverside triangulation to that of the Ordnance Survey, Bullock worked down river and far out into the estuary where, after seventeen years, his great survey of the Thames and approaches was completed as far as the Kentish Knock Sand, thirty miles seaward from the Nore. He used a succession of boats and paddlers, his first being the steamer *Echo* and his last the *Porcupine*.

By the time Bullock reached the estuary the Queen's Channel, which had been found by Mackenzie and Spence and buoyed by Trinity House in 1775, was proving inadequate for the increasing draught of vessels entering the river by the southern route. Bullock re-surveyed the swatchway further to seaward which Mackenzie and Spence had charted as Prince's Channel; this was now found to carry twenty feet of water, as opposed to the fourteen feet in the Queen's Channel. Prince's Channel was accordingly marked with three lightships, the *Girdler*, *Tongue* and *Princes*, and brought into service for navigation.

As his predecessors had done, Bullock found a swatchway, even more to seaward, through the long finger-like sandbanks, and named it Bullock Channel. This entrance to the Thames remained unmarked and unused for another fifty years, finally to be renamed the 'Duke of Edinburgh's Channel', which is today the main entrance to the Port of London from the south.

Bullock's work on the Essex side of the estuary showed Spence's northern route to be shoaling in the swatchway between East and West Swin. But no deeper route was opened here until the beginning of the twentieth century when Trinity House buoyed the Barrow Deep.

The deeps, and the connecting swatchways through the dangerous sandbanks which divide them, form the ever-changing pattern of channels which give shipping access to London's river port. To find the channels, and then to buoy them for navigational use, fixed marks on the drying sandbanks are required to guide the surveyor, for land is low-lying and distant.

Bullock commenced by using flags secured to iron posts driven into the sand, but these lasted a few tides only so strong are the streams in the estuary. His beacons became more ambitious in design and permanent in structure, until he came to his masterpiece on the Goodwin Sands, set in a concrete base and having a crow's nest from which to take his angles. This he left as a refuge for shipwrecked sailors, the crow's nest stocked with biscuits and a gallon of rum. When I grounded in my survey boat on the Goodwins on a cold winter's day during the Second World War I dearly wished that Bullock's beacons and supplies had survived the years.

Bullock's name will always be an important one in connection with the opening of London's river. He died an Admiral in 1874; his son, also a surveyor, rose to the rank of Captain after taking over the surveys on the coast of China on the death of Bate at Canton.

The Mersey is another of England's great navigable rivers and in 1830 the port of Liverpool was rapidly expanding under the pressure of increasing industrial trade. Recent shoaling of the channels across the estuary was causing great alarm: what use was it to chart foreign lands in an effort to expand overseas markets if the ports at home were unable to ship the exports? Eleven thousand ships, including a regular steam packet service to Ireland, were leaving the Mersey every year, but silting channels had now reduced the operation of the port to but eight hours in every twelve-hour cycle.

The Dock Trustees, a permanent committee of the Liverpool Corporation, appealed to the Admiralty for help in 1833. Beaufort sent for Lieutenant Henry Denham who had been working in the Bristol Channel for the last four years.

The Mersey estuary had some similarity to that of the Thames, on a smaller scale, in that the Formby and Rock Channels which had been traditionally used ran near to the northern and southern shores of the estuary, and by their proximity to land marks were easy to follow.

Denham realised that on every tide a great quantity of water was temporarily stored in the great expanse of shallows which stretched three miles wide and fifteen miles upstream to Runcorn. He saw the narrows between Liverpool and Birkenhead as the neck of this storage bottle, through which the ebb tidal stream flowed swiftly out across the Burbo Flats. If the Rock and Formby Channels were closing up, then there must be another exit. By the end of his first summer Denham had found the 'New Channel', far out in the centre of the estuary, and the port of Liverpool began to live again.

The following year the Freedom of the Borough of Liverpool was conferred on Lieutenant Denham for his services in reopening the port. In 1835 he was promoted Commander and permitted by the Admiralty to accept the post of Marine Surveyor to the Port of Liverpool at £700 per annum.

Great were Denham's activities during the next few years; he charted both in the estuary and far up the river; he took samples with a closing water bottle, devised by himself, at various depths on ebb and flow so that he could gauge the massive quantity of sediment carried out to the Burbo Flats on every ebb tide. He became convinced that only by maintaining the rapid ebb flow through the 'neck of the bottle' and out into Liverpool Bay could the New Channel be kept open and the sediment carried to the deep sea beyond. Encroachments by developers upstream would reduce the size of the 'storage bottle' and must at all costs be curtailed.

Denham read a paper before the British Association in 1837 describing his work at Liverpool, and possibly indicating to en-lightened listeners that the conservation of the whole of the Mersey, so vital to the storage bottle concept, was a task for a body with wider powers than those available to the Dock Trustees.

The New Channel bar had shown signs of shoaling in 1837 and Denham had put into practice a routine of harrowing the seabed here with spiked cables secured to a hardwood beam, towed by a steamboat during periods of ebb-flowing tidal stream.

It was his increasing demands for a steamboat, and probably also his British Association paper, which increased the resentment the hard-headed northerners of the Dock Board had begun to feel against this somewhat tactless, overbearing, but ruthlessly efficient naval commander.

A great storm in January 1839 finally brought matters to a head. Both the Rock and Formby lightships were driven from their stations, as were many of Denham's buoys marking the New Channel. He had no steamboat either to recover or replace them, nor was he permitted by the Dock Board to hire a tug for the purpose. It took Denham over a week to get the port back into operation and his subsequent report to the Dock Trustees revealed his feelings: 'The previous two months have been mortifying enough, kicking about in chance steamers, one of which sunk under our feet at the only spot which can save the Port of Liverpool from being pronounced a bar harbour at half tide next June. The weekly applications to be allowed to proceed in this rigorous season were as replete with cold receptions and reasonings as they ought to have been with cheering on . . . The vital exigencies of the Port have been this awful week the sport of chance and official help-lessness. In a word then, if the local revenue of the Port cannot afford better means I or any person of my pretensions would be robbing it as well as destroying himself morally and physically by remaining.' On receipt of this report the Dock Trustees unani-mously agreed to dispense with Denham's services.

Although he departed under a cloud, Denham left behind him an open thriving port with 16,000 ships a year entering and leaving, and detentions of steam packet vessels due to the tide reduced from about 250 to but 30 instances per year.

The formation of a permanent hydrographic service in this and other large ports around the British Isles stemmed directly from Denham's efforts. The Dock Trustees found that they had to engage another surveyor to watch the changing channels and advise on removal of silt from the port. Liverpool led the way in establishing its own hydrographic service, and today every port worthy of the name maintains such an organisation, leaving the Hydrographer of the Navy free to deal with the charting of the high seas.

In fact, Denham was next employed by Beaufort beyond the port limits working northwards along the coasts of Lancashire and Cumberland.

On return from Owen's African survey Commander Mudge had been placed in charge of the survey of the east coast of Ireland using hired boats. His assistant was Lieutenant George Frazer who, like Denham, had been a pupil of Commander Martin White in *Shamrock*, had been to the Cape Verdes with Bartholomew in *Leven*, and served with Captain Bayfield in the St. Lawrence. Consequently when Mudge died at Howth in 1837 as a result of a chill caught in open boats, he had a highly experienced successor in Frazer, who for the next fifteen years worked on the Irish Coast in boats, in paddlers and the ketch *Sparrow*. Frazer was honoured by the City of Dublin in recognition of his work in opening up that port.

Glasgow was another river port requiring charts, not only of the river itself but the extensive and intricate area embracing the whole of the outer approaches to the Clyde as far as the Mull of Kintyre, and including the many lochs which stretch like fingers into the very heart of the Highlands. For this stupendous task Beaufort selected Commander Charles Robinson in 1838, who then spent ten years on the work in the paddlers *Gleaner* and *Shearwater*.

Robinson was another who had sailed round Africa with Owen and had further accompanied him on the subsequent expedition to Fernando Po. As a lieutenant he had proved his worth in hired boats on the north coast of Wales from 1833 until he went to the Clyde.

William Sheringham is unusual in that he started his career as a surveyor by assisting Beaufort in the office, but his obvious qualities and his enthusiasm resulted in his being sent as a Lieutenant in 1832 to work with Slater in Scotland. Three years later he was on his own with hired boats on the coast of Wales, moving on to the north coast of Cornwall in 1840. From there he was ordered suddenly to Portsmouth, promoted Commander and given a paddler for an urgent survey of Portsmouth and Spithead. From here in the years following he moved outwards along the south coast, until by 1853 he had connected Bullock's work in the east with that of Commander White at Start Point in the west. The section of coast from here to Falmouth, charted by White in *Shamrock* prior to 1828, was the only stretch that Beaufort accepted from an earlier period, and is his tribute to Martin White who had been selected by Hurd in 1817 when he first formed his corps of surveying specialists.

The jig-saw puzzle is nearly complete. We have a gap around the Isle of Man and in the extreme west, Land's End and the Scillies. For this work Commander George Williams, another man of experience, was chosen; he had served with Hewett in *Fairy*, in the Mediterranean with Graves in *Beacon* and, finally, with Beechey in the paddler *Lucifer* in the Irish Sea. He in turn graduated to a paddler, the *Bann*, for the boisterous work about Land's End.

The picture is complete and by 1855, the year of Beaufort's retirement as Hydrographer, the coasts of the United Kingdom were charted, including the unfrequented coastline of western Ireland where Commander Richard Beechey had been working since 1835 and Commander George Bedford since 1844. It is on this first survey under Beaufort that all subsequent charts of our shores have been based. The process of recharting never ceases; the constantly changing shape of the seabed along our eastern shores and in our estuaries; the demands of shipping for larger and larger-scale charts; and constant instrumental developments making charting a more exact science, are the forces which drive us on. But still can be seen on our coastal charts much of the original work that was done under Beaufort's guidance.

CHAPTER SEVENTEEN

Arctic and Antarctic

At the commencement of the Beaufort period, but without assistance from the Admiralty, for Barrow was no friend of John Ross, the latter sailed for his second attempt at finding the elusive Northwest Passage in a steam vessel of 150 tons named *Victory*, provided by the wealthy gin distiller, Felix Booth. Sailing as second-in-command was Ross' nephew, Commander James Clark Ross.

The expedition sailed south through Prince Regent Inlet into the Gulf of Boothia on the east side of a peninsula which Ross named 'Boothia Felix'; and from Felix Harbour extensive sledge journeys were made by James Ross. These land journeys enabled him to locate the North Magnetic Pole over which he raised the Union Flag.

But that is as far as the expedition went, for *Victory* was fast in the ice for two long winters and only moved a mile or so in the intervening summer. She had to be abandoned and the crew travelled northwards to Fury Beach where they survived a third winter on supplies which Parry had landed during the unsuccessful salvage operations of the *Fury*.

In the summer of 1833 the party set out in *Fury's* boats and were eventually fortunate, when clear of the ice in Lancaster Sound, in falling in with the whaler *Isabella*. She was the same ship in which John Ross had made his first voyage to Lancaster Sound in 1818 and from whose decks he had declared the Sound closed by mountains. *Isabella* was just about to leave her fishing

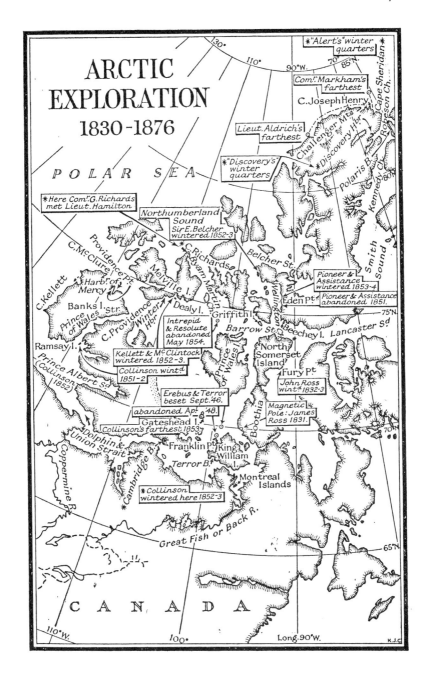

ARCTIC
EXPLORATION
1830-1876

POLAR SEA

* "Alert's" winter quarters *

Com.r Markham's farthest
C. Joseph Henry

Lieut. Aldrich's farthest

* "Discovery's" winter quarters

Challenger Mts.

Discovery Hbr.

Polaris B.

Cape Sheridan
Robeson Ch.

Kennedy Ch.

80°

* Here Com.r G. Richards met Lieut. Hamilton

Northumberland Sound
Sir E. Belcher wintered 1852-3

C. McClure Pt.

Providence Pt.

C. Richards
Byam Martin

Melville I.

Belcher St.

Wellington Ch.

Smith Sound

Pioneer & Assistance wintered 1853-4

Pioneer & Assistance abandoned 1851.

Eden Pt.

C. Kellett

* Harb.r of Mercy

Banks I.

Prince of Wales Str.

Dealy I.

Winter Hbr.

C. Providence

Griffith I.

Barrow St.

Beechey I. Lancaster S.d

75°N.

Intrepid & Resolute abandoned May 1854.

Ramsay I.

Kellett & McClintock wintered 1852-3.

Collinson wint.d 1851-2

Prince Albert S.d (Collinson 1852)

Prince of Wales

North Somerset Island

Fury Pt.

John Ross wint.d 1832-3.

Erebus & Terror beset Sept. 46.

abandoned Ap.l '48.

Gateshead I.

Collinson's farthest 1853

Magnetic Pole: James Ross 1831.

Boothia

70°

Dolphin & Union Strait

Coppermine R.

Cambridge B.

Franklin Pt.
King William I.

Terror B.

Montreal Islands

* Collinson wintered here 1852-3

Great Fish or Back R.

65°N.

C A N A D A

110°W.

100°

Long. 90°W.

K.J.C.

station and carried the adventurers back to England. Both John Ross and Felix Booth were knighted—a happy ending to an early sponsored expedition.

The discovery of the North Magnetic Pole and the increasing use of metal in ship construction gave impetus to the study of the earth's magnetic field. In 1838 James Ross was employed on a magnetic survey of the British Isles when he was called to his office by Beaufort with an exciting proposal. He should command an expedition to the Antarctic for the purposes of magnetic research and geographical discovery; Ross would lead in the bomb *Erebus* with Captain Francis Crozier, a veteran of Parry's voyages, in *Terror*. Both ships would be strengthened for the purpose of forcing their way through the pack ice which had effectively stopped both Cook, and, fifty years later, the Russian navigator Fabian Bellingshausen in the vicinity of 70° South.

The expedition sailed and Ross established the main magnetic observatory in the Derwent River near Hobart, with the generous assistance of Sir John Franklin, now Governor of Van Diemen's Land. From here Ross commenced his operations in December 1840 by sailing eastwards and then south in the longitude of New Zealand until he met the pack ice. It was his triumph that he, with his strengthened vessels, was the first ever to force his way through the ice to the open sea beyond.

Sailing south, a range of mountains was sighted and Captain Ross soon landed on a small off-lying island to claim Victoria Land for the Queen. A few days later the volcano of Mount Erebus, 13,350 feet high, was sighted, its dark smoke plume billowing from its icy summit, and the ships moved into the Ross Sea. Here the Irish blacksmith Sullivan in *Erebus* can take up the tale:

'A Description of the Great Antarctic Barrier Latitude 75 South. At the South-East end of Mount Erebus and joining the Main Land of Victorias continent begins the Barrier or as I should call it natures handy work, in the evening we commenced running thinking from the Declination of the Barrier from the distant view from the Mast head that we may run it down by midnight. But as far and as fast as we

ARCTIC AND ANTARCTIC

273

run the Barrier apprd. the Same Shape and form as it did when we left the mountain. We pursued a South Easterly Cource for the distance of three hundred miles. But the Barrier appeared the Same as when we Left the Land. On the first of Febry we stood away from the Barrier for five or six days and came up to it again farther East, on the morning of the Eight Do we found our Selves Enclosed in a beautiful bay of the barrier All hands when they Came on Deck to view this the most rare and magnificent Sight that Ever the human Eye witnessed. Since the world was created actually Stood Motionless for Several Seconds before he could Speak to the next man to him.'

In April the expedition was back at Hobart for the southern winter and Sullivan reports:

'The Governor Sir John Franklin and the inhabitants of Hobart Town welcomed us all hands were in Good health and Spirits, Fresh grub, Liberty on Shore with a drop of the Creator—Soon made our Jolly Tars forget the Cold fingers in the Frozen Regions . . . for very Little they thought of 78 South while Regealing them Selves at Charley Probins the Sign of the Gordon.'

New Year 1842 found the vessels again penetrating the pack ice, both ships secured to a drifting iceberg awaiting a sailing breeze. Captain Ross, in the true Parry manner, led the junketings in a ballroom built by the sailors from iceblocks on the berg. Dressed as Miss Ross, the leader partnered Captain Crozier for the opening quadrille.

Getting through the pack demanded all Ross' courage, persistence and seamanship as well as his human touch. On 18th January James Savage, sailor in *Erebus*, wrote:

'The Great Storm in the Packed ice Latitude 67 South. On the evening of the 18th Sprung up a Strong wind. By Midnight it blew a perfect hurricane the Sea runing high but breaking. We were in an awful position the Ships dashed from berg to berg, we were in Ememinent danger with the

Ships Broad Side to the wind. Every Crash treatning to Shake her timbers to pieces we Expected to see the masts fall over board Every moment.'

And after the storm:

'We Cast anchors again to repair the damages in the best manner we could the *Terrors* Rudder was Literally Split to atoms. Our Rudder was Split in two and otherwise damaged. We got the blacksmith and Carpenters to work at both Rudders, we got them repaired by the 22nd and Shiped. The ice Still thick and heavy untill the 2nd of Febry it cleared up all of a Sudden at Eight oclock p.m. not a bit of Slack ice to be Seen. Thank God and British Built Ships we See Our Selves Once more in the boosom of the open Sea After being closed up in the center of our Enemy for the space of 47 Days.

'After Getting Clear of the ice we made a straight cource for the South untill Wednesday 23rd we came up Close to the Barrier Some hundreds of miles farther East and Seven miles farther South. No more hopes this Season. We returned for the Faulkland Islands, South America, there to remain untill the next Season. We had Fine Steady Breeze untill we met with Accidence on the 13th of March.

'Our Miraculous Escape from Awful Shipwreck

'Sunday Morning March 13th 1842 we Escaped through Providence one of the most frightful cases of Ship Wreckd. that Ever occured on the high Seas. At one oclock a.m. we were in Company with the *Terror*. She was runing into One ice Island and we in another under Close Reefed top Sails.

'It was blowing a gale of wind at this time the watch was on the fore yard takeing in the last Reef the night was Exceedingly dark we Could Scarcely See a hundred yards off. When Low we were Runing into a Cluster of Ice islands at the rate of 7 Knots per hour. Poor James Angelie Since Drowned Cried out from the foreyard an Iceberg ahead.

'The Mournful Cry on deck was General all hands all hands Soon Brought our naked tars on Deck. Before they

Could all get on Deck Both Ships Struck with Such force we thought all was over.

'When we reached the Deck the Awful Catastrophe presented to our View. Shocking to Relate, the *Terror* to Avoid instant danger put her helm hard a port, we put our helm hard a Starboard. All this Occurred in the Space of one minute the *Terror* had more way And Canvas than we had. The *Terror* was trying to Gow to Leeward of the *Erebus* but the ice berg would not moove out of the way. The officers in command was Actually Stupefied what to do at this perilous moment they did not know. For if they hit against the berg they would Certainly be lost to avoid Either the berg or the *Erebus* was impossible.

'Now the dreadful and memorable Scene took place. After the first Stroke a heavy sea Elevated the *Terror* with our Bow Sprit Entangled a Cross her bows. The bow Sprit was Snaped to atoms, Fore top mast soon followd. fore top mast booms yards stays and every gear connected with the Ships fore castle was torn away. At this time we expected the *Terror* would sink but she rose the victor to despute the conquest. From this time out we were the sufferers the bow sprit carrying away Saved our lives. Five minutes longer would do the job but God decreed it not.

'The *Terror* was at this time next the ice berg crackling along. She broke away our bower anchor And with the Elevating Sea the *Terror* was inclining towards us. But before the anchor Could get clear Both Ships Struck with Such force as to bury the anchor in our Starboard Side. We carried it for the Distance of 700 miles through a heavy sea. Such my friend must be the Effect so terrible a Collision a weighty stroke 4000 tons. My friend the next wave Lifted the *Terror* above our Main Top mast.

'The most awful and Tremendous Sight we See yet at this moment, we poor pilgrims of the Ocean thought it was our last in this Life. Some uttered a feint Shriek through instant Surprise. But the Almighty God helped our Sinking Spirits when we thought we would have a Dreadful Stroke from her.

Like a Shot from a gun She made a leep a Stern and the next Sea carried her Quite clear of us.

'If both Ships was forty Seconds Longer in contact They would Gow down together and no Person would live to tell the tale but God decreed our Separation.

'When *Terror* had Got clear of us then we had another Great danger to Encounter we were no more than Eight yards from the iceberg. Tremendous Sight to See we could not distinctly discern the top of the berg. But a bluff projecting Summit far above our masthead. A heavy Sea pitched us against it. At this Thomas Abernethy the Gunner was on the ice plank he Cried out a Loud Back the main yard. It was instantly done, the Ship heeled a little, the wind caught the main top Sail and with the draw Back of a heavy Ebbing Sea with Gods help we Got clear off with every succeeding wave. After a Little time we Discovered we were in a cluster of ice islands. To help our Revived Spirits The Carpenter announced the pumps to be free and clear. all went on well, by this time began to bestow a thought on the *Terror*. For actually we thought when she Leaped astern in her confusion and She having a Deal of sail on that She hit Some of the bergs and went down. Our Consorts Crew were more alarmed about our fate. For they thought we were Gone and no Certainty of Escape. But Stop a Little before day Light we hoisted a blue Light. Immediately the *Terror* answered. Judge my Friends our Feelings at Both Sides. God almighty, My friends, alone that Saved us from a miserable death 3000 miles from any land.

'At Four oclock the day began to dawn the happiest Sight we any of us ever welcomed its now with open day Light we Could See the Eminent and awful Danger we were placed in a Little before. With a good resolution all hands Set to work to clear away the Wreck, the Sun Shone Beautiful, the day was calm but the Sea run high we had fine weather for a week Thursday Evening we had a jury bow Sprit rigged. Fore top and Gallant masts and yards and all the Wreck well Supplied for rounding the Tempestuous Cape horn. We Lost a man rounding the horn in the gale of wind and on the 6th of April we Cast Anchor at Port Louis, Barkleys Sound, Faulkland islands South America. If our Ships were Merchantmen this Scribbled Description i give of our Miraculous Escape would never reach Great Britain. But thanks to our noble Strong Barks they done their duty . . .'

Ross had not discovered the South Magnetic Pole, but he had sailed along a sufficient length of the ice shelf to learn that a great continent existed, and that far inland the Magnetic Pole was surely to be found. Not only had he discovered the southern continent, but by good fortune he had located the Ross Sea, which leads towards the very heart of the continent and was the natural entry for the great expeditions of the twentieth century.

The Ross Antarctic Expedition is not only renowned for its geographical, but also for its scientific discoveries. John Richardson, perhaps the first of the great surgeon naturalists to serve with the Royal Navy, who had accompanied Franklin twice to the shores of the Polar Sea, was at the naval hospital at Haslar by 1838; here he taught young Assistant Surgeons to be also naturalists. Richardson arranged with Beaufort that one of his brightest pupils, J. D. Hooker, should sail with Ross to the Antarctic. His presence resulted in the publication of six volumes describing the flora of New Zealand, Tasmania and Antarctica; but in addition to this, Hooker was an enthusiast with the dredge.

Ross was an enthusiast with the deep-sea line. During his uncle's voyage to Baffin Bay in 1819, in *Isabella*, a 'deep-sea clamm' had been used for sounding which had brought back greenish mud from a depth of 1,000 fathoms. On one occasion a starfish was found entangled with the line close above the clamm which seemed to indicate some form of life existing at 1,000 fathoms.

This had fired James Ross' enthusiasm and he and Hooker planned to take deep soundings and use the dredge on the seabed during the Antarctic Expedition.

To take his deep soundings Ross had prepared a line over 3,000 fathoms in length, fitted with swivels at regular intervals, and stowed on a vast reel. When the weather was calm at sea a boat was lowered into which the reel was fitted; a 76-lb. weight was secured to the end of the line which was allowed to run out freely. The time of each 100-fathom mark passing out over the gunwhale was noted, and when these intervals were seen to increase significantly it was assumed that the bottom had been reached. In this way Ross made the first oceanic sounding of 2,425 fathoms on 3rd January 1840 in 27° 26′ S 17° 29′ W. In the mid-1960s this area was surveyed by U.S. Survey Ship *Discoverer* which found the actual depth at this position to be only 2,100 fathoms. Similar soundings using the method pioneered by Ross were taken in the deeper parts of the ocean by surveyors in the mid-nineteenth century; these too have proved to have been too deep when checked by modern-day methods.

There are reports that Hooker used the dredge frequently to depths down to 400 fathoms from which much evidence of animal life was brought. Unfortunately these deep-sea zoological collections do not seem to have survived the voyage, or if they did they were subsequently lost to science.

The Antarctic Expedition returned to a great welcome. They had, as Laird Clowes has said, gained 'a glorious peace victory'. The two vessels had proved their strength and their ability to batter their way through the pack ice. On the resulting rising tide of enthusiasm for polar exploration the two ships were selected by Barrow and Beaufort for a renewed attack on the Northwest Passage. Parry's influence resulted in fitting them with engines and screws: surely *Erebus* and *Terror* would force their way through to the Pacific.

Sir James Ross, who had now been knighted, would have made the ideal leader and was offered command. He declined because of his age, but as he was only forty-five perhaps it was because he was newly married that he did not wish to add to the nine winters and fifteen navigable seasons he had spent in the polar regions.

Sir John Franklin, in his sixtieth year and new back from Van Diemen's Land, was most anxious to command the expedition; and surprisingly he was selected by Beaufort and Barrow, though his experience in ice navigation was negligible. He had gained his fame coasting the shores of the polar seas in boats, and that twenty years earlier. He cannot be considered a good choice and Beaufort must have wished many times in the years ahead that he had chosen a younger man to command an expedition of such importance.

The two ships sailed from Chatham in May 1845, Captain Crozier still in command of *Terror*, and cheered on their way by the crews of *Herald* and *Pandora* which, under Captain Kellett, were shortly to leave to continue surveying the Pacific shores of America.

Franklin entered Lancaster Sound and during the first summer attempted to sail northwards through Wellington Channel, where the vessels were eventually stopped by impenetrable pack. They wintered at Beechey Island during 1845–46 and in the spring sailed southwest between North Somerset and Prince of Wales Island, now known as Franklin Channel. Again the vessels were stopped by pack ice west of King William Land, discovered by James Ross on his sledge journeys from *Victory*.

Franklin must have known that the American mainland was near, but during the summer of 1847 the pack never released its grasp on the two ships, and Franklin died in June, Crozier taking over.

It was during the third winter, the second to be spent in the pack, that the poor quality of the preserved meats took its toll, and a heavy responsibility for the eventual disaster must fall upon the contractor who had provided them. By the spring the crews were greatly weakened and not fit for arduous travel; but it was now essential to abandon the ships and it is believed Crozier decided to make for the Great Fish River, explored by Back in 1834. The men set off hauling boats on sledges and with all the provisions which were still edible. Every day members of the party fell behind and died in the tracks of the survivors, the very last of whom probably succumbed at the end of the summer of 1848 in the vicinity of the mouth of the Great Fish River. All this only came slowly to light many years later and the facts are still a subject of argument. About the time that the last survivor was dying of extreme cold, hunger and fatigue, uneasiness about the fate of the expedition began to grow in London, and the great series of searches began. In all, between 1848 and 1860 about twenty search expeditions were launched; half of these were official and organised

The Arctic Council meeting under the chairmanship of the Hydrographer in 1851 to discuss the search for Sir John Franklin. By Stephen

by Beaufort, the others being equipped and sent out by Lady Franklin, Franklin's second wife, and her friends.

Beaufort, having been largely instrumental in mounting the expedition, felt it incumbent on him to lead in organising the searches, many of which were planned by the Arctic Council of which he was chairman, and among whose members were all those with an intimate knowledge of the polar seas. A print by Stephen Pearce shows the Arctic Council gathered about their chief, and here we can see James Ross, Edward Sabine, and George Back among others, whilst portraits of Sir John Franklin and John Barrow are seen on the wall behind them. A new chart of the Arctic lies on the table before them, the search for Franklin is under discussion.

The story of the many searches must be as briefly told as that of the expedition itself, for much has already been written of both elsewhere. I am merely recording the part which surveyors took in the searches, and here and there indicating the additions to hydrographic knowledge which resulted.

Herald was the first ship overseas to be ordered to search. She was at work upon the fever-infested shores of Central America and her debilitated officers and men were happy indeed to turn their attention to this new task, confident they would find their fellows whom they had cheered away from Chatham three years before.

Captain Kellett was ordered to take his ship to the Bering Strait and search eastwards into the Arctic; he could also expect *Plover* to arrive there to be stationed as permanent relief ship summer and winter.* The obvious base was Kotzebue Sound, from which *Herald* searched alone and without success that first summer of

* *Plover* remained as depôt ship in the Bering Strait until 1854. During her final two years Commander Rochfort Maguire, who had been First Lieutenant in *Herald* from 1845–51, was in command. Together with the surgeon, John Simpson who had already served in *Plover* from 1848–51, Maguire made friends among the Eskimos living in the vicinity of *Plover's* winter quarters in Elson's Bay close to the east of Point Barrow.

Maguire's Journal and Simpson's Essay on the Eskimos of northwestern Alaska provide an early record of how Europeans and Eskimos could establish a working relationship. See Bibliography—Bockstoce.

1848; returning again to Kotzebue the following spring she found *Plover* and *Nancy Dawson*, a Royal Thames Yacht Club schooner there to help. *Herald's* people found the barrel of flour buried by Beechey for Franklin on the shores of Kotzebue Sound twenty-three years before, when he had awaited in vain Franklin's land expedition. The flour was still sweet and Kellett gave a dinner party for the officers of the three ships at which all the pies and puddings were made from this flour.

The three ships then proceeded to Icy Cape from where Kellett despatched Lieutenant William Pullen in *Plover's* boats to search the shores as far as the Mackenzie River, up which he was to make his way in two whaleboats into the heart of Canada, a remarkable journey which Pullen successfully achieved but without finding traces of *Erebus* or *Terror*. He reached the Hudson Bay Company's Station at Fort Simpson on 3rd October where he passed the winter.

Plover was left at Kotzebue throughout the winter of 1849–50, *Herald* and *Nancy Dawson* going south, the former to return for a third time in the spring of 1850. At the opposite side of the Arctic other search expeditions had been active. In the summer of 1848 Sir James Ross had set off once again for the polar seas with *Investigator* and *Enterprise*. It had been a bad season; the vessels had failed to get past North Somerset Island, and returned to England at the end of the year with no news of Franklin. The vessels were re-commissioned, and with Captain Richard Collinson in *Enterprise* and Commander Robert McClure in *Investigator*, the two barks sailed for Magellan Strait to cross the Pacific and join the search from Bering Strait.

Meanwhile a new expedition was mounted from the east under Captain Austin. He had sailed with Parry on his third voyage to the Arctic and had found himself in command of *Chanticleer* on that tragic day back in 1831, when Foster fell to his death from a canoe in the Chagres River.

Austin's expedition was well planned and excellently managed; two 400-ton sailing barks, *Resolute* and *Assistance*, had been chosen, with the screw sloops *Pioneer* and *Intrepid* to tow as required.

In the summer of 1850 this squadron reached Barrow Strait

where they were held up by ice, having, however, found Franklin's first winter quarters at Beechey Island, but no clues as to whither he had sailed. During the winter, whilst the ships were icebound, vigorous plans were made for sledge journeys in all directions as soon as spring came, and by the summer's end a vast area of the north had been covered without any further evidence of Franklin's expedition.

Meanwhile *Investigator* and *Enterprise* became separated during their long journey across the Pacific. *Herald* met *Investigator*, off Cape Lisburne, and Kellett was much impressed. He inspected her and declared, 'I was highly pleased with the comfort and cleanliness . . . He parted with me at midnight, with a strong north-east wind and, under every stretch he could carry . . . steering to the North.' Pim, one of Captain Kellett's lieutenants, wrote in his journal, '*Investigator* intended to "take the pack" at any risk.'

Three years later Kellett and Pim were to meet McClure again at the other side of the Arctic.

Kellett was home in *Herald* in 1851 and was made second-in-command of yet another expedition to sail from the east in 1852. The ships were those used by Austin, and whilst Captain Kellett commanded *Resolute*, the command of the expedition and of *Assistance* was given surprisingly to Captain Sir Edward Belcher. This time Beaufort's choice of a leader seems almost unbelievable; every ship Belcher had commanded he had made a hell afloat. The humanity, the tact, and the leadership which men like Parry, James Ross and Austin had shown to be vital in the Arctic were beyond the reach of Belcher, no matter how he tries to explain away his failures in his account of the expedition which he titled *The Last of the Arctic Voyages*.

The squadron sailed from the Nore in April 1852. In addition to the *Assistance* and *Resolute*, there were the two screw sloops *Intrepid* (Commander M'Clintock) and *Pioneer* (Lieut. Sherard Osborn), and the sloop *North Star* as supply ship. This latter vessel was under the command of Pullen, now a Commander. He had spent the winter of 1849/50 at Fort Simpson and travelled in the spring by river and lake across Canada, towards York Factory on Hudson Bay. On 25th June, when nearing the Great Slave Lake, two Indians in a canoe met Pullen and, to his astonishment, delivered a message from Admiral Beaufort. In this remote place Pullen read that he was promoted to Commander and urged to make a further search on the shores of the Polar Sea. Undaunted he turned back and another winter passed before he finally took ship for England from York Factory.

Commander George Richards was second-in-command onboard *Assistance* and he really knew his Belcher. He had served with him in *Sulphur's* commission and it is not surprising that he decided to keep a diary of every happening onboard. Richards was determined that if, on return to England, Belcher court-martialled his officers, as was his habit, the facts of every situation should have been recorded on the spot. I have seen this diary with its many revealing facts but I will not quote them. Richard's foreword to the diary explains its purpose: 'If any person ever makes public the writings in this diary may he be haunted by my ghost in this world and the next.'

It does not need an exhaustive study of this diary, or more than a casual perusal of Belcher's book, to make one realise that Richards acted as the buffer, and by his tact and his knowledge of Belcher, maintained the peace.

Belcher writes: 'Our departure from Upernavik, to use the seaman's well-known expression, was "the hoisting in of our long boat". Henceforth we must be considered at sea, and dependent on our own resources. Cut off, for a series of years, from any but our own companionship, and dependent in no small degree upon the *bona fide* constituents of our society, power ceases, and the will of the least amongst us may create *bella, horrida bella*. Upon what a volcano do we stand! The sullen chief, if he be so, must chew the cud, and vegetate year after year in sullenness and vexatiousness of spirit. No such purgatory could exist, better calculated for a man of narrow mind—none so dangerous to a sensible mind. Such then being our feelings, I proceed, in charity with all men, not perfect myself, and willing to overlook all faults in others, provided they do not, when I tell them of it, still continue to tread upon my corns.' So wrote Belcher as the vessels sailed into Lancaster Sound. His corns were to suffer quite a bit during the next two years.

In Lancaster Sound the expedition was divided into two. Belcher in *Assistance* with *Pioneer* formed the eastern division and sailed northwards up the Wellington Channel, whilst Kellett took *Resolute* and *Intrepid* to Melville Island. *North Star*, the supply ship, remained at the site of Franklin's first winter quarters, Beechey Island.

Nothing had been heard of McClure in *Investigator* since he said farewell to Kellett in *Herald* in 1850. Collinson had failed to get into the Arctic that summer, but after wintering at Hong Kong in *Enterprise* he passed through the Bering Strait in 1851, since which date he too had been lost to the world. It was therefore a subsidiary task of Belcher's expedition to keep a good look-out for signs of these two vessels.

By the end of the summer the Eastern Division were iced in well up the Wellington Channel and winter quarters were established. Autumn sledge journeys were begun, and in the depth of the winter preparations were made for spring travel both to the north and to the west. Sledges and sledge boats had been provided by Woolwich Dockyard, and whilst these were designed to be hauled by manpower, dogs had also been purchased at Upernavik.

Commander Richards started travelling on 10th March, and Belcher soon after, and on 10th April Richards commenced an epic ninety-five day journey. He set out with six sledges, hauled by fifty-seven men, each sledge also under sail when the wind served, and with its own silk banner flying bravely from the stern; these had been lovingly embroidered by wives and sweethearts and presented onboard before leaving Woolwich.

During the journey Richards searched and surveyed a great area of the islands and channels on the northern side of Melville Sound. On 18th May he noticed fresh sledge tracks and by following them up he met Lieutenant Hamilton with his party, twenty-one days out from *Resolute*. He had much to tell. The Western Division had failed to establish satisfactory quarters in Parry's Winter Harbour and had fallen back to Dealy Island. At Winter Harbour, under Sandstone Rock, Lieutenant Mecham had found a note from Commander McClure, who had recently travelled there by sledge from *Investigator*, held fast in the ice for the last three winters at

'Harbour of Mercy' on the north side of Banks Island. In all this time *Investigator* had lost but one man.

As soon as travel was possible in the spring of 1853 Kellett sent a party to the Harbour of Mercy. On 6th April Commander McClure saw from his decks a strange figure approaching across the ice. 'In God's name who are you?' he cried. 'Lieutenant Pim, late of *Herald* and now of *Resolute*. Captain Kellett is in her at Dealy Island.'

It was a great moment, the first time that two parties, one from the east and one from the west, had met across the Arctic wastes. Only about 150 miles of impenetrable pack ice separated *Resolute* at Dealy Island from *Investigator* in the Harbour of Mercy, and this was as near as anyone ever came in the nineteenth century to discovering the long sought after Northwest Passage.

Having heard this exciting news from Hamilton, Richards travelled on round the north side of Melville Island and, after meeting Lieutenant Pim also on a journey from *Resolute*, he reached Kellett's two ships on 3rd June. There were a few invalids from *Investigator* onboard, but the majority of officers and men, including the Captain, were away on searches or visiting *Investigator*.

Richards waited until Captain Kellett returned, and after an excellent dinner, as game was plentiful here, and a long talk, he set out to return to *Assistance*, travelling south about Melville Island and northwards by Byam Martin Channel. He was telling Belcher the news on 11th October 1853.

Belcher had a difficult summer trying to get clear of the ice; there had been many days of dangerous and tedious work. It was a bad year and he was many times held fast, even in August.

After each success Belcher's confidence rose, 'What the sensations were of those around, I was unable to discover; but I had the deep satisfaction of feeling that I had, by the blessing of God, effected my object, and impressed all the well-disposed men under my command with the determination which will, I trust, under the blessing of God, enable me to do my duty, and that where I *decide*, no puny obstacle or difference of opinion shall deter me from the accomplishment of any service I may deem it necessary to execute.' Or when held up: 'Here then our present prospects were at least painfully delayed, and by many were considered entirely frustrated for the season. But although opinions were perhaps too openly expressed, I deemed it prudent to be prepared for taking the pack again' . . . 'Unfortunately, the *Pioneer* shortened sail some miles astern, and before she reached the gap by which we entered, it had closed, and separated her so far as not to be of further assistance until the communication was opened.'

Lieutenant Sherard Osborn in command of *Pioneer* had also had a difficult period. He had towed *Assistance* from every possible angle under the guidance of Belcher calling with his megaphone from the deck. As Belcher remarks: 'Hailing and straining the lungs to people always half deaf, is not pleasant to either party, and is productive, by repetition of orders, when not heard or obeyed, of very unpleasant feelings.' On one occasion Belcher became so exasperated with Sherard Osborn that he crowded on sail and rammed *Pioneer*, inflicting considerable damage, an incident he was at pains to get his officers to forget.

By summer's end *Assistance* was wintering again, still over fifty miles north of Beechey Island in the Wellington Channel, and Sherard Osborn had been relieved of his command.

In February 1854 Commander Richards was sent off by sledge to the Western Division with instructions from Belcher to Kellett to meet him at Beechey Island by 24th August, with the crews of all vessels including the *Investigator's*. In a private letter Belcher gave Kellett instructions to abandon his ships.

Lieutenant Hamilton from *Resolute* arrived in March by dog sledge having missed Richards and with news from Kellett. The Western Division had been blown out of their winter quarters in a gale in August and were now frozen in the Melville Sound. Kellett was intending to send the *Investigator's* crew to Beechey Island during the summer, whilst he planned to remain a further winter. His men had already searched and surveyed over 1,600 miles without clues of Franklin's expedition, but he intended more.

On 20th April Commander M'Clintock came on a dog sledge from *Resolute*. Kellett had received Belcher's orders to abandon his ships with surprise, and he sent M'Clintock to question whether they were imperative. Belcher was beside himself and penned a stiff letter ordering Kellett to batten down the vessels and abandon them. The crews were to repair eastwards at once, leaving M'Clintock, the bearer of this message, to await the return of absent sledge parties before bringing them also to Beechey Island.

On 3rd May Richards arrived back to report that the 'Investigators' had reached the rendezvous, leaving four food depots along the route to assist the Western Division crews to come in.

As summer went on the struggle was resumed to navigate *Assistance* and *Pioneer* the fifty miles south through the pack. Leaving Richards in charge of this difficult task Captain Belcher went south with his gig in July to take command of the assembling crews awaiting evacuation in the little sloop *North Star*. Belcher explains that without the presence of his own command he needed the presence of his gig, with pendant flying, to maintain his authority.

Kellett, M'Clintock and various officers in charge of sledge parties had come in. Lieutenant Mecham, who last year had found McClure's note at the Sandstone, now had more exciting news of Captain Collinson and *Enterprise*.

In the early summer he had made a long journey southwest from Dealy Island. He crossed the old hummocky flows at the west end of Melville Sound which formed the obdurate barrier between east and west. He entered Prince of Wales Strait between Banks Island and Prince Albert Land and travelled south to the tiny Princess Royal Islands, humped among the floes. Here he saw a cairn and to his delight it contained a note from Collinson. Whilst *Enterprise* had sailed up the west coast of Bank's Island as far as 73° N. Collinson had gone by sledge as far as the south shore of Melville Island. Further information was to be found on a small island at the southern entrance to Prince of Wales Strait. Mecham hurried on and found the note from Collinson indicating that in 1853 he was searching further south and east.

Mecham's sledge journey had been an epic one, judged even by the high standards now achieved by the naval surveyors. In seventy days he had covered 1,336 miles. He had no dogs and had averaged twenty miles daily on the long homeward journey from the southern end of Prince of Wales Strait to Beechey Island, much of the route over hummocky sea ice.

In fact Collinson had passed through the Dolphin and Union Strait and on as far as Cambridge Bay in the southeast of Victoria Land, before being forced back by ice and making his eventual departure through Bering Strait. So in fact he came nearer than any other in all the great expeditions to the scene of Franklin's final disaster.

After a last visit to the *Assistance* and *Pioneer*, still trapped in the ice, and Collinson not having made his appearance, Belcher gave the order for all the crews to embark in *North Star* on 26th August 1854. Hardly had the overburdened vessel got under way when a steamer towing a bark was reported. They were the *Phoenix* and *Talbot* with further stores and instructions to abandon the search and to withdraw ships and crews if there was no new evidence to encourage further search. The men were happy to avail themselves of this unexpected comfort for the voyage home.

On 28th September 1854, the vessels reached Cork, and Belcher, Kellett and McClure, three shipless captains, set out by rail for London. Court-martial inevitably followed. McClure's vessel had been honourably abandoned on the very verge of a breakthrough of the Northwest Passage, Kellett held written instructions from Belcher to abandon his ships, but Belcher himself had left behind four out of the five vessels which had set out so bravely under his command for the 'Last of the Arctic Voyages' in 1852. No word of praise or comment was passed by the court-martial board when they acquitted Belcher.

A year after Belcher's return, in September 1855, Captain James Buddington in the United States whaling bark *George Henry* sighted in Davis Strait in 67° N. a ship which, when he boarded her, proved to be the *Resolute*. With a party of eleven men from his own crew Buddington managed to sail *Resolute* clear of the ice and south to New London where he arrived safely on Christmas Eve.

The United States purchased *Resolute* from Buddington for 40,000 dollars, and after refitting her and finishing her down to the finest detail, sailed her to Spithead under the command of Captain Hartstein, U.S. Navy.

Here, with Queen Victoria onboard, Captain Hartstein officially handed over the vessel, 'not only as an evidence of a friendly feeling to your Sovereignty, but as a token of love, admiration and respect to your Majesty personally.'

Belcher never had any love for the 'Yankees' and now, by returning in perfect condition a ship he had ordered to be abandoned, they had inflicted upon him, quietly employed as he was in writing Sailing Directions at the Admiralty, a last bitter blow at the end of a querulous lifetime at sea.*

---

* In 1880 when *Resolute* was finally broken up, a desk six feet by four feet with movable slope and inkstand was made from her timbers by Messrs. Morant, Boyd & Blandford of 91 New Bond Street at a cost of £330. This desk was presented to the President of the United States. The late President John F. Kennedy found this massive desk in the furniture store and used it for his daily work until the day he died. In 1994 Admiral Austin Yeager, National Ocean Service, informed me that President Clinton had moved the *Resolute* desk back into the Oval Office as his daily working desk.

CHAPTER EIGHTEEN

War and Washington

Belcher's return and the subsequent court-martials passed almost unnoticed, for war with Russia had broken out in March 1854. During the previous year the Tsar had issued an ultimatum to the Ottoman Porte demanding that every Orthodox subject of the Sultan should be placed forthwith under the protection of the Tsar. This was quite unacceptable to the Porte and appeared to be but the first step proposed by the Tsar for carving up the Turkish empire for his own purposes. Both Britain and France reacted to this threat of Russia reaching the Mediterranean and long before war was declared their combined fleets had moved up to Constantinople.

The utter defeat of a Turkish squadron convoying supplies to Sinope on the Black Sea coast of Asia Minor by the Russian fleet; the failure of a conference of powers called to Vienna to restrain Russia; and the refusal of the Tsar to evacuate the Danube Principalities which he had overrun, resulted in the formal declaration of war by Great Britain and France against Russia.

The war, which lasted until January 1856, was, except for a few minor operations in the Far East and the White Sea, confined to the two major campaigns in the Black Sea and the Baltic. There were no fleet actions in either theatre, the Russian fleets playing a passive role within their heavily defended harbours, whilst the British and French forces relied upon naval bombardment or combined operations. As the war progressed the screw and paddle vessels showed their final ascendency over the sailing ships, whilst the role of the shallow-draught gunboats and mortar vessels became an increasingly important one.

The need for the allied fleet to navigate inshore waters, the requirement to station themselves with accuracy for the bombardment of fortifications and the necessity for locating landing beaches and approach channels all called for the special skill of the surveying officers, who made a name for themselves and their branch in both campaigns in somewhat difficult circumstances.

Since Smyth had begun his survey work in Sicily at the request of the Commander-in-Chief at the close of the Napoleonic wars, there had been a continuing history of his successors at work in the Mediterranean and their activities were well known to the Fleet. One of the great naval personalities in the Mediterranean had been Thomas Graves. He had learnt his surveying trade with Smyth in the *Adventure* and had gone for five years in that same ship to Magellan Strait before returning to the Mediterranean in 1832 to command the surveying brig *Mastiff*. First in this vessel, then in the brig *Beacon*, the corvette *Volage* and finally, in 1850, the paddler *Spitfire*, Graves had worked in the Greek Archipelago, or the 'Arches' as they were familiarly called by the Navy. Over a hundred charts had resulted from his labours, but they were far more than charts for, urged on by Beaufort, he mapped the archaeological sites encountered in his work, sketching with rare beauty those ancient ruins which still stood, so that Graves' lovely original documents record historic sites which one may look for today in vain.

In 1850 Captain Graves had accepted the post of Superintendent of the Port of Malta, where he was well known to officers of the Fleet until his untimely death three years later at the hands of a Maltese boatman, who stabbed him for reasons I am unable to discover.

Since 1832 Tom Spratt had assisted Graves in all his work, first as a Midshipman and then, rising through the ranks and learning his surveying, drawing and archaeology from his master, he finally took over *Spitfire* as a Commander when Graves went to Malta in 1850.

The Commander-in-Chief, Admiral Sir James Dundas, had been in the Mediterranean for over two years when war broke out and so he knew of Spratt's work, and thus the surveyor moved easily and naturally into his wartime role, bringing with him in *Spitfire* three competent assistant surveyors in Lieutenant Arthur Mansell, Acting Lieutenant George Wilkinson and Mr. Edward Brooker, Master.

Spratt's early success was to find a coal mine at Erekli on the Asia Minor coast, an asset for the many steam vessels now involved; and by constant activity around the shores of the Black Sea *Spitfire* soon became a sort of intelligence headquarters to which the Commander-in-Chief and his second-in-command, Vice Admiral Edmund, Lord Lyons, frequently turned for information and advice.

By June 1854 the Russian fleet had shown no inclination to quit their stronghold of Sevastopol and the Russian army had retreated north of the Danube. It was accordingly decided that the combined French and British land forces should invade the Crimea. An extensive reconnaissance was made of the coast of the Crimea by the smaller steam vessels, whilst the ships of the line lay offshore in support.

Eupatoria, thirty-five miles north of Sevastopol, was chosen as the landing place, the town being easily captured before the two armies advanced southwards. Left in command of Eupatoria, which he defended during numerous attacks throughout the war, was Captain Thomas Brock, another surveying officer who had spent years surveying in the 'Arches', and has left us a series of beautiful watercolours of the Greek Islands.

After success at the battle of the Alma the allied armies bypassed Sevastopol to the east and south. Admiral Lyons captured from seaward, and Spratt surveyed, the bay of Balaclava, which proved suitable for the landing of the heavy equipment now needed by the armies for the siege of Sevastopol. A month later Spratt and his officers directed their attention to the accurate placing of British, French and Turkish vessels for a day-long bombardment of Sevastopol, the entrance to the harbour of which had now been blocked by scuttled vessels of the Russian fleet. Little damage resulted from the bombardment, nor did it enable a successful attack to be launched by our land forces.

With the Russian fleet now immobilised within the fortified harbour it became necessary to find other destructive work for the allied fleets. Accordingly *Spitfire* was sent off to make a reconnaissance on the western side of the narrow neck of land which seemed to form a lifeline between the Crimea and the Russian mainland. The water here proved extremely shallow preventing close approach even in small craft, but Spratt's intelligence system revealed that in fact the main military road lay thirty miles to the eastward of this neck of land, being formed by a floating bridge southward from Genitchi to the long spit of land known as the Tongue of Arabat, separating the Sea of Azov from the Putrid Sea, along which it then ran southwards many miles to Arabat in the Crimea.

Admiral Lyons took over as Commander-in-Chief in December 1854 and a more offensive spirit prevailed. In the spring of 1855 an expedition under Lyons landed troops near Kerch, capturing it, and Yenikale to the northwards, giving the allies control of the narrow Straits of Kerch, the entrance to the Sea of Azov, into which a light raiding squadron under Captain Edmund Mowbray Lyons, second son of the Admiral, in the *Miranda*, a fifteen-gun screw vessel, was piloted by the surveyors.

This squadron ranged at will sinking every Russian craft they met and frequently landing parties to blow up or set fire to vast granaries and forage stores. They paid particular attention to Genitchi and Arabat, the two terminals of the military highway, whilst they even entered the extreme shallow waters in the approach to the River Don. By mid-June the squadron was back and Captain Lyons was killed in a routine night engagement with one of the Sevastopol forts.

Commander Sherard Osborn, no longer a towing master for Captain Belcher, now took a second light raiding squadron into the Sea of Azov, his ship being the paddler *Vesuvius*. The military road across the Arabat spit again came in for attention and during a brisk action off Genitchi Able Seaman Joseph Trewaras earned the V.C. by cutting away the floating bridge carrying the road, although under heavy fire from the shore. For four months this squadron ranged freely, striking unexpectedly, repeatedly and successfully at the Russian supply lines.

Sevastopol finally fell to attacks by French and British troops on 9th September 1855, only some mortar vessels and the naval brigade representing the fleet in the final assault. The Russian fleet was found scuttled within, which now released the whole of the allied naval forces for any task they wished to perform. The mouths of the Danube had long been blockaded, and now it was decided to curtail navigation into the Dnieper and Bug rivers; both flowed into a long gulf called Kherson, in the northwestern part of the Black Sea. The entrance to the gulf lies at the western end, narrow and intricate, between the mainland to the north and the long spit of land which forms the southern side of the gulf. The fortress of Kinburn lay at the terminal of this spit, there forming the key controlling the waters within.

The expedition consisted of ten screw ships of the line with about eighty auxiliary vessels, gunboats and mortar-boats in which were conveyed about 8,000 allied troops. Three French floating armoured batteries made their first appearance and a devastating impression on this occasion—the first armoured steam ships in the world.

Admiral Lyons commanded the British and Admiral Bruat the French divisions, the larger vessels of which were carefully placed to the west and south respectively by Spratt for the bombardment of the fortress.

On the first night Brooker, *Spitfire's* master, went with Lieutenant Marryat in his gunboat *Cracker*, to search out and buoy the channel between the fort and the mainland which, when complete, enabled other gunboats to join them to the northeast of the fortress.

During the following day the troops were landed on the south side of the spit to the east of the fortress, and after being held up a day by bad weather a carefully planned bombardment was commenced on 17th October. As fire from the fortress decreased an increasing number of screw and paddle vessels passed through the buoyed channel to get to the northeast of the target, whilst the ships of the line were enabled, due to Spratt's careful sounding, to move in on the west and southern sides until they had but two feet under their keels. So great was the encircling fire now brought to bear that the Russians in Kinburn fortress surrendered before nightfall.

With the Danube, Dnieper and Bug rivers now sealed, Sevastopol taken, the Straits of Kerch in our hands and a flotilla ranging at will in the Sea of Azov Russia was totally blockaded from the south and peace seemed clearly on the way. Still, *Spitfire* kept busy surveying the bays, the channels and the anchorages on the Russian coast whilst opportunity remained. Smyth's lesson had been handed down—the closing stages of a victorious war are the days of harvest for the surveyor in foreign fields.

Spratt had been Admiral Lyons' constant adviser throughout, often holding discussions far into the night in the Admiral's quarters in *Agamemnon*. Captain William Mends, the Flag Captain, had sat in on all these meetings and his comment at the war's end was concise: 'Spratt was the mainspring of all the operations, whilst Lord Lyons held the key.'

Promoted to Captain, awarded the C.B. and given a newer paddler, *Medina*, Spratt resumed at the war's end his surveys in the Mediterranean.

The surveying officer whom Beaufort despatched to assist in the Baltic campaign was Captain Bartholomew James Sulivan whom we last heard of in *Beagle* with FitzRoy. He had returned as a Commander to South American waters in the years 1842–1846 in *Philomel*, a beautiful brig, for surveys of the Falkland Islands and the River Plate. By this time General Rosas, from whom Darwin had borrowed horses on his ride to Buenos Aires, had completed his campaign against the Indians and was installed as President of the Argentine Republic. His powerful army of gauchos was still about him, and his territorial ambitions now extended to the north bank of the River Plate, resulting in a siege of Monte Video, the capital of the Banda Oriental, whose independence was guaranteed by Britain and France. A combined naval squadron, to which *Philomel* was attached, was eventually prepared to take action in 1845 against Rosas who had thrown a boom across the stream and erected strong fortifications at Obligado on the Parana River, thus sealing off the independent state of Paraguay from the outside world.

In boats, with muffled oars, Sulivan led a party by night to sound out the vicinity of the boom, so close to the fortifications that they could hear the gauchos talking. The resulting chart was used to plan the attack by the combined squadron which resulted during a fierce action in the forts being destroyed and the boom cut. Sulivan's task had then been to pilot naval and merchant vessels 800 miles up the uncharted Parana River to open trade with Paraguay. It took him two months of daily sounding and marking in open boats or standing on the paddle boxes of the steamers to direct them under a burning sun from dawn to dusk.

Sulivan had thus shown his suitability for any piloting or surveying which might be required by a fleet in foreign waters and Beaufort wisely selected him for the Baltic. He was provided with the tiny paddler *Lightning*, 100 h.p. with three guns and drawing seven feet; she was the first successful steam vessel built for the Navy and originally used for surveying in the Irish Sea by Belcher in 1835.

Beaufort's instructions show the farsighted attitude which contributed so greatly to the success of his long reign, now nearly over.

> Sir Francis Beaufort to Captain Sulivan
>
> Sir
>
> My Lords Commissioners of the Admiralty having selected you to the command of H.M. vessel *Lightning* to join Vice Admiral Napier for the purpose of assisting with the important operations of the Baltic fleet, by making such skilful and rapid reconnaissances, as well as occasional hydrographic surveys, wherever it may be considered necessary, I scarcely consider myself warranted in supplying you with any special instructions as to the service on which you will be employed; still for the sake of preserving that connection which has so long subsisted between you and this office, and I may add with such beneficial results to H.M. Service, I would exhort you to keep all our surveying rules and habits always in your

mind, so as to render everything you do more or less subser-
vient to the great object of improving our charts; never to
defer to the following day writing the remarks and observations that you may have collected, as they may be of lasting
value long after the campaign in which you are engaged has
passed away; to give descriptions of the characteristic features
of the land, or of the leading peculiarities of the different districts
of the Baltic navigation.

In your partial and desultory surveys take great care to
establish the connection of some one permanent and conspicuous object with your triangulation or bearings by which you
may subsequently adjust any new work, or by which any new
labourers may bring every fragment of fresh information into
harmonious agreement with former acquisitions.

Considering you as one of the Admiral's eyes, and knowing
that through it he will see everything that he ought to see, I
feel sure that at the end of the campaign he will exclaim, as
Sir William Parker did in China Sea, 'Without those admirable
surveyors I should have done nothing'.

> I am, Sir
> Your Obedient Servant
> F. Beaufort
> Hydrographer.

With these instructions Sulivan sailed for the Baltic to report to
the Commander-in-Chief whom he found onboard his flagship
Duke of Wellington, anchored with the fleet in Kiel Bay. Sixty-nine-
year old Sir Charles Napier appeared to be quite ignorant of
Sulivan's former services in the Parana when the latter handed his
appointment 'for surveying and pilotage duties' to him. 'I do not
know what you have come out for, or what is the use of a surveying
ship, unless to make a fire-vessel of!' said the Admiral in front of
several officers who were gathered in his cabin. It was not an
encouraging start.

The attitude of the Commander-in-Chief may be attributable
to the Master of the Fleet, George Biddlecombe, who, being
responsible for the navigation, should have welcomed the surveyors,

but appeared to regard their presence as an encroachment upon his preserve.

Despite the fact that Napier spoke constantly of the shortage of pilots, *Lightning*, with a post-Captain in command, and three surveying officers onboard, including the very competent Master, Frederick Evans, was used for domestic tasks within the fleet. She was sent from ship to ship with messages; despatched to distant harbours with the purser in search of meat and supplies; and, most humiliating of all, ordered to Swedish ports to collect indifferent pilots when the excellent Russian charts which had been supplied to the fleet by the Hydrographer were completely adequate for navigation, except in the narrow waters and anchorages where *Lightning* should have been busily employed.

Whilst the elderly Commander-in-Chief remained nervous, unsure of himself and afraid to approach the land, Sulivan and his officers were desperately anxious to commence reconnaissance of Bomarsund, the fortress in the Åland Islands commanding the entrance to the Gulf of Bothnia; to explore the approaches to Helsinki and the nearby fortress of Sweaborg; and, above all, to reconnoitre Kronstadt, the island fortress at the mouth of the Neva where the Russian fleet was said to be lying.

As the fleet moved cautiously up the Baltic Rear Admiral Plumridge was sent on ahead to reconnoitre with his paddlers to the retreating ice-edge in the Gulf of Finland. While this expedition was being discussed with the C-in-C, Sulivan managed to catch Plumridge's eye, and by signs persuaded him to ask that *Lightning* go with him. Plumridge put it to Napier who agreed, and further suggested that Evans be lent to Admiral Plumridge for pilotage duties.

Sulivan saw his initial task as the finding of suitable anchorages for the fleet and, sailing with Plumridge, he made his first plan in the Faro Sound at the northern end of Gothland.

By the time *Lightning* returned, the Commander-in-Chief had seen by chance a paper prepared by Sulivan on a proposal for organising seaman battalions for service ashore. This was a hobby horse of Napier's and from that day he saw Sulivan in a new light. Sulivan was amazed to find himself in the presence of the Commander-in-Chief being bombarded with questions about buoying shoals, seeking anchorages, piloting vessels, making reconnaissances and many similar tasks for which Sulivan had waited so long. Evans was ordered to rejoin, and *Lightning* was despatched to examine Hango and Wormso anchorages, one on the north and the other on the south side of the entrance to the Gulf of Finland.

These tasks were eagerly undertaken, including a reconnaissance of the fortifications at Hango and the location and buoying of the Apollon shoal ten miles north of Wormso.

The next task ordered was a thorough reconnaissance of Bomarsund as the charts of the Aland Islands held by the fleet were quite inadequate and the strength of the fortifications unknown. For this Sulivan set out in *Lightning* on the evening of 28th May with the paddler *Driver*, six guns and drawing 14 ft. 6 in., to assist. Commander the Hon. Arthur Cochrane, a worthy son of Lord Dundonald, a naval officer of great energy and resource, was in command of *Driver*. With him in *Lightning* Sulivan took Captain Nugent, R.E., one of the engineers attached to the fleet. Sulivan found Cochrane an able and zealous companion, whilst Nugent was immediately acceptable to the highly religious Sulivan for he always had a Bible lying on the table amongst his plans. They had also with them a Swedish interpreter, for the Aland islanders were Swedes and were believed to resent the presence of the Russians who had occupied the islands in 1809. Much intelligence might be gained from the local inhabitants.

Having reached Led Sound at the southern end of the islands their first efforts to contact the villagers were unsuccessful, the inhabitants taking flight at the approach of the boats. At last the sailors got hold of an old man at Degerby, and by showing him some kindness some women were encouraged to come to the beach and from them eggs, milk and cream were purchased. Soon word of the Englishmen's friendliness spread through the islands and as Sulivan progressed he met young men and girls who had been employed in building the forts at Bomarsund and much intelligence was thus collected. The only channels leading into Lumpar Bay which were considered safe for navigation by the Russians were from the north and overlooked by the fortifications, so that Sulivan decided to try to find an entrance from the south through one of the more complex and unguarded channels. Next day the two ships worked themselves through intricate passages from Fogle Fjord up the east side of Lumpar Island and through between Michelso and Lumpar Island into Lumpar Bay, whence the forts of Bomarsund could be seen two miles away to the northwards. The channel in the vicinity of Ango Town was but 300 yards wide as it passed between 300-foot-high rocks on either side. A regiment of riflemen was said to be stationed in the town and could be expected to make the passage unpleasant for a squadron of vessels necessarily advancing one by one. It was therefore deemed advisable to search for another channel between the islands further to the north.

No possible entrance was found here so *Driver* and *Lightning* anchored east of Michelso Island. Sulivan, Cochrane and Nugent then set out in the two gigs with two cutters, one armed, the other rigged for sounding. They passed south of Kalfholm Island and round to the west point of Michelso. One cutter was then sent to sound the channel between Michelso and Lumpar Island, the other anchored to keep guard whilst the three officers landed from the gigs, stationed sentries in the woods, and scaled a high rocky cliff. At the summit they found a plateau where stunted pines gave them shelter as they stretched out on the sparse dry grass and pine needles and focused their field glasses on the fortifications at Bomarsund but a mile and a quarter distant.

All three sketched busily. The large central fort reminded them of a terrace at a fashionable English watering place with its numerous square window-like casemates surmounted by a steeply sloping roof. This fort appeared to house 92 guns, and there were three subsidiary forts, each with 24 guns, distant half a mile to the north, south and west of the main fort respectively. The western fort stood on a commanding hill, the one to the south was still under construction.

The sketching was almost complete when a hail from the cutter far below indicated that the enemy were landing on the island to the southeast. Cochrane and Nugent scrambled down the cliff. Sulivan ran through the woods to collect the sentries. The sounding cutter was recalled. Soon all were embarked and the boats were

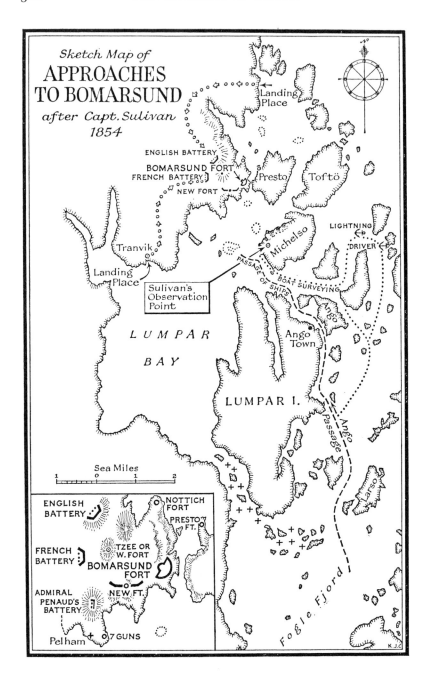

Sketch Map of
APPROACHES
TO BOMARSUND
after Capt. Sulivan
1854

Landing
Place

ENGLISH BATTERY
BOMARSUND FORT
FRENCH BATTERY
NEW FORT

Presto   Toftö

LIGHTNING

DRIVER

Michelso

Tranvik

PASSAGE OF SHIPS

BOAT SURVEYING

Landing
Place

Sulivan's
Observation
Point

Ango

Ango
Town

L U M P A R

B A Y

LUMPAR I.

Ango Passage

Larso

Sea Miles
1   o   1   2

ENGLISH
BATTERY

NOTTICH
FORT

PRESTO
FT.

FRENCH
BATTERY

TZEE OR
W. FORT

BOMARSUND
FORT

ADMIRAL
PENAUD'S
BATTERY

NEW. FT.

Pelham   7 GUNS

Fogle Fjord

K J.C

pulling southeastwards along the shore, hastened on their way by a long wide shot from the battery at Bomarsund, and with Sulivan's fine gig's crew drawing ahead. He expected the soldiers round every headland, then he saw them, five men being feverishly ferried from a little island to the mainland in a tiny skiff. The gig put on a spurt and were within thirty yards of the dinghy as the soldiers abandoned their boat and scampered into the woods, the last, by his uniform a man of some authority, brandishing his revolver as he ran.

If this was the calibre of the riflemen at Ango Town it now seemed worth completing the survey of Ango Passage. It was the southern entrance that was difficult, for a rock with six feet of water over it all but blocked the passage. Eventually a way past was found and the two vessels ran through the tortuous passage without molestation and out into Lumpar Bay where they anchored one and a half miles from the forts. The boats were sent away to sound the anchorage, during which task they went within 2,000 yards of the forts of Bomarsund but never a shot was fired.

Next day the two vessels retreated through the Ango Passage and worked northwards from Toftö for some days in foul weather in an attempt to find the approach channel to Bomarsund from the north. After much boat sounding a navigable passage was found between South Grano island and the mainland, two and a half miles north of the forts.

By 10th June Sulivan was back with the fleet at Hango. Napier was delighted with his report and agreed with Sulivan that troops would be needed for a successful attack on Bomarsund. Accordingly a report requesting troops was sent home to the Admiralty.

Whilst awaiting the arrival of the troops the fleet made a reconnaissance in force to within eight miles of Kronstadt, whence Sulivan was sent on in *Lightning* with three other small steamers to reconnoitre. He anchored within 3,000 yards of the fortifications on the south, within three miles on the north and paid three visits to an abandoned lighthouse six miles west of Kronstadt, from the summit of which he was able to sketch the fortifications and eighteen ships of the line within. Some of these were moored head and stern so that their guns covered the channel from the only gap in a continuous line of fortifications. The place was well-nigh impregnable. The only Russian vessel taken during the war was a crude model of a brig left by the lighthouse-keeper which Sulivan took for his sons.

News was now received that British and French troops had arrived in the Baltic and the operations against Bomarsund began. On 28th July little *Lightning* confidently led Rear Admiral Chads' squadron of five sixty-gun screw vessels through the tortuous Ango Passage, Commander Otter, the surveyor in *Alban*, shepherding from astern. Once safely through, Admiral Chads anchored his vessels in Lumpar Bay as Sulivan had proposed, whilst he and Otter went to find the southern landing beach for the troops.

The next three days were spent by *Lightning* taking the British and French masters through the intricate channels so that they could pilot in the steamers. Finally *Lightning* was used to conduct the Commander-in-Chief and both Army Commanders to the south and north landing beaches and, with the arrival of the troops, the scene was set.

On 8th August Admiral Plumridge's squadron, guided in by *Lightning*, landed 700 seamen and marines, 70 sappers and 2,000 French marines on the north beach; whilst the French steamers, guided by Otter in *Alban*, landed 10,000 men on the southern beach. Both landing forces had artillery which was taken inland and used successfully to reduce the western outpost, Fort Tzee, and then to bombard the main fortifications from the west, whilst Admiral Chads bombarded from the bay to the southeast. Thus ringed with fire the Russian Commander surrendered on the evening of 15th August. So ended a copy-book combined operation largely planned, and certainly made possible, by the surveyors, and the only really successful action in the whole Baltic campaign.

Once the ice had sealed the Russian fleet in the Gulf of Finland the allied fleets dispersed to return in the spring of 1855. By then Sulivan had acquired a new paddler, *Merlin*, and as soon as the ice was clear he was making a reconnaissance of Kronstadt. Once again he was at the summit of the lighthouse, which had been thoughtfully scrubbed out and refurbished in his absence. He found that the Russians had not been idle in other directions; new

H.M. Surveying Ship *Lightning* (Captain, J. B. Sullivan) leading a squadron of Royal Navy screw vessels through the Ango Channel to attack Bomarsund, 1854. By O. W. Brierly, R.A.

defences had been thrown up on the island to the west to prevent landings; new gunboats were in evidence; obstructions were being laid in the sea on the formerly undefended north side; and, as *Merlin* was shortly to find out, infernal machines were moored beneath the surface of the surrounding waters. The gilded steeples of Kronstadt gleamed confidently in the evening sun, which aided Sulivan's visibility to such an extent that he could discern the golden dome of St. Isaac's Cathedral and the needle spires of the Admiralty, inviolate as ever in the heart of St. Petersburg on the banks of the Neva far to the eastward.

Rear-Admiral the Hon. Richard Dundas, who had relieved Napier as British Commander-in-Chief, was more approachable than his predecessor and Sulivan persuaded him that the best chance of a success in the Baltic lay in an attack on Sweaborg, now that British and French mortar boats were available. Sulivan had visited Sweaborg twice in 1854 with the flag of truce exchanging prisoners, and had kept his eyes open and during the first four days and nights of August he now carried out an intensive survey of the area.

The plan of attack, which commenced on 9th August, was almost entirely Sulivan's, and the execution so successful that the great arsenal of Sweaborg was almost completely destroyed by bombardment and the resulting fires by the time action was broken off on the morning of 11th August. The success lay in the most careful placing of the mortar boats in a crescent seaward of a group of offshore islets, every boat being exactly 3,300 yards from her target, with the mortars loaded and elevated so that their first and every succeeding shot fell accurately upon their selected targets.

To create a diversion and draw the enemy's fire to targets less vulnerable than the moored mortar boats which they now screened, all the gunboats of both fleets bombarded the fortifications whilst under way in preselected and carefully buoyed areas among the islets.

This necessitated a chart, true to scale and well triangulated, and showing every islet, rock and submerged shoal. Carried out in four days, in the very face of an enemy who was occupying much of the area, this survey of Sulivan's is a brilliant example of the type of work Belcher had envisaged in his textbook twenty years before.

The Master in *Merlin* was Richard Dyer and we can get an insight into life with Sulivan during the second year of the Baltic campaign from letters written by Dyer many years later:

> 'Being a surveying-ship, the men had many advantages, and were not at all of the ordinary man-of-war type. Everything went on smoothly and without friction of any sort. Discipline was maintained strictly and firmly, and there was a remarkable absence of crime and punishment. The utmost attention was paid to the comfort and well-being of the men in every detail, the result being that our Captain was universally beloved and respected. When surveying coasts I was always struck with his profound knowledge and the rapid conclusions he arrived at. Indeed, it was a common remark amongst his officers that he had an instinctive knowledge of the bottom. He always knew where to place buoys and beacons long before those around him had completed their calculations. As a pioneer on a coast in time of war he had no equal . . .'

Halfway through the Russian war in January 1855 Beaufort was finally permitted to retire and hand over to Captain Washington. The selection of this officer to be Hydrographer of the Navy did not pass without comment by surveyors with much overseas service, and many of them, employed as they were in distant parts of the globe, would have used Belcher's term to describe Washington as a member of 'the feather bed crew about Charing Cross'. Washington's service in surveying had neither been as long nor as distinguished, they believed, as that of many who had toiled for Beaufort.

He had shown his enterprise when first promoted Lieutenant in 1821 by returning to England from Valparaiso by his own route. He rode over the Andes to Mendoza by a track later followed by Darwin, and then on across the Pampas to Buenos Aires. He became Secretary of the Royal Geographical Society in 1836, but he did not get his first surveying appointment until, as a Commander, he took over the paddler *Shearwater* in 1841 from Captain Hewett, posted to the ill-fated *Fairy*.

After four years in the paddler *Blazer*, when he extended Hewett's work in the North Sea, he went to the Hydrographic Office in 1847 and served in the Railway & Harbour Department. In connection with the establishment of a new form of lifeboat, a subject in which he was intensely interested, Washington visited Russia, Sweden and Denmark in 1853. Their Lordships instructed him that whilst on this mission he should collect intelligence on the Russian Navy.

He succeeded in seeing every ship of the Baltic fleet, including a division at sea, a sight never repeated during the Baltic campaigns. He also got a close look at the fortifications at Kronstadt, Sweaborg and Bomarsund, and collected copies of Russian charts with which the British and French squadrons were subsequently provided by the Hydrographer.

Thus, although he lacked wide experience of surveying overseas, in the midst of a war with Russia he was a good choice for Hydrographer.

Turning from the wars, Washington directed his efforts to increasing the publication and sale of charts. Under Beaufort every chart was scrutinised and checked by the Chief before final printing and publication; this practice, in some ways admirable, created a bottleneck resulting in much unpublished data remaining in the archives of the Hydrographic Office. The time had come for decentralisation, yet Washington believed that every chart should be subjected to careful scrutiny by the seaman's eye, so that he had to look to his naval assistants to perform this duty; the capable Captain Becher was the Chief Naval Assistant throughout Washington's tour of Office, and by 1862 there were five junior naval assistants.

With F. Higgins, a draughtsman, retiring in 1855 and Michael Walker, Assistant Hydrographer, in 1861 after fifty-five and fifty-two years respectively, the old order in the draughtsmen's office was changing. Captain George Bedford took over as Assistant Hydrographer; he was a man of wide experience having commenced his surveying career on joining the Navy in 1823 with George Thomas in the old *Investigator*.

The engraving of the copper printing plates had long been done by contract, and now the printing of the charts themselves was taken over by Messrs. Malby & Sons. Only the compilation of the charts on paper in preparation for transference to copper by the engraver was performed by the six draughtsmen in the Hydrographic Office, the first proofs struck from the copper being finally checked by a naval assistant.

Fifty-six sub-agents under Potter of the Minories were selling the Admiralty chart at home and abroad; whilst sales overseas were increasing the position was not satisfactory at home, where many British shipping masters were still using privately published charts although these were generally more expensive than their Admiralty counterparts; for instance James Imray & Sons listed 132 such charts in 1856. Washington discussed this situation with Sulivan who had taken over from Beechey as the professional officer at the Board of Trade.

A circular letter from the Hydrographer to all chart agents resulted, calling for a better service to seamen. Important points made were that charts were to be sold at the prices engraved upon them; that agents would be given a 33⅓% discount to offset the cost of employing a competent person to keep the stock of charts corrected by Admiralty Notices to Mariners; these, giving details of new dangers, changes of buoys and lights etc., and the numbers of the Admiralty charts to be corrected, would be regularly supplied to the agent.

Washington's efforts in reorganising the office and encouraging the agents had substantial results which mark his particular contribution. The Admiralty were listing 2,500 charts for sale in their catalogue in 1864, showing an increase of over 500 since Washington took office in 1855, whilst sales through the agents were about 75,000 bringing in £5,000 or more; the Navy were using about another 50,000 charts annually.

To maintain this increase in publication it was necessary to increase the number of surveys, and despite having to revert once again to hired boats, Washington had more surveys in hand at one time than any other Hydrographer before or since. Eight Captains, seven Commanders and nine Masters were in charge of surveys at home and abroad.

Captain Bayfield, after twenty-five years, completed his great work in charting the River and Gulf of St. Lawrence; Captain Richards was in British Columbia, where he joined the United States Commissioners in defining the boundary with the United States in those intricate waters; Denham was in the Fijis; extensive surveys were under way in China and a commencement had been made in Japan; Captain Bate, who had surveyed extensively off the Chinese coast since taking part in the China campaign of 1842, was killed at the second capture of Canton in 1857; surveys were also going forward on the coasts of Australia and New Zealand. To add to all this, with the taking over of the East India Company's responsibilities by the Crown in 1861, the survey work formerly directed by their Hydrographer John Walker became the task of the Admiralty Hydrographer, and here there was much leeway to be made up.

The Royal Navy had paid little attention to the deep oceans beyond the continental shelves except to search for detached shoals far out in the oceans, known as 'vigias', which were frequently reported but seldom found when searched for. Under the influence of Maury, the United States naval survey had been developing a technique for deeper sounding using a small engine to recover the line and a 'lead' formed of a hollow metal tube carried to the depths by weights which were automatically released when striking the seabed. The tube was forced into the ooze, a simple flap valve retaining the sample when hauled back to the surface.

Several long voyages by the U.S.S. *Dolphin* using such equipment enabled Maury to construct the first bathymetric chart of the North Atlantic, which was available to Washington soon after taking over as Hydrographer. The urgency to add to these comparatively scanty soundings was almost at once apparent with the emergence of proposals on both sides of the Atlantic to join the two continents by a seabed cable for the transmission and receipt of telegraphic signals.

Washington selected Lieutenant Joseph Dayman to sound out a line from the West Coast of Ireland to Newfoundland using the paddler *Cyclops*, whilst in the following two years two more lines were explored by Dayman, now a Commander, in the paddlers

Gorgon and *Firebrand*. A more devious route via the Faroe Islands, Iceland, Greenland and Labrador was followed by Captain Sir Leopold M'CLintock, a veteran of four Arctic expeditions, in *Bulldog*, who took with him Dr. Wallich who examined the seabed samples collected with a modified form of the lead used by the Americans. Hempen line was used in these vessels and a Massey's sounding machine was attached close above the lead to record the depth. Such machines recorded distances lowered by the revolutions of a propellor rotated by its fall through the water and automatically locked for the ascent. The deepest sounding recorded was about 2,000 fathoms.

Two abortive attempts were made to lay the transatlantic cable in Washington's time, but it fell to his successor to give the greatest assistance in the opening up of the world's telegraphic communications.

Washington early turned his attention to the Compass Department and Observatory at Woolwich for he considered it of major importance 'now that steamers dash along at ten to twelve miles an hour'. He appointed Evans, still a Master and recently back from helping Sulivan in the Baltic, as the Superintendent, a post he was to hold with distinction until 1874.

The rank of Master was one to which Washington gave much thought. For nearly 200 years these specially entered officers had been the navigators and pilots of the Fleet, and only an occasional one who became 'Master of the Fleet' could achieve Commander's rank. The majority, like poor old George Thomas, soldiered on for their whole lives with no hope of promotion.

Except in surveying ships, other officers onboard men-of-war, including the Captain, paid little attention to navigational matters; there were even cases where a Captain failed to take his ship to sea as his Master was onshore.

In the Baltic Sulivan had found that the situation was almost impossible, for the Masters had no experience in such complex waters and, until the Commander-in-Chief began to rely on the surveyors, the fleet never moved without a flock of unreliable local pilots.

There were no Masters in small paddlers under the command

of young Lieutenants and the latter soon showed that after a few hair-raising days and nights they had become competent in pilotage and bold in ship handling. The general abolition of Masters would make every officer in the Fleet a navigator, said Sulivan, and Washington largely agreed.

These views, widely expressed, were popular neither with Masters, nor with executive officers. Washington served on a committee in 1862 where his opinions were overruled, but a year later his proposals were adopted and a gradual move was made towards the complete abolition of the rank. Masters with fifteen years service were promoted to Staff Commanders with an avenue open to Staff Captain; whilst three years later all Masters under fifteen years seniority were made navigating Lieutenants and gradually the special entry declined and suitable executive officers moved into the specialisation of 'Lieutenant N' which thus superseded the 'Master' for ever.

As many Masters had been employed in surveying ships it was inevitable that a number of Staff Captains and Staff Commanders lingered on in the surveying service to the end of the century. Evans was the only Master to rise through these ranks to become Hydrographer.

Washington was of a nervous and sensitive nature and he felt deeply the unpopularity he gained within the service as a result of these measures. Thus it was unfortunate that about this time three accidents at sea occurred in quick succession, each of which was attributed to the Admiralty chart—a course that many navigators have adopted over the years, sometimes with but often without good cause.

H.M.S. *Bacchante* grounded in Esquimalt Harbour on a rock which had been missed in the survey. The merchantman *Genevieve* struck in the approaches to Otago on the South Island of New Zealand, the Master claiming before a board of enquiry in Mauritius that no channel existed as shown on the chart. The Hydrographer admitted an error in the first instance, but in the second it was clearly an excuse for a navigational error.

However, it was the great loss of life and the questions in the House of Commons, which resulted when H.M. cruiser *Orpheus* was lost in New Zealand, that brought Washington to the depths of depression.

It happened on the Manukau Bar off the west coast of the North Island. Here the sand spits at either side of the river mouth curve out in two great arms meeting to form a shallow bar five miles out in the Tasman Sea. Today it is one of the most treacherous resurveys the New Zealand Navy has to tackle; the launches often come near to broaching to as the great swells sweep stealthily in to form crashing breakers on the bar. The distant leading marks ashore, resited after every survey, are difficult to see when approaching; in those days local knowledge was conveyed by signals made to the incoming vessel from the shore.

An enquiry revealed that *Orpheus* had onboard a notice describing the leading marks as unreliable; and that the local signals were badly made to her from the shore. The chart may have given the wrong position for the deepest part of the bar, but no chart of Manukau will ever be correct for long; the first great storm, and there are many in the Tasman Sea, will change overnight the positions of the sand bars so carefully and dangerously surveyed.

Washington went into a decline, and leaving for Le Havre to be away from all these troubles for a while, he left faithful Becher in charge. He died there, a Rear-Admiral, in 1863, a victim of overwork and criticism which a more robust character might have withstood. Such a man had now to be found.

CHAPTER NINETEEN

The Antipodes

It was during Washington's period in office that a series of agreements was drawn up with the Australian colonies, whereby they provided boats and crews for use by officers lent from the Royal Navy to chart the coasts and shoal waters in the approaches to the rapidly developing townships, communication with which was seriously hampered by the frequency of shipwreck.

Before examining these important agreements it will be well to go back and trace the progress of sea surveying in the Antipodes since Captain P. P. King returned from Australia in 1823, after six years' work in the little cutter *Mermaid* and the sloop *Bathurst*. He had done much to close the gap left by Flinders on the Northwest Coast.

It was King's discovery of the excellent harbour of Port Essington in the Northwest that resulted in two attempts to form a settlement there. An unsuccessful venture during the years 1824 to 1829 was followed nine years later, in 1838, in the official establishment of a settlement at that place: troops were taken there from Sydney in H.M.S. *Alligator* (Captain Sir Gordon Bremer), and H.M.S. *Britomart*, a brig commanded by Lieutenant Owen Stanley, eldest son of the Bishop of Norwich. Although *Britomart* was not a survey vessel Owen Stanley did carry out some surveying in the Arafura Sea. He was a surveyor of wide experience, having served in *Adventure* in South America under Captain P. P. King, in the Mediterranean in *Mastiff* with Graves and in 1836–37 he had sailed with Captain George Back to the Arctic in *Terror*.

By this time thriving townships had developed at Melbourne on the Yarra River at the head of Port Phillip, at both Hobart and Launceston on the Tasmanian rivers, at Adelaide in St. Vincent Gulf, at Albany in King George Sound and on the Swan River in Western Australia. Captain King had, on retirement after his Magellan Strait surveys, come out to take over from Sir Edward Parry, the former Hydrographer, as Manager of the Australian Agricultural Company, and lived at their settlement at Port Stephens on the east coast of New South Wales.

Only Northern Australia had in no way been settled and this was now considered desirable. Port Essington lay on the southern flank of the sea route now developing between Sydney and British Indian possessions, including Singapore. Shipwrecks in Torres Strait were frequent and the islanders were enthusiastic wreckers so that a settlement at Port Essington would act as a refuge for shipwrecked mariners, although many would have preferred Cape York as the site on this count.

These developments had convinced Beaufort that it was time for more detailed surveys of the Australian coast and that the days of the running survey were over. He turned his attention to the Northwest Coast, and the Gulf of Carpentaria, both so little known, and to the Bass Strait, where ships were frequently cast away through a lack of knowledge of its many hidden and undiscovered dangers.

To take up these tasks *Beagle*, newly returned from her world voyage, was chosen, many of her officers and men electing to remain in her. John Wickham, the First Lieutenant, took over command from FitzRoy when the ship re-commissioned at Woolwich, whilst Lieutenant John Lort Stokes became the senior assistant surveyor, and Surgeon Bynoe, who had learnt much from Darwin, was well suited to make the natural history collections.

Wickham's instructions urged upon him the necessity of 'proceeding from the known to the unknown', for which purpose he carried the charts of Dampier, Flinders and King. Australia is a continent of few notable rivers and as such waterways are the keys to the development of the hinterland special importance was attached to their discovery.

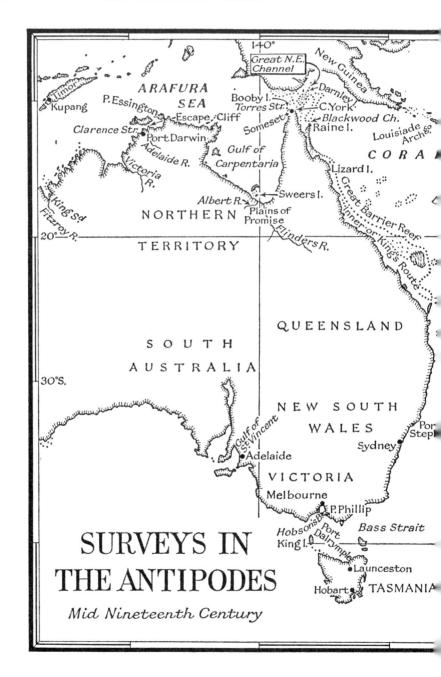

140°

Great N.E. Channel

New Guinea

ARAFURA SEA

Timor

Kupang

P.Essington

Clarence Str.

Escape Cliff

Booby I.
Torres Str.
Someset

Darnley
C.York
Blackwood Ch.
Raine I.

Louisiade Archo

CORA

Port Darwin

Adelaide R.

Victoria R.

Gulf of Carpentaria

Lizard I.

King Sd

Fitzroy R.

Albert R.
Plains of Promise

Sweers I.

Great Barrier Reef

Inner or King's Route

NORTHERN

Flinders R.

20°

TERRITORY

QUEENSLAND

SOUTH

AUSTRALIA

30°S.

NEW SOUTH

WALES

Por
Step

Gulf of St.Vincent

Sydney

Adelaide

VICTORIA

Melbourne

P.Phillip

Hobsons B.
Port Dalrymple
King I.

Bass Strait

Launceston

Hobart
TASMANIA

SURVEYS IN
THE ANTIPODES

Mid Nineteenth Century

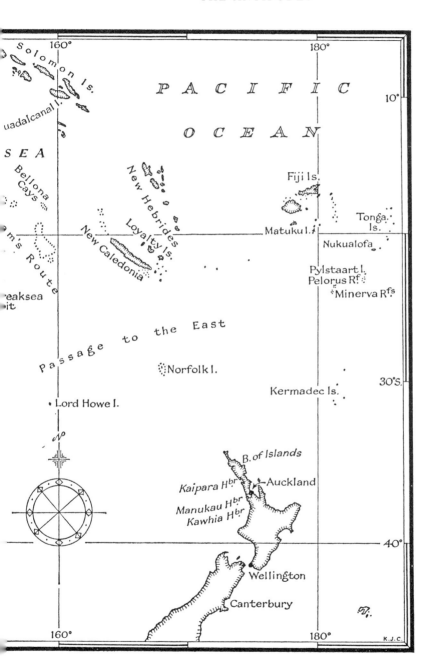

Beagle reached the Swan River settlement by the end of the year 1837 and sailed in the New Year for the Northwest Coast to return five months later, having surveyed 300 miles of coastline and penetrated ninety miles up a river which Wickham was pleased to name FitzRoy after his old Commander. It was, like so many Australian rivers, disappointing, deteriorating after many shallow reaches into a series of stagnant pools awaiting the infrequent rains.

Everywhere ashore the mosquitoes and flies had been very troublesome and it was noticed that the few aborigines the surveyors encountered kept their eyes almost closed to avoid the flies and when in conversation held their heads well back so that they might see the person addressing them. This peculiar attitude of the head had been noticed 200 years before by Dampier when he visited and named 'Roebuck Bay' after his ill-found vessel.

Wickham had taken with him from the Swan River a native named Miago as interpreter, but he proved quite unable to converse with his fellow black men only a few hundred miles from his home; this proliferation of languages was found to be a feature of almost all the aboriginal tribes around the coasts of Australia.

Miago's desire was to steal one of the native gins (women), a feat of prowess which, unlike the language, was common to every native in Australia when encountering another tribe. Miago's bravery, however, evaporated when faced with a group of spear-wielding blacks with whom he had no word in common.

Wickham now moved to the Bass Strait survey, calling at Hobart in Tasmania for discussions with the Governor, Sir John Franklin.

As might be expected Franklin had not been idle regarding the navigation of the Derwent River, where Hobart stood, or the dangerous D'Entrecasteaux Channel forming the approach. He had obtained the services of Lieutenant Burnett, appointed marine surveyor to the Colony by the Admiralty. Burnett was working in the D'Entrecasteaux Channel when his boat was capsized by a sudden gust of wind, so prevalent hereabouts, and he lost his life. A fine lighthouse on Bruny Island which guided *Beagle* into the channel remained his monument.

Franklin was, of course, always interested in any surveying expedition, whilst his hospitality and that of Lady Franklin was well known. There were opportunities for ample sport in this rapidly growing settlement. Stokes and other officers were mounted for a day with Mr. Gregson's hounds and Stokes reported as follows:

'A thoroughly English appreciation of all that provided sport, led a large party of us to join the meet, at a place called "The Neck". The turnout was by no means despicable: the hounds were well bred, though rather small—perhaps an advantage in the sort of country over which their work lies. A tolerable muster of red coats gave life and animation to the scene, and forcibly remined us of a coverside at home.

'The hounds found a large kangaroo almost immediately upon throwing off and went away with him in good earnest. There was a burning scent, and from the nature of the country, over which we went for some distance without a check, the riding was really desperate.'

The first step in the Bass Strait survey was the setting up of an observation spot inside Port Phillip at Hobson Bay to which all subsequent positions fixed in the Strait were to be connected. The coast to the westwards was surveyed before crossing the Strait via King Island to the north coast of Tasmania; this part of the survey terminated at Port Dalrymple on the Tamar River and the ship then ran a meridian distance back to the observation spot in Hobson Bay.

After Christmas a triangulation was carried up the Yarra River to the flourishing town of Melbourne and Stokes rode out to Flinders' Station Peak, which overlooks the whole of Port Phillip, so that all *Beagle's* work might be connected by theodolite angles with that of Flinders.

In early March, with a strong southwester astern, *Beagle* left the stormy area of 'the funnel', as Bass Strait was locally known, and arrived in Sydney to draw charts and prepare for the northern cruise to the new settlement at Port Essington.

Stokes found Sydney at this time the happy hunting ground of land jobbers, the prices of land rising so quickly that fortunes could be made, but he believed the labouring classes throve best: 'They can in tolerably prosperous times, earn sufficient in three of four days, to support themselves throughout the week. During the remainder of the time, the sober and industrious man employs himself in building a house; but I am sorry to say that the generality repair to the vast number of public houses that swarm on every side, and get drunk.'

The ship was away by the end of May 1839, but on encountering a strong and enduring gale it was decided to put into Port Stephens to take a new chronometric departure, as the chronometers had been severely shaken. It was also an opportunity for discussions with Captain King whose knowledge of the Australian coast was unique.

From Breaksea Spit the inner route inside the Great Barrier Reef was taken, then through Endeavour Strait and on to Port Essington, where Mr. Crawford Pasco of the *Britomart* met them in the approaches with a chart of Port Essington, newly constructed by Charles Tyers, Master of the *Alligator*. Pasco had been in the *Blonde* in South America and was known to many in *Beagle*, but owing to his suntanned features and flowing black locks, he was taken for a Malay and ordered to 'Leap up, Johnny'. Before *Beagle* left Port Essington Pasco joined her by exchanging with one of the mates.

A short voyage was made from Port Essington to Clarence Strait to the southwestward, which had been explored and named by King back in 1820 and was called after the Duke of Clarence when a sailor prince, before he became Lord High Admiral or King William IV. A fair-sized river flowing into the Strait, found and charted by *Beagle*, was named Adelaide after William's now-dowager queen. The river was found to be navigable for small vessels for about fifty miles.

Both green ants and Australian aborigines were troublesome during the expeditions onshore, and at Escape Cliffs took place an unusual occurrence when Mr. Lewis Fitzmaurice and Mr. Charles Keys literally danced for their lives. They had landed on the beach below some twenty-foot-high cliffs for magnetic observations, and had just set up their instruments when a stamping noise directed their attention to the cliff-top, where a large party of natives with

spears poised and quivering were champing on their beards, recognised as a sign of extreme excitement.

Fitzmaurice and Keys, facing the spearmen on the cliff, began
to dance and shout, which puzzled the natives who lowered their
spears and stared curiously; but whenever the dancers slowed their
pace, or attempted to reach towards their firearms on the beach,
the natives at once raised their weapons menacingly again. It
seemed to the dancers a very long time of great activity on their
part before the aborigines were distracted by the arrival of one of
the ship's boats, and they were able to relax their dancing and
recover their firearms. Desperate at the time, the incident caused
many a laugh in recollection onboard, and Fitzmaurice drew an
'eye-witness' sketch of the curious scene.

On return to Port Essington *Beagle's* officers and men were
happy to receive mails brought by H.M.S. *Pelorus* which had
arrived to relieve *Britomart* as guardship. With three H.M. Ships
in harbour Owen Stanley took the opportunity to mount his
long-awaited play which he had written in keeping with tradition
as an old Arctic explorer. The performance was much appreciated
in this extremely remote settlement.

In September 1839 *Beagle* returned to Clarence Strait where a
fine natural harbour was found, and named by popular consent
'Port Darwin' after the former shipmate who had been so well
respected onboard. To the inner harbour was given the name
'Bynoe Haven', after the ship's surgeon who had been now many
years in *Beagle,* and by his assiduous attention to the collection of
natural history specimens was carrying on the work that Darwin
had shown him how to do. Hundreds of bird skins, preserved by
Bynoe, were invaluable to John Gould, the English ornithologist,
in preparing the first great standard work on the birds of Australia.

Bynoe was in a unique position to study the marsupials of the
continent, and carefully examined between 200 and 300 wallabies.
In all this number he never found an embryo in the uterus, and
this fact, together with the discovery of a 'thin transparent tube'
apparently containing 'the rudiments of an animal' in one specimen he dissected, led him to believe that the young might pass
through the tube and 'become attached to the nipple in an inverted

state'. He was doubtless influenced by the colonists' theory that kangaroos were 'born on the nipple' and refused to envisage the possibility that a creature so small and helpless might make its way after birth to the mother's pouch and there firmly attach itself to her.

The Victoria River was next discovered. A gap in the high land noticed from seaward led Wickham to suspect a river mouth. Wickham and Stokes decided to explore and in Stokes' words:

> 'Our preparations were rapidly made, a few days provisions were stowed away in the boat, and as the western sky glowed red in the expiring light of day, the gig was running before a northwest breeze, for the chasm in the distant high land, bearing South 20 degrees East, twelve miles from the ship. As we advanced, the separations in the range became more marked and distinct, as long as the light served us, but presently darkness wrapped all in impenetrable mystery. Still we ran on keeping close to the eastern low land, and just as we found that the course we held no longer appeared to follow the direction of the channel, out burst the moon above the hills in all its glory, shedding a silvery stream of light upon the water, and revealing to our anxious eyes the long-looked for river, rippling and swelling, as it forced its way between high rocky ranges.
>
> 'As we ran in between the frowning heights, the lead gave a depth of eighteen and twenty fathoms, the velocity of the stream at the same time clearly shewing how large a body of water was pouring through. "This is indeed a noble river," burst from several lips at the same moment; "and worthy," continued I, "of being honoured with the name of her most gracious Majesty the Queen".'

Eventually *Beagle* was moored in Holdfast Reach, fifty miles from the sea where, on weighing a month later, she lost both anchors in the muddy riverbed. The boats penetrated 125 miles upstream and Stokes led a party on foot onwards for another week, following the line of pools and dividing river bars far into the interior. The heat was terrific and Stokes was fortunate not to lose two of his party who suffered heatstroke.

Some days after leaving the river Stokes was observing equal altitudes of the Sun on a beach below the cliffs; the morning observations went off without incident and he returned confidently for the afternoon observations. When landing he met Mr. Bynoe, returning from a day's specimen shooting, who assured Stokes that he had seen no trace of natives.

Stokes reached the station he had occupied in the morning, and turned to hustle on the two members of the boat's crew who were bringing the instruments. He was staggered by a violent and piercing blow. Before the spear had ceased to quiver in his side a savage shout revealed a party of spearmen on the cliff-top. As they scrambled down in pursuit of their prey, Stokes, desperately wounded in the lung and losing blood rapidly, stumbled towards his two companions. The boat, which had returned to the ship anchored nearby, was rapidly despatched by Pasco who had rushed from the chartroom on hearing the natives' howl of triumph. The arrival of the boat's crew on the beach halted the spearmen in their tracks within thirty yards of their victim. It was many weeks before the patient care of Bynoe resulted in Stokes' recovery, but to the end of his days he felt pain when actively employed.

Christmas 1840 found *Beagle* at Sydney, Stokes now fortunately fit to take over from Commander Wickham who, exhausted, was invalided home. The Gulf of Carpentaria was the first survey taken up by Commander Stokes in the New Year. He made for Sweer's Island and anchored in Investigator Road to visit the wells dug by Flinders forty years before; these were found marked by a tree with the word '*Investigator*' carved clearly on the bark. '*Beagle*' was added to the other side of the tree, and new wells were dug close by at Point Inscription.* This was yet another of the ever-growing number of observation spots around the shores of the great continent, each of which was fixed for latitude by observation, for longitude by chronometric traverse, and where the magnetic variation was

---

* In 1887 this tree was uprooted by a cyclone. Part of it on which some letters of the ships' names remained was retrieved and given to the Queensland Museum (see Bibliography—Marsden Horden).

measured, the times of high water at the Moon's full and change recorded, and the direction and speed of the tidal streams assessed.

Two notable rivers were found in the Gulf of Carpentaria: the first, near Investigator Road, Stokes named after Flinders, for, said he, 'monuments may crumble but a name endures as long as the world.' The second river, up which he was able to penetrate fifty miles by boat, Stokes named the 'Albert', as a companion to the Victoria River. Eventually shallow water and submerged tree trunks halted the boats, and Stokes proceeded a few miles further on foot, until gazing out on limitless and apparently fertile lands, he named them the 'Plains of Promise'.

After completing 200 miles of coastline in the Gulf of Carpentaria, Stokes sailed to Port Essington and round the continent westward, filling in many gaps as he went to Hobart. Here Franklin lent him the colonial cutter *Vansittart* which, with Charles Forsyth in command, assisted by Pasco, enabled the Bass Strait Survey to proceed more rapidly.

There were two accidents with guns whilst in the Gulf of Carpentaria, which, although small incidents in themselves, give an insight into the religious beliefs of the surveying officers of those days and the overriding importance attached to the work itself. Stokes' attitude in both cases is wholly typical and shows us two reasons why the surveyors overcame the endless difficulties with which they so frequently were faced. Lieutenant Gore, subsequently lost in the North with Franklin, was in the boat one day with Stokes exploring an inlet. White cockatoos swarmed in the tree-tops like snow and Gore decided to shoot some for the pot. With his first shot from the boat his gun exploded in his hand, cutting it terribly, whilst pieces of the weapon whizzed close past the ears of both Stokes and the coxswain who were, however, unharmed. 'Our preservation can only be attributed to Him whose eye is on all his creatures and who disposes of our lives as it seemeth good in his sight. Without intending to be presumptious we may be permitted to believe that we were spared partly on account of the service in which we were engaged—so beneficial to humanity, so calculated to promote the spread of civilisation, which must ever be the harbinger of Christianity. At any rate it is not, in my humble opinion, any impeachment of the wisdom of the Almighty, to imagine that he determines the fortunes of men according to the work in which they are engaged.' Stokes had no doubts about the value of his work to mankind.

The other accident occurred when Mr. Fitzmaurice had the misfortune, whilst with a detached party, to receive the accidental discharge of a gun in his ankle and was maimed for life. Stokes reported, 'Mr. Fitzmaurice had fortunately, before he was disabled, completed his examination of the coast between Flinders and Van Diemen's Inlet, with his usual praiseworthy activity.'

A visit during the Bass Strait work to Sydney for stores found orders for home awaiting *Beagle* and her reliefs arrived before she sailed to complete her work in 'the funnel'. These were the sloop *Fly* and the schooner *Bramble* as tender, with Captain Francis Blackwood in command of the expedition, their task being to delineate the outer edge of the Great Barrier Reef.

By reducing the scale of the survey, and employing *Vansittart* to the full, Stokes managed to complete the Bass Strait work to his satisfaction before leaving for home. The weather, as usual in this area, was difficult, but here, at least, the natives were not troublesome. The sealers, who had followed Flinders and Bass so quickly to the islands of the strait, had by now almost decimated the seal population, but they had lived on in their turf-covered houses in the sheltered bays of the islands. They earned a living collecting mutton birds and their downy feathers, both of which were marketable in Tasmania. The first generation of 'Straitsmen', as they called themselves, had abducted native wives from the mainland, and now a generation of wiry half castes thinly peopled the islands where they welcomed *Beagle's* men when they came to barter ships biscuits for scraggy sheep and stunted vegetables.

On 6th May 1843, *Beagle* sailed from the Swan River for Mauritius, the Cape and home, and as she reached the southeast trades she hastened onwards at eleven knots. Commander Stokes looked back over six years adventuring in Australia and eighteen years' continuous service in *Beagle*. For a ship of a class referred to by the General Service as 'coffins' the little brig had done the surveyors well.

Merchant vessels were now increasingly using the Torres Strait,
and during the northwest monsoon eastward passages were not
infrequently made. There was considerable controversy as to the
best route to follow from Sydney to Cape York. The inner route,
known generally as 'King's Route' after Captain King who had
surveyed it, had the advantage of calm water within the sheltering
barrier, but frequent coral patches necessitated nightly anchoring
which was unpopular in ships with small crews. Consequently
undermanned vessels preferred the outer route, but this, as Flinders
had pointed out years before, required a good knowledge of the
ship's latitude after many days at sea, often in overcast weather,
and also charts which showed with accuracy the known gaps for
passing through the reef. It was the outlining of this northern part
of the barrier reef and the location of the gaps that was Captain
Blackwood's particular task. If passages were located he was to
attempt to find channels leading westwards from them to Cape
York and to place a beacon on a reef near the most suitable
entrance so that it might be surely found from seaward.

On his way north from Sydney Blackwood entered the inner
route at Breaksea Spit and re-surveyed this route northwards on
a larger scale. On reaching Lizard Island he moved to the outer
edge of the barrier where he commenced his work in June 1843.
In two further surveying seasons Blackwood's little squadron
which, in addition to *Bramble* (commanded by Lieutenant Charles
Yule) included the ship's pinnace *Midge*—modified to operate
independently—and the colonial cutter *Prince George*, succeeded in
charting the outer edge of the Great Barrier Reef northwards to
the coast of New Guinea. From here they worked eastwards along
that unexplored coast for 140 miles. Further south an entrance
through the barrier was found near Raine Island, and the 'Blackwood Channel' was surveyed from there across to Cape York. He
next selected Bligh's Entrance in the Northeast as an alternative
channel and surveyed its whole length into Torres Strait. Today
it is known as the Great Northeast Channel.

To mark the entrance to Blackwood Channel, Blackwood
proposed that a permanent beacon be erected on Raine Island. In
January 1844 twenty picked convicts, mainly masons and quarrymen,

were embarked in *Prince George* at Sydney, together with a quantity of materials and tools for the building of the beacon on Raine Island, and the months of June to September were spent on the work.

Plans for a massive structure had been drawn up by Mr. Stephen Moore, the *Fly's* carpenter. The island, about half a mile long, was at no place more than twenty feet above high water; it was alive with young frigate birds and boobies and the whole place 'stank like a foul hen-roost'. The construction party, consisting of the convicts and seamen under Lieutenant John Ince, erected tents and portable wooden huts, soon to be crawling with bird-lice and ticks. The site for the beacon was at the eastern end of the island and here a quarry was opened for the extraction of coral rock, which was hewn into square blocks. The lime was procured by burning the large shells of the tridacna (or giant clam) found on the reef at low water, whilst wells were dug to obtain brackish water with which to slake the lime.

There being no anchorage near the island, *Fly* lay twelve miles to the southwest inside the outer barrier. *Bramble, Prince George* and *Midge* were busy ferrying provisions and stores from the ship, and fresh water from Sir Charles Hardy's Islands where two streams were dammed. It was necessary to cut much wood on the islands near the mainland for burning the lime. Beams of wood for the building were obtained from the wreck of the *Martha Ridgway* which lay on the reef some twenty-five miles south of *Fly's* anchorage.

The beacon was complete at the end of September, a circular stone tower 64 ft. above ground level and 74 ft. above low water and diameter 30 ft. It had three floors inside and was roofed by a dome-shaped frame of wood covered with canvas which drained into *Martha Ridgway's* water tank placed at the base of the tower. Coconut trees, pumpkins and maize were planted in a garden nearby so that the islet might serve not only as a guide but also as a refuge for the mariner. Towering above this lonely scene the white structure was impressive; its five-foot-thick walls remain to this day, and it is still in use by mariners.

With Blackwood sailed John Macgillivray, a zoologist employed by the Earl of Derby, whilst a geologist, Beete Jukes, was appointed to the expedition, together with an artist, Mr. Harden Melville.

During the four-year voyage of the *Fly* both Macgillivray and
Jukes collected thousands of specimens, many of which went to
the British Museum and to the Geological Society. Jukes particularly interested himself in the natives, and by developing a technique for befriending them he was often useful in keeping them
occupied whilst the surveyors got on with their work.

Jukes' practice was, on the approach of natives, ostentatiously
to lay down his gun, an armed sailor in the background covering
him meanwhile. Making welcoming gestures he would then dance
before them, and if his reception was friendly the gift of a red
nightcap, a knife or a handful of brown sugar established friendly
relations.

Even apparently friendly natives would suddenly become hostile
and a tragic case occurred on the mainland of Australia when,
sensing this change of attitude, Yule ordered his observing party
back to the boat. A seaman, Bayley, brought up the rear, a musket
under one arm and the artificial horizon under the other. Jukes
came on the scene just in time to see one of the aborigines take
aim from behind at Bayley with his spear. Jukes immediately
attempted to shoot him, but the gun, 'a rubbishing piece of Belgian
goods' that he had borrowed from Yule missed fire with both
barrels and Bayley fell. It proved impossible to remove the barbed
point and the seaman died onboard three days later.

On another occasion on Darnley Island Mr. Frederick Evans
had the unpleasant experience, whilst observing a meridian altitude with the artificial horizon, to feel the point of an arrow being
drawn across the back of his neck by a native of that island.

Jukes found the people of Darnley and Murray Islands, on the
Barrier to the east of Torres Strait, to be an entirely different race
from the aborigines of the Australian mainland. Whilst the
Australians at Cape York were thin-legged, spare and lanky, the
men on the islands were well-made, stout and muscular; whereas
the mainlanders' dark skins had been scarred and cicatriced, and
their centre front teeth had been removed, the men of the islands
bore no such primitive disfigurements; whilst the islanders lived in
large huts and cultivated produce which they were willing to
barter, the Australians lived in the open, had no gardens and were

uninterested in the Europeans' desire for trade. This difference in
the natives coincided with a contrast in the vegetation: on the
mainland there were but a few leafless gum trees and scrub, whilst
on the nearby islands there grew coconut palms, bamboos, plan-
tains and yams all utilised by the inhabitants, whom Jukes later
found to be similar in nearly every respect to the Papuans on the
mainland of New Guinea. Jukes' extensive observations on the
various natives encountered, illustrated by Melville, make his narrative of the *Fly's* cruise a significant contribution to the ethnog-
raphy of the regions visited.

The little squadron spent the lie-up period of 1844–45 at Sura-
baya, where they were hospitably received by the Dutch and the
local rajahs. *Prince George* went to Singapore where she delayed
her sailing hoping for the arrival of the English mail, but in vain,
which was a sad blow to officers and men of the squadron. 'I thus,'
wrote Jukes, 'was obliged to enter on the second twelvemonth
without news from friends at home, and it was more than half
expired before I received any. A year and a half without news
from home is a period which few persons are now compelled to
pass in this age of rapid transmission of intelligence.'

Fly made a passage to Singapore in mid-1845 with survivors
from two ships wrecked in Torres Strait, and at the end of that
year left Sydney for home. Meanwhile Lieutenant Yule continued
in *Bramble* the surveys of the south coast of New Guinea, assisted
by the small colonial schooner *Castlereagh*, which he managed to
obtain at Sydney, with Lieutenant David Aird in command.

Captain Blackwood was thirty-two when appointed to command
the expedition and *Fly* was the first surveying vessel in which he
had served; but he had a scientific bent and throughout his life
showed an interest in navigation, geography and astronomy. It is
apparent from the warm dedication to him in Jukes' account of
the voyage, and from references in the Preface and the text, that
he was sympathetic and congenial to the scientists and showed a
keen interest in their discoveries.

In mid-1847 the 500-ton frigate *Rattlesnake* arrived at Sydney,
with Captain Owen Stanley in command, to carry on the good
work of Blackwood. Like his predecessor he was a comparatively

young man, but unlike Blackwood he had extensive surveying experience. Owen Stanley's particular instructions were to continue the survey of the inner route northwards from Lizard Island, and then to examine in detail the channels of the Torres Strait. He was also to continue the work of *Bramble* on the south coast of New Guinea, including the Louisiade Archipelago running south-eastwards from the eastern tip of New Guinea. The surveying seasons 1848–49 and 1849–50 were spent in two extensive cruises to perform the work: the first cruise dealt with the northern portion of the inner route comprising an unbroken series of triangulation over 600 miles from Lizard Island to Cape York, whilst the second cruise began in the Louisiade Archipelago and worked westward along the coast of New Guinea to the Torres Strait, where no less than eight separate channels were surveyed on a comparatively large scale. In all this work Owen Stanley had the invaluable assistance of Yule in the *Bramble*.

Shortly after arriving in Sydney at the end of the second of these long cruises Owen Stanley died suddenly. He had shown increasingly obvious signs of weariness of the constant anxiety such work entailed, and the sudden news of the death of both his brother and his father seemed to add that feeling of complete depression that caused his tragic end. Lieutenant Yule took the ship home to England with a number of women onboard, including Owen Stanley's brother's widow and Mrs. Yule.

Owen Stanley's name is perpetuated in the great mountain range in New Guinea where, in the dense jungle, the battles of World War II were so desperately fought; whilst *Rattlesnake* herself is remembered for the part she played in setting one of Britain's greatest naturalists upon the road to success.

Sir John Richardson was still training surgeon naturalists at Haslar, and T. H. Huxley, showing promise, was appointed to a surveying ship. His commission in the *Rattlesnake* resulted in turning this young man's life from medicine to science.

However, on 10th December 1846, when the young assistant surgeon commenced his diary in Plymouth Sound, his thoughts were only on his modest natural history collecting programme which he so eagerly wished to commence: 'Thank God! Fitting out is at last over. We have no more caprices to fear but those of the wind—a small matter after having been exposed to those of the Admiralty.'

Macgillivray had come from *Fly* as the ship's naturalist, whereas Huxley engaged in scientific work when he could be spared by Dr. Thomson, the surgeon. Mr. O. W. Brierly, subsequently to become a war artist in the Baltic Campaign, was a guest of the Captain onboard and he left an interesting pictorial record of the commission, including a superb painting of the *Rattlesnake* and native craft entitled 'First Arrival of White Men amongst the Islands of the Louisiade Archipelago'.

Huxley, only twenty-two when the voyage began, was a highly sensitive young man with a very natural enthusiasm to get ashore in the many fascinating places visited by the ship, in order that he might collect specimens or study the natives. He was extremely critical in his diary of the cautious attitude of Owen Stanley, both towards the safety of his ship and the avoidance of any sort of affray with the Papuans.

'There lies before us a grand continent,' he wrote of New Guinea in his diary, 'shut out from intercourse with the civilised world—more completely than China, and as rich if not richer in things rare and strange. The wide and noble rivers open wide their mouths inviting us to enter. All that is required is coolness, judgement, perseverance, to reap a rich harvest of knowledge and perhaps of more material profit. I beg pardon, that is not all that is required; a little risk is also needful.'

After complaining of the infrequency with which ships' boats landed parties on the shore, and of the many days and nights spent rolling and pitching at sea in the *Rattlesnake* whilst *Bramble* searched for safe anchorage, Huxley concludes: 'If this is surveying, if this is the process of English discovery, God defend me from any such elaborate waste of time and opportunity.'

Anchorages were not easy to find in the Louisiade Archipelago, for they existed only within the reefs and the narrow entrances took a great deal of locating. Huxley's diary for 14th June 1849 gives a description of the finding of such an anchorage, near Peron Island, whilst Brierly illustrated the same occasion in two watercolours dedicated to Sir Francis Beaufort.

'A continuation of this reef stretches out a long way to the north westward so that we began almost to despair of finding shelter. However the *Bramble* coasted along, and finding a practicable looking break, about the middle of the day, stood off and on while Yule went in one of his boats to make a more minute examination. Between two and three o'clock a signal at the *Bramble's* mast had turned all eyes towards her and not without astonishment we read, "A practicable opening if you are not busy". What our being busy had to do with the matter was not so clear, but presently they found out their mistake and hoisted the proper flags which were to the effect that the opening was practicable but narrow.

'So we signalled to her to lead in and followed in her train. The opening is very narrow (a tenth of a mile nautical, about 200 yards), and it looks rather ticklish to see yourself passing within a stone's throw of roaring breakers on either hand, however loudly the leadsman may sing out his "Deep nine" or "By the mark fourteen".

'But we passed in without let or hindrance and now are safely at anchor within a huge harbour formed by several high islands on the one side while to windward the reef which we have had so much trouble to thread defends us as a natural breakwater.

'After we came to anchor, Captain Stanley signalised to Yule inviting him to dinner. The answer was "plunging". But as the Lieutenant came, he must doubtless have meant something else.'

Signalling has never been the surveyor's strongest suit!

Huxley's great interest during the voyage had been the capture and study of floating marine organisms, subsequently known as plankton; and these he had taken with a tow net made of flag bunting, the first record of a plankton-net being used in a British ship. He was interested in three great groups amongst the creatures he captured: first the tunicates which included sea squirts, pyrosoma (colonies of tunicates having luminescence) and salps; next molluscs, his particular interest here being the headed types

H. M. Surveying Ship *Rattlesnake* navigating a narrow passage through the reefs of Louisiade Archipelago, located by the tender *Bramble*, seen within, 1849. By O. W. Brierly, R.A.

such as cuttlefish, octopus and squids; and lastly coelenterates which embrace medusae, jelly-fish, men-of-war and siphonophora. He was the first worker to classify the types of zooplankton by their basic structures, however different they might appear at first sight, rather than by their similarities of habit and behaviour. He followed the single cycle of each animal he studied right through from one fertilisation to the next, and realised that an individual might be incorporated in a floating colony or live alone.

During the voyage he wrote a paper on the Anatomy of the Medusae which Captain Owen Stanley sent to his father the Bishop of Norwich, who communicated it to the Royal Society and it was published in the *Philosophical Transactions*. It was this paper which brought him to the notice of men of science, and the refusal of the Admiralty to publish his further work which led him to leave the Navy and enter wholeheartedly the exciting field of biology, now unfolding as a separate science.

He was elected a Fellow of the Royal Society at the extremely early age of twenty-five soon after returning from his voyage in *Rattlesnake*. He became in time a wholehearted supporter of Darwin, and did more than anyone else in the nineteenth century to bring the world of natural science to the attention of the layman.

In later life Huxley looked back upon the value to him of his years in *Rattlesnake*.

'Life on board Her Majesty's ships in those days was a very different affair from what it is now, and ours was exceptionally rough, as we were often many months without receiving letters or seeing any civilised people but ourselves. In exchange, we had the interest of being about the last voyagers, I suppose, to whom it could be possible to meet with people who knew nothing of firearms—as we did on the south coast of New Guinea—and of making acquaintance with a variety of interesting savage and semi-civilised people. But, apart from experience of this kind and the opportunities for scientific work, to me, personally, the cruise was extremely valuable. It was good for me to live under sharp discipline; to be down on the realities of existence by living on bare necessities:

to find how extremely well worth living life seemed to be when one woke from a night's rest on a soft plank, with the sky for a canopy, and cocoa and weevilly biscuit the sole prospect for breakfast; and more especially, to learn to work for the sake of what I got for myself out of it, even if all went to the bottom and I along with it.'

The growing colonisation of New Zealand in the early forties and the trouble between the colonists and the Maoris resulted in the first Maori War. A small British Naval squadron took part, and the need for new charts of the coasts of New Zealand was at once realised. The 1839 Admiralty Chart Catalogue lists 'Chart 1212— Island of New Zealand—Captain James Cook and subsequent navigators', together with eleven lesser charts. Now that there were sizeable settlements in the Bay of Islands, Auckland and Wellington, and with Otago and Canterbury about to be formed, it was time to make coastal approach sheets and plans of the sheltered anchorages along these windy shores.

Lort Stokes, now a Captain, was selected in 1847 for the work in New Zealand and given command of the five-gun paddle-sloop *Acheron*, the first surveying vessel with auxiliary power to be sent to Australasian waters, and of particular value in New Zealand where the prevalence of high winds is always prejudicial to surveying.

Stokes suffered a great personal loss on his way out to New Zealand when his wife, whom he had married in Australia whilst in *Beagle* in 1841, and who was accompanying him in *Acheron*, died at the Cape.

Commander George Richards was second Captain of *Acheron*, whilst her master was Mr. Frederick Evans, recently in *Fly*; thus two future Hydrographers assisted in the survey of New Zealand.

Acheron remained on the coast until 1851 when Captain Byron Drury, in his 400-ton brig *Pandora*, continued the work until its completion in 1856.

Pandora's surveys included the extremely dangerous bar harbours of the North Island, then more in use than they are today, such as Kaipara, Manukau, and Kawhia. Drury made the results of his work immediately available to navigators on the coast by giving detailed accounts of harbour entrances, anchorages, etc., in the *New Zealand Gazette*.

During World War II an Australian soldier clearing bomb debris in London found the diary of John Joliffe, *Pandora's* surgeon, which is now in the Mitchell Library. Joliffe had a good sense of humour and has many tales to tell, including an account of how he retrieved the surveyors' sextants as they floated away on the waves in their wooden boxes when *Pandora* was driven ashore in a gale. On another occasion he met a comely Maori girl on the shore who beckoned to him to follow her into the bush which he willingly consented to do, only to find at the end of a long walk that she wanted to sell him a large pig. The First Lieutenant also had an eye for the girls, so Joliffe told him of the smiling beauty on the beach but did not disclose her intention. Next day the First Lieutenant returned from a long walk in the thick bush, hot and exhausted and extremely annoyed with Joliffe.

Near panic ensued one night when, *Pandora* twisting and wrenching violently at her cable as a result of an earthquake tremor, many of the crew ran on deck to get the boats away, some shouting that the end of the world had come. But an old quartermaster calmed the excitement by pointing out that, if the end of the world had come, there would be nowhere for the boats to pull.

In 1851 came the Australian gold strike and the consequent rush, not only from England but also from California. This added greatly to the numbers of ships sailing between America and Australia and led to petitions being made to Her Majesty's Government to chart the eastern approaches to Australia, so encumbered with islands and reefs.

H.M.S. *Herald*, a vessel of the same class as the *Rattlesnake*, had just returned with Kellett from the eastern Pacific and was at once fitted out for Australia, whilst Beaufort selected a man of great experience, Captain H. M. Denham, to command. He reached Sydney in 1852 and with the paddle-steamer *Torch* as his tender, commanded by Lieutenant William Chimmo who had just spent six years in *Herald* surveying on the West Coast of America under the Command of Captain Kellett. The results cannot be better described than by the President of the Royal Geographical Society in his annual address in 1862, the year after Denham's eventual return to England at the end of a memorable nine-year commission.

'The region of *Herald's* special exploration very soon became suggestive of a distinct oceanic designation, and that of "Western Pacific" was adopted, implying that all that space embraced by the meridians 150° and 180° E. between the equator and 45° S.

'By determining the salient positions both of the islands and reefs belonging to the New Caledonia, Loyalty, New Hebrides, Fijian, and Tonga groups on the *north*, and also of Lord Howe, Norfolk, and Kermadec Islands, with the warning banks of soundings, which range about the parallel of 30° S., a clear passage is indicated of 300 miles wide for the first 1,600 miles directly eastward of Australia. On this track the harbour of Matuku (the southernmost island of Fiji) is of easy access; it is adapted for a coaling-station; while the chiefs and a Christianized population present every facility.

'Having mapped all that space embraced by New South Wales, New Zealand, Kermadec group, Tonga, Fiji, New Hebrides, and New Caledonia, so as to open up the first stage of communication between our Australian colonies and Western America, and having landed and established the Pitcairners at Norfolk Island, a detailed survey of the Fiji group was taken in hand, which however, had to be relinquished (when only its southwestern section had been delineated upon a three-inch scale), to meet the demand for a similar development of the Coral Sea as that which this expedition had wrought directly eastward of Australia; in the course of which Captain Denham traced the fate of Mr. Benjamin Boyd, of the R.Y.S. yacht *Wanderer*, and punished his murderer at Guadalcanal of the Solomon Group. The space to which Captain Denham's researches were then directed is bounded to the westward by the great barrier reef of Australia, and to the northeastward by New Caledonia, Solomon Islands, and the Louisiade range—the trends of which converge on Torres Strait. This coral sea, heretofore beset with vaguely charted dangers, and rendered the more perplexing by many *reported* reefs, caused sad disasters, which, however, did not deter voyagers, who looked upon a *northwestern* route to India as a great facility for ships of Tasmania, Melbourne, New Zealand, Sydney, and Queensland. In due course, however, this sea with its isolated reefs (coming adruptly awash, though with no soundings around), became mapped; and now presents a clear 1,200 mile route (free of current and within the steady southeast trades, of 150 miles width; a route which may be availed of upon three successive courses—viz. N by W. ¾ W. 240 miles, N.W. ½ W. 700 miles and W. ½ N. 220 miles—after crossing the parallel of 25° S., upon the meridian of 156° E., until sighting the (about to be lighted) Raine Island Tower in Torres Strait.

'This "Coral Sea" development indicated such postal and commercial benefits as suggested the compliment of designating it the "Denham Route"; for, by it, and through Torres Strait, steamers of one-half the size now employed round Cape Leeuwin, can make the passage to Singapore in smooth water in one-fifth less time. Nor is it restricted to western monsoons for shipping to get to the *southward* through the Coral Sea, as the *Herald* worked the passage against the southeastern monsoon and trade, in twenty-six days.

'. . . by October, 1860, she sailed homeward by Torres Strait, determining its middle passage, settling the position of its western dangers (Cook's Reefs, Proudfoot, etc.) and then proving that the parallel of Booby Island, 10° 36' S., is a clear track down the Arafura Sea, until abreast of Timor, when soundings jump so abruptly from 100 to 12 fathoms, as to demand a "good look-out" and to indicate a bottom adverse to submarine telegraphic connection of Australia by its northwestern Cape.'

The artist Glen Wilson sailed with Denham and has left us a fine pictorial record of the voyage, particularly of the Fiji Islands and

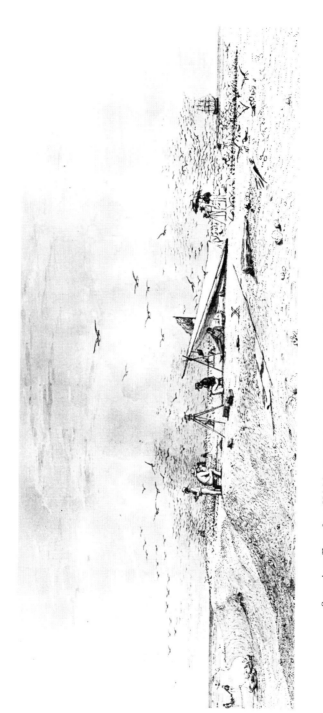

Surveying officers from H.M.S. *Herald* at work on Observatory Cay, Bellona Reefs, 1858. By Glen Wilson

of the beautiful sailing craft encountered there. Wilson's water-colour sketch of the *Herald*'s officers and men at work on South Bellona Cay shows a typical scene when charting a reef and its anchorage, which many of those flanking 'Denham's Route' so conveniently provided. We see an officer using the artificial hori-zon for his sights to fix the island's position; a party of men are preparing to measure a base across the cay; an officer is setting up his theodolite to observe the angle of a modest triangulation; left a party of sailors are catching turtles for fresh provisions; the ship lies at anchor in the distance, and in the shade of a sail set up as an awning we see someone resting from the hot sun; I like to think this is the Captain.

During several visits to Sydney Denham had sought interviews with Denison and FitzRoy, Governors of New South Wales, and had corresponded with the governments of Victoria and Tasmania in his efforts to bring about the colonial hydrographic agreements which the Hydrographer, Admiral Washington, wished to estab-lish. The names of the surveyors appointed by the Admiralty to each colony which was willing to provide boats and crews are given in detail by Geoffrey Ingleton in his book, *Charting a Conti-nent*, together with an account of the work each performed, but here there is space to list them only briefly with some remarks about their earlier surveying experience.

Commander Henry Cox, with two Masters and a draughtsman, was the first to arrive at Melbourne for the Victorian Survey. He had previously served with both Belcher and Vidal. He was suc-ceeded in 1866 by Lieutenant George Wilkinson who had served with Spratt in *Spitfire* during the Crimean War.

Lieutenant Edward Brooker was next to arrive in Tasmania in 1861 with a Master to assist him. He had been in *Rattlesnake* with Owen Stanley and also in *Spitfire* with Spratt. But once the survey of the principal part of Hobart was complete, and the chart published, the Tasmanian Government lost interest and Brooker was released to return to England.

Commander F. W. Sidney, previously employed surveying in many parts of the world, arrived in Sydney in 1861 with two Masters to assist him, John Gowlland and Francis Hixson. Gowlland took over from Sidney in 1868 when the latter's eyesight failed, and was drowned when his sounding boat overturned in a sudden squall in 1874.

Lieutenant John Hutchinson, who had served in *Herald* with both Kellett and Denham, was promoted Commander and with two Masters, Messrs. Frederick Howard and Michael Guy, was placed in charge of the South Australian Survey. He soon took over the survey of the 'Northern Territory' which was administered from Adelaide. Hutchinson died in 1869, the year in which a settlement at Port Darwin was finally decided upon. Howard carried on until 1880.

Hixson and Howard had also served in *Herald* in the South Pacific and had been happy to return to Australia where all three of the former Heralds married their former sweethearts.

The opening up of the sugar and cotton industries on the Queensland Coast called for increased surveying activity there, and Mr. James Jeffrey, a Master who had served with Belcher, and with Otter in Scotland, was assigned to the work. He was given much assistance by Commander George Nares in H.M.S. *Salamander*, more particularly in the further opening up of the inner route, which received new impetus when a coaling station was established at Somerset on the Queensland coast about five miles south east of Cape York.

These agreements between the Home Government and the Australian Colonies, which did so much towards opening up the continent, form an important stepping stone in hydrographic history. It was the first time that a colony had recognised its responsibility for charting its own shores, and this led in the twentieth century to the formation of independent hydrographic services in the Dominions, nearly all of which formed their surveying services as a part of their navies according to the British pattern by then so firmly established.

CHAPTER TWENTY

Richards and the Rise of Oceanography

There were three entirely eligible aspirants for the post of Hydrographer at the time of Rear-Admiral Washington's unexpected death in 1863; all have played a leading part in our story—Captains Lort Stokes, Thomas Spratt and George Richards, the youngest of whom, the last mentioned, was selected by the Admiralty. A brief review of his record shows that he was well suited to take over as Hydrographer. He had served twice for long periods with Belcher, remaining unscathed: in fact he was one of the few officers ever to receive praise from him. Belcher wrote as follows: 'He has at all times borne the character of an exemplary and steady officer, and is one of the few officers of the *Sulphur* of whom I can speak with unqualified praise, not only for his assiduity in surveying, but for his gallantry during the operations at Canton, and for his exemplary conduct when the other officers of the *Sulphur* were in a state of insubordinate alienation from their Captain.'

There is little doubt that Richards' presence in *Assistance*, as second-in-command during the search for Franklin, did much to ameliorate the difficult relationships which developed between Belcher and his subordinates.

Meanwhile, between these two voyages Richards had served as a Lieutenant with Sulivan in *Philomel*, where he was an assistant surveyor for the work in the Falkland Islands, and led the landing parties at the battle of Obligado. His service in New Zealand with Stokes was mentioned in the last chapter.

In 1856 Washington gave Richards his first command, the steam sloop *Plumper*, for surveys in British Columbia, where he remained until 1863. A more suitable vessel, the commodious paddle sloop *Hecate*, was sent out to Richards in 1859; in her he was on his way home at Sydney in 1863 when he received news that he had been appointed Hydrographer.

Until he arrived in England the post was occupied by Captain Becher, the Chief Naval Assistant, who retired when Richards took up his duties. Apart from two short spells at sea as First Lieutenant in *Fairy* in 1839 and in command of *Mastiff* in 1847–8 when he completed the survey of the Orkney Islands, Becher had served forty years in the Office where he had maintained continuity since Parry's day.

Before examining the developments at sea during Richards' term, it is intended to examine the organisation which had been developed in the office. Richards wrote, largely for his own benefit, a brief history of the department and set down details of the current arrangements in the office in 1868, about midway through his tenure of the post. By this time he had been successful in obtaining an increase in staff from the Board of Admiralty headed by Lord Somerset. Such an increase was clearly desirable for the decade 1860–70 marked a rapid extension of commerce in all parts of the world, with a resultant call for British Admiralty Charts which were so widely in use in ships of all nations.

The Hydrographer's Staff at that time was composed as follows: Staff Captain Frederick Evans, Assistant Hydrographer, also in charge of the Magnetic Department at Woolwich, daily becoming more important with the advent of Britain's iron navy. After him came five Naval and three Civil Assistants; a writer; a Naval Captain as Superintendent of Charts in charge of six Draughtsmen; and four Chart Packers who doubled as Office Messengers. Evans had, to assist him at Woolwich, a Naval Superintendent of Compasses and an Assistant.

Two of the Civil Assistants were in fact retired naval officers. The third was a civilian in charge of the payment of pilotage within the Fleet and of the arrangements for the examination of Navigating Officers in pilotage, a duty taken over from Trinity House by the Hydrographer in 1866.

The Hydrographer's, or 'Scientific' Vote, provided the funds for running the following establishments: the Hydrographic Office, the Royal Observatory at Greenwich, the Cape Observatory, the Nautical Almanac Office and the Surveying Service at sea. Broadly stated, the Hydrographer's responsibilities were to arrange for the execution of accurate surveys in all parts of the world visited by British men-of-war or merchant ships, and to publish such surveys in the form of charts. The associated publications such as Sailing Directions, Light Lists, and world-wide Tide Tables were prepared by the Hydrographic Office, and together with the Nautical Almanac, were published by the Stationery Office.

In addition Richards had introduced a new series of physical charts of the oceans which were of assistance in planning the voyages of vessels, for they showed graphically the prevailing winds, currents, temperatures and other predominant meteorological data.

The Walkers of Holborn having retired, the copper plates were now being engraved by a number of London firms, and the completed plates were stored at the Admiralty whence they were collected as required by Malby & Son, the printers.

It was the First Civil Assistant's duty to supply the chart boxes to the Fleet, whereas merchantmen were provided through the sub-agents of J. D. Potter of The Poultry, London, who was now the sole agent through which the Admiralty sold charts commercially. Potter was permitted to deal direct with Malby in the ordering of charts, the account being settled monthly.

With 2,500 charts now in the catalogue, and sales of approximately 100,000 annually, the problem of stocks was a considerable one. The Admiralty Chart, being regularly corrected by Notices to Mariners, cannot be sold unless it is kept up-to-date by hand, so that it is always a delicate matter to maintain a sufficient supply on the shelves to meet demands, and yet not to exceed the numbers which may be corrected by the small staff available.

There were four ships working abroad at this time. The advent of steamships had given a new importance to the narrow Magellan Strait, for such vessels took this route in preference to the exposed passage round the Horn. Here Captain Richard Mayne, who had served under Richards in *Plumper*, was making a modern survey in the screw sloop *Nassau*.

Staff Commander John Reed was in command of the screw sloop *Rifleman* delineating the reefs on the flanks of the main shipping route between Singapore and Hong Kong. The more sheltered yet longer route, the Palawan Passage, had been charted by Commander Bate in the brig *Royalist* some fifteen years earlier.

Trade was now open with Japan, and owing to the large number of accidents to foreign vessels occurring on that coast permission had been granted to the British to conduct surveys in the approaches to Japanese ports and in the Inland Sea. This work was being done by Commander Edward Brooker in the screw sloop *Sylvia*.

Commander George Nares was in command of the screw sloop *Newport* in the Eastern Mediterranean, an area of growing importance with the impending opening of the Suez Canal.

In addition to these vessels *Lightning* was carrying out the first of a series of scientific cruises in the Atlantic of which more will be told later.

The parties working on the Australian coast at this time have been described in the last chapter; there were also parties in hired ships or boats at the Cape of Good Hope, in the West Indies, in Newfoundland and British Columbia, also at home in the Channel Islands and at Portsmouth.

Such is a typical pattern of work in hand at any one time during the second half of the century.

In 1829 Lieutenant Thomas Waghorn, R.N., had opened across the Isthmus of Suez what became known as the 'Overland Route', organising the carriage of passengers and mails from Alexandria to Suez; ten years later the Peninsular Shipping Company added 'Oriental' to their title and operated two shipping services from Alexandria and Suez to coincide. In 1849 Captain Bate and Mr. Pasco went out by the Peninsular and Oriental Company ships to join the surveying brig *Royalist* in the Far East; Pasco gives a concise account of the journey through Egypt:

'We all became deck passengers from Alexandria, through the Mahmodel Canal and up the Nile to Cairo, where, after a few hours at Shephard's hotel, the first batch of three or four vehicles with passengers started soon after sunset for the desert and Suez. Two hours later the second batch started, which included our party, and a third two hours later, so that the same horses, after two hour's rest, went on again at the different stages. Luggage and loading of various descriptions came at the same time on camels, so that during the journey you might see sundry articles of your own on transit, but the owners had no trouble whatever about it. All that you might leave in your cabin at Alexandria, whether a portmanteau, a fiddle, or a tooth-brush, all would be found safe at Suez in due time.'

De Lesseps started digging his Canal in April 1859, with no help from England, whose rulers believed the scheme impracticable.

The Red Sea and the Mediterranean were joined by the Canal in March 1869 and Britain had to accept a *fait accompli*. Her steam merchant vessels soon formed the majority of those passing through the Suez Canal, but before permitting Royal Naval vessels or Indian troop transports to use the Canal the Government sent out Hydrographer Richards and the Director of Engineering and Architectural Works at the Admiralty, Colonel Clarke, to examine the Canal and report.

They joined the *Newport* at Alexandria in January 1870 and Captain Nares took them to Port Said, the new High-Light there being sighted twenty-five miles distant. The British Consul took them to see the Egyptian Governor and the French officials of the Canal Company. All drawings and documents were placed at their disposal and a French liaison officer was attached to them for the duration of their visit.

The plan was to transit the canal both ways in *Newport*, sounding continually and running contour sections across the Canal at intervals. A party was left at Port Said to survey the entrance, the construction of which had always been considered most delicate. The eastward drift of the current could be expected to carry silt from the never-ending supply of the Nile Delta to cause shoaling in the entrance to Port Said. To prevent this a long breakwater had been built out on the western side of the approach and *Newport's* survey showed that silt was accumulating against it and might build up to form a shoal beyond the breakwater. Richards saw no insuperable difficulty here: the breakwater could always be lengthened, a process that has in fact been repeated more than once since those days.

Parties, left at certain places along the Canal to measure the tides, were recovered on *Newport's* way north. They found the range of the tide varying from five or six feet at Suez to a few inches in the Bitter Lakes; the northern part of the Canal had no tidal rise, but a one-quarter-knot northerly current was measured.

The Canal was 88 miles long, 22 miles of it through the lakes. It was 325 ft. across with a central channel 26 ft. deep and 72 ft. wide. *Newport's* 52 traverses along the Canal revealed 4 or 5 weak spots only, where the depth was less than 26 ft., but at each of these dredgers were either at work or shortly to commence. There were five curves in the length of the Canal which Richards believed would be difficult to navigate, but these were being widened by the Canal Company.

There were a number of stations or 'gares' along the Canal where increased width and bollards on the banks permitted vessels to pass, or moor for the night. Telegraph stations were in course of construction at these points so that competent nautical officials would be able to regulate the movements of passing vessels.

As yet there were no buoys to mark the shallow sides of the Canal, but Richards was assured that these were under construction at Trieste, and were shortly to be laid along the 16-ft. depth-contour of the Canal at intervals of one-fifth of a mile throughout the entire length.

Richards and Clarke concluded that if the improvements being carried out were completed the Canal would be a safe route for naval vessels except the heavy iron-clads, only one of which was stationed in the Far East. Ships would save 5,000 miles and approximately thirty-six days on a passage from England to Point de Galle (Sri Lanka); but they would burn one third more coal for neither the Mediterranean nor the Red Sea were good sailing routes, whilst the Canal dues for a frigate would be approximately £350 with a further £50 for pilotage.

They did not recommend that the British troop transports to India should use the Canal, for the vessels were far too big and unwieldy. Troops should continue to be carried across Egypt by train as had been the practice for some years.

Nares made a further inspection in *Newport* in 1871 to see that progress with the improvements had been made, and subsequently he accompanied a small British Naval squadron through the Canal, proving it a satisfactory route for the Royal Navy.

In 1875 came Disraeli's dramatic purchase of Khedive Ismail's share in the Suez Canal, at a cost of nearly £4 million, which made Britain an equal partner with France in running the now flourishing enterprise.

The opening of this seaway had shown the necessity for modern surveys of the Gulf of Suez, the navigation of which was believed to be difficult. This work was done by Nares in *Newport*, thus giving the name to 'Newport Rock' and the lighthouse that now stands upon it to guide vessels into Suez Bay.

When Richards came to office in 1863 communications with India were being developed in another way, for Charles Bright (later Sir Charles) was laying a telegraphic cable to India through the Persian Gulf, the Mediterranean link to Alexandria from Malta having already been achieved.

In 1851 a successful telegraphic cable had been laid on the seabed between Dover and Calais, and, after four attempts, a cable was laid between Scotland and Ireland in depths down to 180 fathoms. Several cables from the Southeast of England to the Continent followed, experience showing that a knowledge of the nature as well as the depth of the sea-floor was required before laying the cable, so easily damaged on rocky ledges.

Thoughts turned towards the Atlantic and the possibility of spanning its narrowest width of 2,000 miles with a telegraphic cable. The Atlantic Telegraph Company was formed, with both British and American interests. Charles Bright was the leading representative from the British side whilst great public interest was taken in this 'feat of the century'.

As already narrated Washington had employed Dayman in the years 1857–59 in the paddlers *Cyclops, Gorgon* and *Firebrand*, obtaining deep-sea soundings along the Great Circle route from Ireland to Newfoundland. The depths averaged about 2,200 fathoms beyond the continental shelf; the soundings were taken with hemp line about every fifty miles along the route, each taking about six hours to complete. Dayman employed a modified form of the Brooke Sounder used by Berryman of the U.S. Navy, one large cylindrical weight being detached when the sampling tube reached the oozy seabed. The ocean-floor samples which Dayman brought home were examined by Huxley and proved to be largely composed of the calcarious remains of minute pelagic foraminifera (zooplankton), which had once lived near the surface of the sea and on death had sunk to form a grey, thick, oozy carpet on the seabed, apparently ideally suited to receive and protect a heavy cable.

The story of the laying of the first Atlantic cable from H.M.S. *Agamemnon* and U.S.S. *Niagara* is one of many disappointments and great determination, ending in success in 1858. Commencing in mid-Atlantic where the cable was spliced, both vessels steamed successfully, streaming their cables, to the two shore terminals, *Agamemnon* to Valentia in Ireland and *Niagara* to Trinity Bay, Newfoundland. The approach to both these terminals had been surveyed with the greatest care so that rocky outcrops might be avoided. Captain Otter, in *Porcupine* specially detached from his Scottish survey, was waiting in Bulls Arm, Trinity Bay, to guide *Niagara* in to the sheltered spot selected for the shore end of the cable.

As the shorter lengths of cable between Newfoundland and Canada had already been laid, communication was soon established between London and New York, Dayman and Otter being among those presented with gold watches by the Mayor of New York to mark the occasion.

The insulation of the deep-sea cable was not satisfactory, however, and within three months the signals weakened and gradually faded altogether. The great venture had showed that the engineering feat was possible, but that the electricians still had much to do before a satisfactory cable was manufactured for deep-sea work.

It took the British public a long time to recover from the disappointment of this failure, particularly those who were in a position to back the Atlantic Cable Company financially. It was not till 1862 that it began to look as if funds would be available for a new attempt and in that year the *Porcupine* was sent with Mr. Richard Hoskyn, Master, in command to re-examine the first 300 miles of the route from Ireland. He attempted to find a more gentle slope in a pronounced incline which had come to light whilst laying the previous cable, when soundings increased quite sharply from 550 to 1,750 fathoms.

Meanwhile the laying of other cables over shorter routes had provided the experience necessary to improve the insulation of the cable, which was being manufactured by the newly formed Telegraph Construction Company, who became the contractors for laying the new Atlantic cable in 1865.

By chartering Brunel's huge vessel, the *Great Eastern* of 22,500 tons, the whole 2,500 miles of cable for the Atlantic lay was embarked in the one ship, to which much improved paying out gear was fitted.

The laying of the cable in the summer of 1865 failed when two-thirds of the way across the Atlantic, and attempts to recover the broken end were unavailing, although much experience was gained. The effort was repeated in the summer of 1866, being completed successfully in fourteen days, after which *Great Eastern* grappled and recovered the broken end of the 1865 cable, when it too was put into operation.

The laying of cables in all parts of the world now gained tremendous impetus, and wherever British cables were laid naval surveying vessels under Richards' direction pioneered the way, sounding the route and examining the sea-floor.

When Richards retired in 1874 he became Managing Director of the Telegraph Construction and Maintenance Company which, during the twenty years he guided them, laid 76,000 miles of submarine cable.

Largely as a result of information gained in the laying of submarine cables there occurred during Richards' period of office a surge of interest in scientific exploration at sea, which he, as Hydrographer and a Fellow of the Royal Society, was able to assist materially.

At the same time as Hooker was dredging in southern waters with Ross in *Erebus* and *Terror*, Edward Forbes, a personal friend and guest of Graves onboard the *Beacon*, was dredging regularly in the Aegean during the years 1840–44. He concluded that there were various depth zones for each species of marine life and that beyond 300 fathoms there was an 'azoic' zone without life.

As a result of his work Forbes suggested that dredgings off the Hebrides and Shetlands, and between Shetlands and Faroes, would add much to our knowledge of deep-sea life, but it was not until Richards came to office that these proposals were realistically investigated, resulting in a series of remarkable cruises by Her Majesty's Surveying ships.

The first voyage was made in 1868 in the paddle steam vessel *Lightning*, under the command of Staff Commander David May, better known for his river surveys of the Niger made during Dr. Baikie's expeditions, and of the Rovuma River when associated with Dr. Livingstone. He now had two very different doctors to deal with, Wyville Thomson and William Carpenter, leading British naturalists, who successfully dredged down to 650 fathoms, and found many exciting things, life being abundantly represented by all the known invertebrate groups with many species as yet unknown. In addition, their deep-sea temperature observations disclosed two adjacent regions where the bottom temperature differed by 15° F., and led the scientists to believe that great water masses were moving in a submarine circulation as stupendous as that of the surface ocean currents which were already known.

In the following year Richards arranged for *Porcupine* to be available; similar to *Lightning*, she was manned by a hired crew, which had become the current practice for surveying ships on the Home Station. *Porcupine* was commanded by Staff Commander Edward Calver, who had for many years been in charge of surveys off the East Coast. Dr. Gwyn Jeffreys joined Thomson and Carpenter onboard for three cruises, to the west of Ireland, the Bay of Biscay and the Faroe Channel, the dredging technique being so much improved that bottom fauna were brought from depths of 2,000 fathoms.

Captain Nares came home in *Newport* in 1870, and he and his officers and men transferred to the screw sloop *Shearwater* to continue the survey of the Gulf of Suez. It was decided that on her way out *Shearwater* should be employed for a time in deep-temperature observations in the Strait of Gibraltar in an attempt to throw light upon the complex water circulation which was believed to exist in the region, surface water flowing into the Mediterranean at the same time as bottom water flowed out. Dr. Carpenter was onboard for this part of *Shearwater's* voyage where he enjoyed singular co-operation not only from the Captain but also from the Navigating Lieutenant Thomas Henry Tizard.

These exciting voyages had stimulated scientific interest, and a desire to explore more widely brought into being the Circumnavigation Committee of the Royal Society, whose object was the launching of a major expedition into all three of the world's great oceans.

Dredging some four or five miles deep, bringing water and sea-bed samples to the surface, and measuring the water temperature thousands of fathoms beneath the ship are difficult processes, even today, as most oceanographers will admit. Sometimes, after many hours, the equipment is recovered and it is found that some unsuspected mechanical malfunctioning has resulted in a fruitless waste of time. The experience gained, however, on the preliminary voyages in the small surveying ships had resulted in a fund of experience and a perfecting of equipment which made it possible, for the first time, to attempt the exploration of the greatest depths.

Once the Circumnavigation Committee had approached the Admiralty it became the Hydrographer's task to provide a suitable vessel for the voyage, to equip her for the work and to provide the best possible surveying officers, whilst the Royal Society nominated the scientists. All this was more difficult to arrange than may be imagined, for then, as now, there were those within and outside the Navy who saw no merit in employing vessels of the Fleet to explore the oceans, yet were ready to point to the success of other nations in this field.

Captain Nares and the officers of H.M.S. *Challenger* (c.1874).

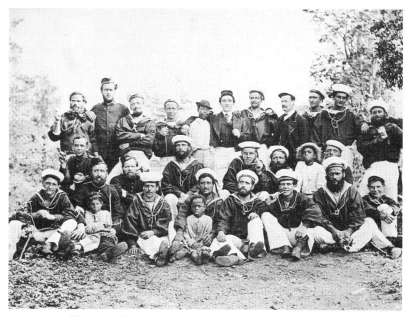

The crew of H.M.S. *Challenger* ashore in foreign parts (c.1874).

The vast amount of hemp rope required to be carried for deep dredging and sounding, the requirement for laboratories and for the storage of specimens, together with accommodation for the large number of seamen needed to operate the equipment rendered any of the small surveying ships then in service totally inadequate. A 2,300-ton naval corvette, *Challenger*, was eventually appropriated. She was 226 feet long, with thirty-foot beam; a 1,200 horse-power engine and huge screw provided auxiliary power, so necessary for keeping the vessel head to wind when using her deep-sea equipment.

Challenger's yards were reduced, her guns were landed and a large steam-winch of eighteen horse-power was fitted on deck, with an axle extending athwartships, a drum at either end. Hemp lines were used for sounding and dredging, being paid out from stowage reels on the forecastle, and recovered by being taken through leading blocks to both drums of the winch and backed by seamen hauling upon them. The sounding line was of 1 in. circumference and 6,000 fathoms long, the dredging lines were of 2, 2½ and 3 in. circumference, the three being spliced together to form a total length of 4,000 fathoms; spares were carried between decks.

With the vast weights entailed when hoisting the heavy equipment on thousands of fathoms of rope from the heaving deck of a ship it was necessary, if parting of the line was to be avoided, to devise apparatus to eliminate the ship's motion as far as the overside equipment was concerned. Large accumulators were used consisting of a number of rubber bands 3 ft. long and ¾ in. thick. These accumulators were secured from the lower yardarms, the sounding and dredging lines passing through blocks attached below the accumulators, which were capable of stretching to six times their length when strains came upon them.

The Baillie Sounder was now in use, a British modification of Brooke's apparatus. An adjustable number of ring weights placed around the sampling tube were held by a wire hoop until detached by contact with the seabed. This permitted easy recovery of the tube with its ooze sample held in by a flap valve in the lower end of the tube. The depth of the sounding was recorded by marks in the sounding line, the moment of striking the sea-bed still being noticed by the deceleration of the rate at which the line ran out.

For deep-sea work a beam trawl was used, similar to but smaller than those used by the fishermen off the English coast. To the line at various depths, and at the surface, were attached long conical nets made of muslin to capture pelagic animals and plants, an adaptation of the type of net first used by Huxley.

An important part of *Challenger's* work was the investigation of the water circulation at all depths, and for this it was necessary to recognise different water masses by their characteristics of temperature and salinity. The termperatures were obtained by lowering maximum and minimum thermometers in protected copper tubes, a type known as the Miller-Casella having proved itself sufficiently robust to withstand the great pressure involved. When hauled rapidly to the surface, after being kept at the required depth for about twenty minutes, good results were obtained which compare favourably with deep-sea temperatures taken in later years with the now well-known reversing thermometers.

For bringing water samples from the depths an ingenious apparatus developed by J. Y. Buchanan, *Challenger's* chemist, was employed. This consisted of a cylindrical brass tube or 'bottle' with stopcocks at either end which remained open as long as the bottle was being lowered; when hoisting began a flat 'tilting plate' attached to a vertical rod connected to both stopcocks was forced by water resistance to close the cocks and retain a sample of water.

To handle a large vessel at sea, when using all this equipment far below, presented novel and complex problems in seamanship, whilst ensuring the smooth working together of naval officers and scientists for over three years called for exceptional tact and leadership on the part of the Commander of the expedition. The post of navigator and senior surveying assistant was also an important one, for observations, however skilfully taken, are of little value unless the vessel's position is accurately and constantly determined by celestial sights, and the ship's courses and hourly log readings precisely recorded. Admiral Richards selected Captain Nares and Navigating Lieutenant Tizard, who had proved their ability for this type of work in *Shearwater*, in which they were still serving together in the Gulf of Suez. Both men subsequently served *Challenger* with the greatest distinction.

No less successful was the choice of scientists made by the Royal Society, the leader being Wyville Thomson, who had played an important part in the preliminary cruises, his personal assistant being a young geologist, also from Edinburgh, John Murray.

Challenger sailed from England in December 1873, returning to England three and a half years later having circumnavigated the globe and made deep-sea investigations in each of the great oceans. A number of popular accounts of the expedition, writtent by those taking part, were published at the time. It is not intended therefore to give details of the famous voyage here.

The true greatness of the achievement in this new field of exploration was not fully apparent until twenty years later, when the last of the many volumes of the 'Challenger Reports' were published from the Challenger Office in Edinburgh where Sir John Murray had edited them subsequent to the death of Sir Wyville Thomson.

The countless specimens of phytoplankton, zooplankton, fishes, bottom-living fauna and sea-bed ooze, together with the voluminous data concerning the temperature and chemistry of the waters within the oceans, were made available to many well-known naturalists of the day. It was their work, in addition to that of those who had sailed in *Challenger*, that contributed to the illuminating 'Reports'. The general narrative was written by Murray, as was 'A Summary of the Scientific Results', whilst Tizard supplied the great mass of important navigational data and supervised the drawing of the many charts required as illustrations.

The *Challenger* voyage thus brought to an interested world the knowledge that the floor of the ocean was a complex of abyssal plains carpeted with ooze, divided by deeps, rises and even rocky submarine mountain ranges; that life in some crude form such as holothurians, or bottom-living worms, existed even at a depth of five miles; and that a vast circulation of water took place within the oceans, the redistribution of nutrients playing a vital role in the massive life cycle of this newly-discovered world.

In accordance with new regulations Richards was placed on the retired list in 1874, and as he believed that the Hydrographer should be an active service officer he vacated the post before

Challenger returned home. However, the part that Vice-Admiral Sir George Richards, as he later became, played in launching the *Challenger* voyage should not be forgotten. He had achieved an ambition, for as *Challenger* sailed he announced his great satisfaction 'that an expedition such as this, which has been the hope and dream of my life, is now on the eve of realisation'.

CHAPTER TWENTY-ONE

Evans and the Importance
of Magnetism

There was little difficulty in choosing a successor to Richards in 1874 for Staff Captain Frederick Evans had been his Chief Naval Assistant since 1865, and in addition to office experience thus gained, he brought to the post a lifetime's knowledge of surveying in many parts of the world, as the frequent mention of his name in our story has shown. His first surveying ship had been the *Thunder* in the West Indies in 1833, where his Captain was Commander Richard Owen. Evans was the assistant master in *Thunder*, and quickly became a surveyor, learning his trade in boats in the Demerara River, off the coasts of Nicaragua and Honduras and in the intricate waters of the Bahama banks.

His last post at sea had been in *Lightning* in the Baltic with Sulivan in 1855, after which he took over as Superintendent of the Compass Department, founded by Beaufort in 1842. He continued in this important post even after becoming Chief Naval Assistant.

The appearance at the bombardment of the Kinburn forts in the Crimea of three heavily armoured French gunboats profoundly influenced the Naval world, and in the fifteen years which followed the 'iron-clad' man-of-war came into service, whilst the long iron-hulled clipper ships began their great races home from Australia and China.

Today, when the gyro compass has become standard and young officers have to be taught the necessity for comparing it with the magnetic compass, it is easy to forget what a vital instrument the latter remained throughout the nineteenth century.

The introduction of iron hulls, and the addition of armour plating, so greatly affected the magnetic compass that for a time it seemed that there would be no satisfactory method of steering courses in the new ships. Evans, with the able assistance of Archibald Smith, an eminent mathematician, set to work on this absolutely vital problem and had solved it brilliantly by the time he succeeded Richards.

Fifty years before, Flinders had shown that a compass needle was affected not only by the variation of magnetic north from true north but also by iron fittings within the ship herself. It was this deviation which now posed so serious a problem that Flinders' soft-iron bar and the correctors devised by Airy, the Astronomer Royal, were totally inadequate to compensate.

The first step in Evans' work was the compilation from the magnetic observations made by surveyors in every part of the world of a chart showing curves of equal magnetic variation for the year 1858. This enabled navigators to assess their value of variation, thus clearing away one of the compass errors and leaving the other clearly exposed. Evans and Smith then got down to work on the deviation problem in various ships of the Royal Navy and in the *Great Eastern*, the largest iron ship afloat. Their results, originally in the form of a report to the Hydrographer, were communicated to the Royal Society and published in the *Philosophical Transactions* in 1860. The paper laid down the best direction in which to build an iron ship on the slipway, the best position within the ship to place the compass, and listed the various sources of error affecting the compass under normal conditions.

The next step was then tackled, the making of improvements upon Airy's system of magnet and soft-iron correctors placed within the binnacle to overcome local interference. The swinging of the compass and the adjustment of the correctors to reduce to the minimum the effect of deviation on the various ships' headings was brought to a fine art by Evans' assistants, who were responsible for every compass within the Fleet.

In 1862 the *Admiralty Manual for Ascertaining and Applying the*

Deviation of the Compass explained the results of the work of Evans and Smith, to be followed in 1870 by a more elementary work for the use of seamen, both of which were translated into many European languages. Evans was elected a Fellow of the Royal Society for his work on magnetism in 1862.

By the time he became Hydrographer he was content to leave the work on iron ships to the Compass Department; he concentrated his interest upon the earth's magnetism, and magnetic observations by surveying officers at home and overseas were intensified.

Ten years after Franklin's expedition had perished in the North, and when the numerous government-sponsored searches had failed to find any significant trace of his men or his ships, Commander M'Clintock, in command of the tiny *Fox*, sent out by Lady Franklin and her friends, found papers on King William's Land which recorded the abandonment of *Erebus* and *Terror*.

There had followed twenty years of national disillusionment with Arctic exploration, only succeeding Presidents of the Royal Geographical Society keeping alive an interest in these remote regions; they slowly instilled among influential persons a desire to resume polar exploration; no one now cared to search again for the Northwest Passage.

Captain C. F. Hall in the United States Ship *Polaris*, although he himself perished, not only gave impetus, but showed the British the way in which they might reach the Pole. His vessel passed through the Smith Sound separating Greenland from Ellesmere Island and wintered in Polaris Bay, as far north as 81° 38' N., on the northwest coast of Greenland in 1871-72.

The Arctic Committee got down to work and the newly appointed Hydrographer was soon busy arranging for officers, men and suitable vessels to undertake a carefully mounted assault on the North Pole. A first class commander for the expedition was essential, one with Arctic experience, and yet the lesson had now been well learned that old men should not be sent on such voyages. The only surveying officer who really fitted the requirement was Captain Nares, for he had sailed as a mate with Kellett in the *Resolute* on Belcher's 'Last Voyage to the Polar Seas' twenty years before. He was now brilliantly leading the Challenger Expedition, and reluctantly Evans decided to relieve him at Hong Kong by an officer from the Fleet, Captain Frank Thomson, Tizard taking charge of the whole of the navigation and surveying work onboard.

Two screw sloops, the *Alert* and *Discovery* were chosen, Nares commanding the expedition in the former and Captain Henry Stephenson, an officer from the Fleet, commanding the latter. The vessels were specially fitted out and provided with sledges to be hauled by men and by dogs, whilst two boats capable of being transported over the ice were provided.

The vessels sailed from Portsmouth Dockyard on 29th May 1875. Arctic exploration had recaptured the imagination of the public; thousands of cheering onlookers lined both sides of the harbour and Southsea beach was thronged. The Queen sent Nares a message from Balmoral wishing him and his officers and men every success.

The lessons of *Erebus* and *Terror* had been well learned. In addition to laying down his main objective as the Pole, to be reached by sledges from the ship at the limit of navigation north of Smith Sound, Nares' instructions included a number of clauses aimed at the safety of the expedition. If the ships had not returned to England by 1877 a relief vessel was to be sent to Lyttelton Island on the east side of the entrance to the Sound. Here Nares was to build a conspicuous cairn, in which were to be placed messages detailing the progress of the expedition and the immediate plans; similar cairns were to be erected every sixty miles or so northward along the shore on notable headlands, messages at each. At the cairns food dumps were to be made to facilitate the evacuation of crews on foot should both vessels be trapped. *Discovery* was not to be taken beyond 82° N., so that should *Alert* be trapped when pushed northwards to the limit of navigation, her people would be able to travel south and join *Discovery* for the return to England.

Two months after leaving Portsmouth, and having made visits to the Greenland settlements to collect dogs, the ships arrived in Smith Sound and commenced the voyage northwards along the western shore. The vessels were constantly harassed by floes driven southward by the prevailing wind. The availability of steam power enabled the ships to force their way past many of the smaller floes, but there were occasions when screws and rudders had to be unshipped to avoid damage when the sturdy ships were nipped. In mid-August both vessels were held up for a fortnight, but strong southwest winds set in, carrying the ice off-shore and filling the sails.

A suitable harbour was found in Lady Franklin Bay in approximately 81° 44′ N. on the eastern side of Ellesmere Island where the slaughter of nine musk-oxen on the first day appeared to be a good omen for the winter's supplies. *Discovery* was left here, giving her name to this excellent harbour.

Nares pushed on, running the gauntlet between the jumbled moving ice floes to the east and the towering black cliffs of Ellesmere Island on the west, the ever-thickening pack ice finally halting the vessel in 82° 24′ N. off Cape Sheridan, when the ensign was hoisted at the peak to celebrate her arrival in a higher latitude than any vessel had ever reached. Here, icebound off the open coast, *Alert* remained from 1st September to 31st July, for 142 days of which she lay in perpetual darkness.

The coast trended away to the northwest; on the other side of the Robeson Channel the coast of Greenland ran northeastwards, whilst to the north lay the Polar Sea. There were those at home who believed this sea would be free of ice and easily navigable, but there it lay, a vast hummocky frozen field, with no sign of land as far as the eye could see, even from the peak of a 2,000-foot mountain scaled by Lieutenant Pelham Aldrich and Able Seaman Adam Ayles.

Reconnaissance sledge journeys were made to the northwest along the shoreline before the long winter set in, during which plans for the spring were made.

Evans had welcomed the opportunity for obtaining a whole winter's magnetic observations at two adjacent fixed stations. Both ships were provided with the latest instruments for recording regularly the values of the three elements: total magnetic force was measured with Dr. Lloyd's needles, Barrow's circle was provided for measuring dip, and a unifilar magnetometer determined the horizontal force. Mr. Fox's portable apparatus was available to the sledging parties for measuring dip and total force in the field, where they also carried a 3-in. prismatic azimuth compass for measuring the variation. Staff Commander E. W. Creak, Assistant Superintendent of Compasses, had instructed selected ship's officers in the use of these complex instruments at the Hydrographic Office before the expedition sailed.

The magnetic observatory built by *Alert's* crew on Floeberg Beach abreast the ship consisted of three houses constructed of snow 10½ft. high and of roughly similar diameter at their base, whilst fifty-three miles to the south *Discovery's* men built their observatory of wood with copper fastenings. At both stations the instruments were frozen into position on snow pillars.

One of the interesting results of the observations was the discovery of a diurnal change of up to half a degree either way in the value of magnetic variation, interrupted frequently by magnetic disturbances, when the needle varied its pointing by as much as 5½°. These movements were correlated at both stations, and the same magnetic storms were subsequently identified in the records of Kew Observatory. Although it had been thought that auroras were connected with these magnetic storms no correlation between visual observations of these phenomena and the recorded magnetic disturbances was apparent.

In March 1876, sledge parties made contact between the two ships and on 3rd April seven sledges set out on their travels northward from *Alert*. 'A finer body of picked men than the crews of the three extended sledge parties were never previously collected together,' said Nares.

Commander Albert Markham and Lieutenant Alfred Parr, after following the coast to Cape Joseph Henry, the northeastern extremity of Ellesmere Island, set out due northwards across the ridged sea ice towards the distant Pole. They hauled the two boats with them in case open water should be met with or cut off their retreat, just as Parry had done on his attempt to reach the Pole fifty years before.

Lieutenant Pelham Aldrich, a surveying officer whom Nares had brought with him from *Challenger*, pushed his way westward exploring the north coast of Ellesmere Island.

A supporting sledge which returned from Cape Joseph Henry reported that both these parties had gone on their way in good health and spirits, and on 3rd May Lieutenant George Giffard, who had been supporting Aldrich, returned with good news of his party up to the twenty-second day out from the ship.

All seemed to be going well when the doctors reported an outbreak of scurvy in the ships, and among those returning from sledging. Nares was seriously worried about the safety of the now distant travellers. With a balanced diet, ample provisions and careful health conduct through the winter, this outbreak of scurvy in a modern expedition was as surprising as it was alarming.

On the evening of 8th June Lieutenant Parr arrived at the ship, having walked alone in twenty-four hours from Cape Joseph Henry, where he had left Commander Markham desperately coping with his men, nearly every one of whom was incapacitated by scurvy. Nares set out at once with a sledge loaded with medical stores and hauled by officer volunteers. One marine had died before Nares got to the party, but the others were brought safely in and eventually recovered.

Markham had reached the furthest north point ever, 83° 20½' N., at an average speed of 1¼ miles a day for 40 days, crossing at right angles an unbroken series of 16 to 20 ft. high ice ridges, each separated by about 100 yards of deep soft snow. For the last 14 days of the journey some of the men were being increasingly affected in the legs by scurvy and became invalids, to be carried every hour further from the succour of the ship as the party hacked their way through the tops of the ice ridges and dug their sledges from the deep snow. The boats they had to abandon. It had been a remarkable feat, but the North Pole remained inviolate 400 miles ahead.

Nares, now more than ever worried about Aldrich's party, sent out Lieutenant William May with a dog sledge and three men to meet the party and help them in. May found Aldrich at Cape John Henry, the condition of his men such that further travel without assistance was impossible, but all were now brought safely in and eventually recovered.

Aldrich had surveyed the north coast of Ellesmere Island for a distance of 220 miles west of the ship, where he named the 'Challenger Mountains' to commemorate the vessel in which he had formerly served so happily with Captain Nares. Increasing pains in the legs were experienced by the men on the outward journey, sore gums, a clear symptom of scurvy, adding to their misery on the way homeward and reducing their strength until they could hardly walk, leave alone haul the sledges.

Captain Stephenson had conducted the exploration of the Greenland coast, a depot having been earlier established at Polaris Bay. He selected Lieutenant Lewis Beaumont to travel with two sledges along the coast to the northeast as far as he was able.

Beaumont came north to *Alert* in April, crossed the ice of the Robeson Channel and set out along the coast in May, when scurvy first struck the party. Able Seaman James Hand was soon unable to walk and Lieutenant Wyatt Rawson and three men were sent back hauling Hand on the sledge to the Polaris Bay depot. On the way all Rawson's men became affected and it was only with the greatest difficulty that they reached the depot, Hand dying almost at the moment of arrival. It was fortunate that Dr. Richard Coppinger, *Discovery's* surgeon, who had been exploring Peterman Fjord to the southwards with Hans, an Eskimo driver, and a dog team, came in about a week later and, with the aid of fresh game and seal meat, managed to save the remainder of Rawson's men.

Meanwhile Lieutenant Beaumont reached his furthest point on the Greenland Coast—82° 18′ N. 50° 40′ W. on 21st May, where he turned back as scurvy was now apparent among his men. Captain Nares' subsequent report describes the miseries of Beaumont's journey back to the Polaris depot: 'By this time two more of the crew showed symptoms of scurvy, and soon after the return journey was commenced, the whole party were attacked until at last Lieutenant Beaumont, Alexander Gray, Sergeant-quartermaster Captain of the sledge, and Frank Jones, stoker, were alone able to drag, the other four men having to be carried forward on the sledge in detachments, which necessitated always double and most frequently treble journeys over the rough and disheartening icy road; nevertheless, the gallant band struggled manfully onwards, thankful if they made one mile a day, but never losing heart; but

Lieutenant Beaumont's anxiety became intense lest relief should arrive too late to save the lives of the worst cases.'

On 22nd June Lieutenant Rawson with Dr. Coppinger set out with Hans and the dog sledge to look for Beaumont, meeting his desperate party twenty miles from the Polaris dept. All were safely brought in, but Able Seaman Charles Paul died soon after arrival.

It was due to Dr. Coppinger's care that only two men died out of those so vigorously attacked by scurvy in Greenland and in recognition Beaumont gave the name of 'Mount Coppinger' to the feature which stood, remote and desolate, beyond the furthest point reached by man in Northern Greenland.

In early July a party was sent across the channel to report to *Discovery*, and Captain Stephenson came over in person to supervise the return of the men, many of them invalids, from Polaris Bay. The ice had begun to move again in the strait making travel hazardous, but coming across in small parties, and using a dinghy, all were safely back in the ship by mid-August.

Throughout the winter *Alert* had lain in the pack, protected from seaward by a barrier of giant grounded icebergs. At the end of July the ice about the ship began to move with the tide, cracks appearing and, later, lanes of open water. The thawing of the larger bergs enabled them, however, to close the shore so that Nares saw that he had little time to waste in getting southward. *Alert* was got under way, steaming when she could, or being permitted to drift in the pack when it moved southwards with the tidal stream. Fortunately the water was sufficiently deep right up to the cliffs to allow the ship to move close in as the melting floe bergs approached the shore, but finally she was nipped against the cliffs by a berg, which grounded. The crew set to work with pick and shovel and succeeded in reducing the topweight of the iceberg sufficiently to refloat it three days later, enabling *Alert* to rejoin her consort in Discovery Harbour where the last men were arriving from Polaris Bay.

The two ships then proceeded together, closely in company so that they could render each other assistance in the ice. Often they were within a few feet of each other and on one occasion fouled but with little damage.

Alert, being driven inshore by a floeberg, grounded forward at the top of high water, and with the tide rapidly falling 14 ft., she lay with her bows high and dry and a list of 22°. At the next high water an anchor was lowered onto a piece of ice which was towed astern by a boat to a suitable position, where, the ice being blown up, a kedge was laid with ease, and the vessel hauled off stern first.

It was a long and tedious passage south and by the time Victoria Head was reached at 79° 15′ N. in mid-September calm weather had permitted the new ice to form a last, and considerable, barrier. Separated by a piece of ice, both vessels charged the barrier together at full speed and broke through, to the sound of cheering seamen, to the open water and the voyage home.

During the expedition out of 120 men involved 60 had suffered from scurvy with 4 deaths. This affliction had proved a major difficulty during the voyage when other expeditions had survived for several years in the Arctic without any such problems. The House of Commons called for an enquiry during which several factors came to light. Firstly the expedition spent much of its time so far north that fresh game was extremely scarce, whilst the long days of complete darkness may have had a debilitating effect upon the men; another factor was that lime juice, rather than lemon juice which has a much higher Vitamin C content, was embarked and sledge parties did not carry lime juice for it would have frozen solid in the large containers available.

The expedition had reached England at the end of October, six months after the return of the *Challenger* Expedition. The two voyages, both launched under Captain Nares' able leadership, invited comparison. The Polar ships had carried two naturalists who had brought back extensive collections, valuable magnetic and meteorological observations had been made by trained officers, and the surveyors had laid down 300 miles of icebound coastline, unlikely ever to be revisited for any useful purpose. Commander Markham had shown that a journey across the ice to the Pole from this starting point was a practical impossibility. How did these rewards for so much hardship compare with the momentous discoveries of the *Challenger*?

Admiral Richards may have been voicing the opinion of enlightened men of the age when he concluded his introduction to Nares' account of his *Voyage to the Polar Sea*:

> 'Geography has little to gain by it, science perhaps less, for whatever science has gained by such voyages—and the gain has been considerable—has been exploration in the neighbourhood of the ship's winter-quarters, and not through the efforts of extended travelling parties, who have neither the time nor the means to devote to it. There are wide fields for geographical and scientific research in other regions, by which the whole human race would be gainers; and though England, as she is bound to do, does more than any other nation in such work, she is very far in these respects from fulfilling her mission. Hundreds of her national ships plough the ocean in time of peace, their almost sole occupation the training and preparation for war, and in the very nature of things, so far as scientific research is concerned, they leave no deeper mark than the track which the sea obliterates behind them, while the few—too few—grudgingly appropriated from the largest navy in the world place their ineffaceable stamp on works of usefulness which last for ever.'

Although suitable ships were made available for these major expeditions, the Hydrographer found indeed that gun-vessels were grudgingly provided for routine surveys, for which it was still necessary to employ about four ships overseas. Typical of these, when Evans took over, was the screw sloop *Nassau* working under Lieutenant Francis Gray on the east coast of Africa. Lieutenant the Hon. F. P. Vereker was the senior surveying assistant onboard, remembered today for his beautiful navigational views of the coasts of the British Isles.

First we find Vereker accompanying his Captain on one of those minor diplomatic duties which are so necessary before flags are hoisted and men commence work on distant shores. His diary reads:

'*21st March, 1874* (Between Aden & C. Guardafui)

'. . . Passed a steamer probably with Livingstone's body on board just off Aluleh Cape.

'*13th April* (Audience with Sultan of Zanzibar)

'Captn., self, Petley, White, Hamilton, Dixon & George, lashed up in cocked hats, epaulettes &c. and about ten proceeded to pay our respects to His Highness the Sultan of Zanzibar. Calling at the Consulate we picked up Mr. Prideaux and accompanied by a crowd of small boys proceeded along the narrow streets to the palace. We passed by his fort which is armed with guns landed from the sailing corvette lying in the harbour. Round the door of the palace, not a very imposing building, was a small crowd of niggers, Arabs &c., and drawn up in two lines on each side of the entrance, so as to form a lane, were the Persian body guard dressed in dark green frocks, dirty white trousers and high caps; not an impressive escort. As we approached the Sultan, "Said Bergash" as natives call him, came down the steps and accompanied by his officers of state advanced to meet us. Shook hands and bid us welcome and then made us *preceed* him into the palace & up a dirty room about 20 yards long & rickety staircase into the presence chamber, a room about 20 yards long with a bare wooden floor, few decorations and small armed chairs all around on which we were invited to be seated, while the Sultan took his place at the end of the room and entered into conversation through the medium of an interpreter with the Consul & Captain. Bad coffee in small gold embossed cups & sherbert highly flavoured with scented rose water & coloured pink was then served on china plates by the attendants and we had time to examine the Sultan. He is a good looking Arab of about 35 I should think with the usual black beard, whiskers and moustache. He was not very richly dressed in the usual Arab dress. An underneath white robe an outside coat of embroidered cloth and worked turban with jewelled arms, sabre, daggers, &c. After about half an hour's conversation he promised the Captn. letters to the governors of the southern ports; we took our departure with the same forms and ceremonies we had used on our arrival, and returned on board very glad to get off our hats coats and heavy epaulettes and indulge in a good draught of ale.

'*1st May* (Partial eclipse of the moon near Lindi)

'About 6.15 p.m. we observed the partial eclipse of the moon very perfectly. A beautiful clear sky and the moon itself being extremely bright tending to help. It lasted till 6.45 about.

'*2nd Aug.* (Seychelles)

'Performed divine service & gave our special leavemen leave till 9 p.m. but they rather abuse it returning drunk and smuggling liquor. Captn. now threatens extreme rigour of the law.

'*28th September* (Amateur Dramatics aboard)

'. . . In the evening our little Dramatic Company played two pieces 'His Own Enemy' and 'My Very Last Proposal' and did them very creditably. "Miss" Ionis entering thoroughly into his part but his whiskers are coming out too strong for the heroine. Although Aldridge was rather tight he made no mess.'

Back in Zanzibar arrangements having been satisfactorily completed with the Sultan we next find Vereker taking charge of a detached survey party on the coast:

'Our gear consisted of—*for surveying*, Theodolite & legs. Pocket & observg sextant. Azimuth compass. Box of instruments. Do. of colours. Indian ink pencils & pens. Inmans tables. Workbook. Protractor & scale. Base chain & pegs. Calico. Drawing, cartridge & tracing paper. Do. cloth. Watch & Drawing board with pins & Notebook. *For Service*. Sword, pistol & ammunition. Signal book. Small portmanteau with clothes. Bedding. *Eatables*. Potted milk, jam, sardines, preserved vegetables, sago & rice—sugar & coffee, cocoa & milk

& grog with some fresh bread.

'*The men* had changes of clothes & blanket clothing. Of course the boat had her sail awnings etc. all in and the regular ship's provisions but we found the *service coppers* a mistake. The captain's orders were very strict about sleeping *in* the boat & *away* from the mangroves. So each night I anchored off just before turning in & let them bathe while preparing breakfast.

'*13th*. Up at 5 AM. and by VI.30 everything was all ready, and as the pipe "Up anchor" went George and self shoved off after a hearty handshake from the skipper and a chin-chin from the rest. Fairly started now we pulled ashore and had a palaver at the big village called Mwanis, where the chief being away in the bush the 2nd man received us most civilly. Having selected a base we measured 4,300 feet and could have got more with an excellent 3rd pt. in the Mushroom or Madjove Pks. After lunch we beat up the river to the small town of Sudi where the Arab governor resides. He received us graciously. He is a very diminutive specimen of an exceedingly dirty Arab and not being much impressed we did not stop long. He pressed us to come and stay off his place so after coastlining up to Lamgogori our sun pt. we came back about sunset and prepared for our grub and a more comical mess I never saw than the mess our fellows got into over the culinary arrangements. The cooks were not skilled in their art and accordingly many strange mishaps occurred. However excepting that we grounded we did all right by Midgt. The governor although professing strict Mohamedism sent down for a bottle of wine *after dark*.

'*14th*. Started the triangulation of the river. Made a good △• on top of Madjovi pkd. Anchored this night off the mouth of a small stream called the Bokaro it being more convenient than Sudi.

'*15th*. Working away at the triangulation and coastline, and commenced sounding. Governor made a great fuss about letting me go on top of the Custom Ho. his Hareem being just behind, but at last consented he accompanying me up. He then "squeezed" for more wine! Made a rough plot in the evening which went down very well.

'*16th*. Continued the survey. Everything very satisfactory.'

About fifty surveying officers were now employed in the Service, but volunteers were difficult to attract for the work was arduous and promotion notoriously slow. Typical was the case of *Nassau's* Captain, Lieutenant Gray, a surveyor of many years' experience who had been carrying out the duties of a Commander in charge of a foreign survey for two years before his promotion was gazetted in September 1875. However, by the time the news reached the ship on her arrival at the Cape in December of that year, Gray had died of fever contracted whilst engaged in climbing to fix a mountain peak in Mozambique.

In 1880 Staff Commander Tizard obtained Command of the hired vessel *Knight Errant*, typically unsuited to surveying, but Evans promised to transfer him to *Triton* as soon as she was complete. She was to be the only vessel built expressly for surveying work in the nineteenth century, and represented a triumph for Evans in his dealings with the Board of Admiralty.

As the *Challenger* voyage had progressed, and officers and scientists had learnt more about the temperature of the deep-sea water, they came to realise that ridges on the floor of the ocean tended to separate bottom water of widely different temperatures and, consequently, different forms of life. Their thoughts turned to the curious results obtained by Wyville Thomson and Carpenter when they had sailed in northern waters in *Lightning* and *Porcupine* in 1868 and 1869. Carpenter had described the phenomenon thus: '. . . two very different Submarine Climates exist in the deep channel (Faroe Channel); a *minimum* temperature of 32° being registered in some parts of this channel, whilst in other parts of it, *at the same depths* and with the *same surface temperatures* (never varying much from 52°) the *minimum* temperature registered was never lower than 46°.'

In 1880 Wyville Thomson wrote as follows: 'During the cruise of the *Challenger*, Staff-Commander Tizard and I had often in our minds the singular instance of continuous areas of widely different temperature conditions which had been examined by Dr. Carpenter and myself . . . it now seemed certain that if our generalisation with regard to the cause of great differences in bottom temperatures within short distances be correct, a submarine ridge rising to within 200 fathoms of the surface must extend across the mouth of the channel between the coast of Scotland and the Faroe banks.'

Both Thomson and Tizard were anxious to put this theory to the test. Despite the inadequacy of the *Knight Errant*, at least she was capable of sailing to the area, and Evans was persuaded to allow her to be used for the purpose.

Thomson's health was now such that he was unable to go to sea unaccompanied by a doctor, so that he remained impatiently at Stornoway whilst Murray accompanied Tizard to the Faroe Channel. It was exciting to find that the soundings showed the presence of the suspected ridge, rising from 500 fathoms to half that depth, the ridge running northwestwards across the whole width of the channel. It was unfortunate that the jury-rigged steam winch was incapable of hauling in the trawl, so that it was impossible to compare the marine life on either side. However, the theory had been elegantly proved.

Tizard planned to return to complete the investigations more satisfactorily and a cruise to these northern waters was one of the first tasks for his new ship *Triton*. She was launched at the Yard of Samuda at Poplar in March 1882, a paddle steamer of 410 tons with two funnels side-by-side athwartships; her frames were of iron, her skin of wood, sheathed with copper; she had two masts for fore and aft sails, or for storm sails, with which she sailed easily with the addition of 'easy steam'; she was comfortable and workable as a surveying ship, which duties she performed into the twentieth century.* By July 1882 Tizard was at Stornoway in *Triton*

---

* *Triton* was used for various duties in World War I and from 1919 she was moored to the West India Docks as a training ship for merchant seamen. She was still sound when scrapped in 1961.

ready to sail with Murray for the Faroe Channel. During August five sounding and temperature sections were run across the ridge, and a number of successful trawls and dredges were made on either side, and on the ridge itself.

Warm water coming from the southwest was easily traced flowing in over the ridge and onwards above the cold water of the northeast basin. Through a 'saddle' towards the northern end of the ridge, and about 100 fathoms deeper than the ridge itself, a comparatively small quantity of deep cold bottom water was traced flowing out. Of marine forms of life taken in the dredge and trawl, 216 species were found in the warm area and 217 species in the cold area: only 48 species were common to both.

Sadly, Wyville Thomson died in the month *Triton* was launched, and did not see the 'finishing up of that very neat Hebridean point' of which he had talked so enthusiastically. Tizard and Murray named the Ridge after him and Tizard's concise report served as an early example of how regional faunal distribution within the ocean may be neatly explained by a study of the morphology of the sea-bed.

Evans had been consulted by Richards in 1873 when he readily agreed that Staff Commander Thomas Hull, an officer of wide surveying experience, should be appointed Superintendent of Charts. It was not long, however, after Evans took over as Hydrographer before difficulties developed between the two men which troubled the Hydrographer for six years.

Messengers have always played an important role in the Office, for it was among their duties to bring from the extensive archives surveys, old and new, as required for the compilation of charts, each of which is a careful blending of the work of many surveyors. It is maddening for the cartographer, engrossed in his work, when, calling for a survey from the distant archives, he is told that no messenger is available. I have found a shortage of messengers to be an unfailing cause of hot tempers and hard words within the Hydrographic Office.

It is therefore not surprising to find that the first friction between the Superintendent of Charts and his Chief resulted from a demand from the former that a messenger should be specially appointed to the Chart Branch. He did not consult the Hydrographer before passing up a letter directly addressed to the Secretary of the Admiralty in which in 'a somewhat imperative tone' he made the request. Hydrographer took Hull to task only to find that Hull considered himself his own master as Superintendent of Charts, and had moreover established direct correspondence with the Captains of surveying ships.

In 1875 Commander Hull, with no reference to Hydrographer, read a paper before the United Service Institution titled *The Unsurveyed World*, a précis following in *The Times* next day. The paper was critical of the Admiralty administration of the Hydrographic Office, claiming that due to shortage of staff many foreign surveys lay on the shelves, their valuable data omitted from the Admiralty Charts. This brought Their Lordships' censure, but little change in Hull's attitude within the office.

Four years later in 1879 a series of damaging articles, anonymously written, appeared in *The United Service Gazette* under the title of *The Rise, Decline and Restoration of Her Majesty's Surveying Service*. Later in the same year a paper was read by a Lieutenant G. T. Temple at the meeting of the Geographical Section of the British Association entitled *Hydrography Past and Present*, which brought about considerable public criticism of the Hydrographer, and certainly bore the stamp of Hull's utterances. Temple was a naval officer employed writing Sailing Directions at his home, and had no previous connection with surveying. Evans traced the printed diagram used by Temple to illustrate his paper to Malby, the chart printer, who had prepared it to Hull's instructions. The Hydrographer prepared a confidential report for the Board of Admiralty describing all his difficulties with Hull which resulted in the latter's supersession in December the same year.

Commander George Stanley succeeded Hull, being appointed as 'The Officer in Charge of Chart Branch'. It was further laid down that in future, to maintain Hydrographer's overriding authority for the charts which bore his name, his direction in writing was to be given as to the use to be made of every incoming item, chart or survey.

There were a number of innovations brought into being by

Evans worthy of notice. He published the *Hydrographical Note*, printed forms issued to all ships in the Fleet, to be completed when sending in Hydrographic information, which are in general use to this day, and do much to encourage the forwarding of useful data by seamen to keep the charts up to date.

In 1879 Evans prepared the first *Hydrographer's Annual Report*, which is laid annually before Parliament and gives details of charts and publications printed and sold during the year, as well as a description of the activities of Her Majesty's Surveying Ships. Today the Report, in a more modern format and with illustrations, is not only seen by Members of Parliament, but is passed to the Press, thus keeping the public informed of the activities of the Surveying Service.

The rapidly improving communications by means of the submarine telegraph enabled time signals to be passed to an increasing number of distant places, bringing a decline in the importance of running meridian distances with numerous chronometers embarked, and an increasing accuracy and reconciliation of the longitude values of the standard places of observation around the world.

Evans advised on the test borings made in the English Channel in 1882 in connection with a scheme for a Channel tunnel, which has taken over 100 years to be realised.

On her return from the Arctic *Alert* was selected, after undergoing a long refit, to sail for a surveying voyage to Magellan Strait. The heavy exterior planking of 'ice-clouts' was left in position and sheathed over with copper. Captain Sir George Nares was again appointed in command, Vereker being First Assistant Surveyor and Navigator. A good deal of deep-sea sounding was to be carried out and for this purpose the ship was fitted with new apparatus, the Lucas wire sounding machine, made by the Telegraph Construction and Maintenance Company under the direction of the Managing Director, Admiral Richards. Both hand- and steam-operated models of this machine, for shallow and deep water respectively, were made, the former, by the speed with which soundings could be taken, making the charting of the world's oceans now a possibility. Another apparatus, which was successfully tried during *Alert's* voyage between 1878 and 1880 and which was to accelerate the acquisition of knowledge of the ocean circulation, was the reversing thermometer, at first in a wooden frame, developed by Negretti and Zambra.

Vereker was promoted Commander at the end of this commission, to command the *Magpie*, a twin-screw gun-vessel which had superseded *Nassau* at Hong Kong. His first task was to go to Borneo to survey the coast of the territory acquired by the British North Borneo Company. Care was to be taken to keep well clear of the border with Dutch possessions, for the question of the exact boundary was still in the hands of the Foreign Office and matters were delicate. 'He must not let his zeal outrun his discretion,' was how authority described such a situation, knowing that zeal was much admired among surveyors.

Vereker took over command in May 1883. His diary is again quoted:

'*28th May*. Joined the ship officially at 9 a.m. and read commission—then mustered by open list and inspected the ship and men. A fine ship's company only 5 second class conduct men. The ship in very tidy order but old and evidently on her last legs. Good spars and should sail well in a stiff breeze. Cabin very roomy and comfortable I having the whole poop and as there is a navigating bridge before the main mast over the charthouse I am quiet too. Getting gear on board and stowed away. In the evening dined in the ward room with the officers.

'*29th May*. Going over all books and documents. Observing sights for chronometer rates. Surprised to find that there are no definite surveying orders on board my predecessor having carried them off. However I have my verbal order to go upon . . .'

On 27th August of the same year, whilst off the coast of Borneo, heavy detonations were heard onboard resembling distant gunfire. For some days afterwards the sun, whilst at a low altitude, assumed a peculiar greenish hue. A message received ashore by telegraphy from the Admiralty some fortnight later advised Vereker of the eruption of Krakatoa, 1,000 miles to the west, and ordered him to repair to the important waterway, the Sunda Strait, where navigation was believed to be endangered by new shoals created by the eruption.

Magpie arrived in Batavia in October to be informed by the Netherlands Government authorities that their surveying ship *Hydrograaf* had sailed for Sunda Strait, but they suggested that *Magpie* nevertheless should visit the scene of the disaster and obtain the latest local information.

'Entering Sunda Strait on 18th October, the surface of the sea was found to be still covered with extensive fields of floating pumice, varying in quality and size from fine dust to blocks two or three feet across. This material had a fine fibrous appearance, as if composed of spun glass, yellowish-brown in colour.'

A running sketch survey of Krakatoa and the adjacent islands, together with some admirable views, were made illustrating the changes in this great centre of eruption.

Commander Vereker, in describing these changes, stated that of Krakatoa Island two-thirds had disappeared, and that from the summit (2,700 feet high) a stupendous cliff abruptly descended nearly perpendicularly to the sea, giving evidence to the violence of the eruption.

The focus of the eruption was not the summit of the island, but a small crater, formed in the preceding month of May, on the northwest portion of the then island: this crater, with the surrounding land, had entirely disappeared, leaving a depth of over 100 fathoms water in its place. The adjacent island—Verlaten—had greatly increased in size, and, like Krakatoa, was at the time of the *Magpie's* visit in an active state. The two new islets to the northward of Krakatoa were almost awash, and composed of mud and pumice: these islets were continually changing in configuration, and, it was said, were at the time gradually subsiding.

Commander Vereker further remarked that the whole of the neighbouring land was covered with a thick encrustation of yellowish-green volcanic mud, overlying the debris of the vegetation, which had been utterly destroyed; and the whole giving an appearance of desolation and ruin hardly possible to describe. The total loss of life was considered by the authorities to be over 50,000, the whole population being, in many places, swept away. During the height of the eruption a terrific whirlwind was experienced.

Captain Evans, on receipt of *Magpie's* description and some almost photographic sketches of the crater, began work on a report of this stupendous act of nature for the Royal Society. This was the last scientific work performed by Captain Sir Frederick Evans, who had received the K.C.B. in 1881, and retired in August 1884 having joined the Surveying Service as a Master and risen to become Hydrographer, the only Master ever to do so.

CHAPTER TWENTY-TWO

Wharton and
Scientific Surveying

From this distance in time it would seem that either Captain Sir George Nares or Staff-Commander Tizard would have held the post of Hydrographer towards the end of the century, but in fact it fell to a younger man, Captain William Wharton, to see the nineteenth century out as Hydrographer and launch his Office into the twentieth century.

There is no doubt that in 1884, at the early age of forty-one, he was well qualified to become Hydrographer of the Navy, being a brilliant scholar as well as a practical surveyor. In 1865 he had been awarded the Beaufort Testimonial, an annual prize for the officer qualifying as the Lieutenant who achieved the best results during the year in Mathematics, Nautical Astronomy and Navigation.

His first experience of surveying was when he served a commission in one of two experimental ships sent out by Hydrographer Richards. They were the *Gannet* (Commander Chimmo) and the *Serpent* (Commander Bullock), placed under the Commanders-in-Chief of the North American and West Indies Station and the China Station respectively. The vessels were men-of-war, to be employed partly on such duties and partly in progressing surveys required on the stations. The joint control between the Commander-in-Chief and the Hydrographer was unsuccessful and the experiment was not repeated. However, it did bring the work of surveying officers more directly before the Commander-in-Chief, and in particular Vice-Admiral Sir James Hope was greatly impressed with the work of Lieutenant Wharton of the *Gannet* in the Bay of Fundy, where tides in excess of forty feet made surveying a particularly difficult task. Admiral Hope subsequently became Commander-in-Chief Portsmouth, and by special arrangement with the Hydrographer, Wharton became unique as a surveyor when appointed his Flag Lieutenant, a post he held for three years. Whilst holding this appointment Wharton wrote a history of his Admiral's flagship, H.M.S. *Victory*, the proceeds for many years being devoted to the Royal Naval Seamen's and Marine Orphans' Home at Portsmouth.

His ability in nautical astronomy earned him temporary duty as First Lieutenant in H.M.S. *Urgent* in 1870, when the vessel carried an expedition to Gibraltar to observe a total eclipse of the Sun.

In 1872, being promoted Commander, he took over *Shearwater* from Nares who had been recalled for the *Challenger* expedition. *Shearwater* worked both in the Mediterranean and in the Indian Ocean, Wharton being responsible for keeping the charts up-to-date for the approaches to the Suez Canal. Examples of Wharton's practical work and his astronomical ability are not hard to find in either theatre.

The apparent continual flow of water from the Black Sea through the Bosphorus to the Sea of Marmora had puzzled men of an enquiring mind for some years, and Wharton set out to solve the question. He devised a 6 ft. square wooden kite, fitted with a wing and so slung and weighted that it maintained its flat surface vertical in the water when lowered to a given depth. The kite was supported by a metal buoy 1 ft. in diameter and 5 ft. high, which presented very little area to the surface water.

From a boat at various stations in the Bosphorus these kites were lowered and allowed to drift, whilst from another boat was released at the same time and place a small buoy, weighted to float awash. Both buoys were then followed, the respective floats being fixed at regular intervals; thus the direction and speed of both surface and deep currents were ascertained. The floats laid in the Bosphorus moved in opposite directions at different speeds, showing that when a current, say of two knots, was flowing out of the Black Sea, a bottom current of, perhaps, a knot was flowing inwards. This was a neat and novel investigation.

In 1874 Wharton played an important part in the arrangements for the observation of the first of a pair of Transits of Venus, plans having been made for British, German, French and Dutch expeditions to observe the phenomenon at five isolated islands in the central Indian Ocean. The Royal Alfred Observatory at Pamplemousses in Mauritius was regarded, at least by Lord Lindsay, as the central station. He was a noted amateur astronomer with his own observatory at Dunecht in Aberdeenshire, and he planned to set up a temporary observatory on Mauritius to witness the Transit, travelling there in his Yacht *Venus*.

The importance of the advent of the submarine telegraph in transferring longitude from Greenwich to a distant station by time signals has already been mentioned. The principle is the same as that of carrying time by chronometer, but the error due to the chronometer's fluctuating rate during the voyage is eliminated.

For years surveys in different areas of the world were connected in longitude by chronometric traverses to the long established observation stations so frequently referred to here. These stations had been designated 'Secondary Meridians' and were listed in the *Instructions to Hydrographic Surveyors*. Thus the longitudes of charts of Southern Africa were related to the Secondary Meridian of the Cape Observatory and of the Magellan Strait to Monte Video or Valparaiso and so on. Modern telegraphy now opened up the possibility of connecting many of these Secondary Meridians to the 'Prime Meridian' of Greenwich.

Mauritius had no telegraph in 1874, yet the more accurately the longitudes of the observing stations were known the more meaningful would be the records of the Transit of Venus. Lord Lindsay determined to connect the Secondary Meridian of Aden by telegraph to Greenwich, and to run his own meridian distance from Aden to Mauritius by chronometers, using a large number so that their daily comparison would give him an accurately determined rate during the passage. Once the longitude of Mauritius was thus established it was the task of the individual expeditions to carry their chronometric meridian distances to their own island observation stations.

Lindsay sent his able young assistant, David Gill, in charge of fifty carefully tested chronometers, by P. & O. steamer to Aden. At Alexandria Gill made arrangements with the Eastern Telegraph Company to pass time signals via Berlin, Malta, Alexandria and Suez to Aden when he should be ready for them.

At Aden, unaided by skilled handlers, Gill transferred his precious and delicate chronometers to the Messageries Maritimes steamship *Godavery* for the vital chronometric passage to Mauritius, which was successfully achieved.

It was then Wharton's task in *Shearwater* to take the British observers under Commander Neate, R.N., to Rodriguez and to make the meridian connection between Gill's longitude of Mauritius and this British station. This he did with the required accuracy, using forty-two of Lindsay's chronometers lent to him by Gill.

It was thus that Wharton first met and formed a lifelong friendship with Gill, who was appointed Her Majesty's Astronomer at the Cape of Good Hope in 1879.

In 1875 *Shearwater* was paid off and the following year Wharton commissioned *Fawn*, another screw sloop, for similar service in the Mediterranean and the Indian Ocean.

In 1877 Russia was advancing again on Turkey and the British Fleet was ordered into the Sea of Marmora to forestall the Russian presence in the Mediterranean. *Fawn* was recalled from Zanzibar, where she was at work, and sent to survey the Sea of Marmora, which Wharton and his officers completed so expeditiously and with such care that they received an expression of Their Lordship's appreciation.

Wharton was promoted Captain in 1880 and for the next two years devoted himself to the completion of his Manual, *Hydrographical Surveying*, which was published in 1882 after he had been appointed to *Sylvia* for surveys in South America. Others had written treatises on surveying, but Wharton's Manual was generally recognised as the up-to-date successor to Belcher's work. It set out in a lucid manner the various steps of a marine survey, the science of astronomical observation being clearly explained and the formulae

well presented. It formed a concise guide for the officers of the
Surveying Service which Wharton ensured they followed when he
succeeded Captain Evans in August 1884.

During *Sylvia's* commission Wharton had furthered his experience in astronomy by observing the Second of the pair of Transits
of Venus in December 1882.

Captain Vereker was the first officer to commission a surveying
ship in Wharton's time:

> 'On the 11th November 1884 I commissioned the *Rambler* for
> a trigonometric survey of the China coast. I had been ap-
> pointed in September . . . with Lt. Pirie and Mr. Beale (Chief
> Engr.) to superintend the fitting out which was slow work as
> numerous alterations had to be made in the ship for boats,
> chartroom, cabins &c with a final result that an excellent
> little man of war was turned into an only so-and-so surveying
> ship being too crowded up in everyway. The old fashioned
> plan of taking a roomy, if obsolete, man of war reducing her
> spars, her armament and her ships company was here re-
> versed and keeping all the old stores, spars, &c, her ships
> company was increased from 97 to 113, the poop cabin was
> docked of nearly one half to make a chart room, the only
> available spare space on deck was annexed for a sounding
> engine and an extra cabin and the already small steerage was
> rendered still smaller by extra chests for Chief Petty Officers,
> a compass room and a chronometer room. Extra cabins were
> also put in below and the shell room alone was taken and
> changed into an extremely ordinary surveying storeroom.
> The poor boatswain already pressed for room found himself
> still further tried by having to stow a great quantity of leads
> and other items. The ships company were unable to be
> berthed on the lower deck and some twenty had to shift with
> upper deck "billets", good enough in hot weather but miser-
> able in cold and wet nights. Even the cook's galley which
> was fitted to cook "from 60 to 90" had now to cook for the
> whole 113 persons.'

Among Vereker's surveying assistants in *Rambler* was Lieutenant

C. H. A. Gleig who, in 1887, published his own work on the surveying service. It is not surprising that after *Rambler's* commission we hear no more of Gleig as a surveyor. A few extracts will be given below from his book *The Bogus Surveyor or a Short History of a Peculiar People by Whitewash*, not only for their humour but also for the insight they give into life in a surveying ship at this time.

Promotion among surveying officers was still extremely slow, slower even than in the Navigation Branch from which many surveyors were drawn, so that competition amongst officers in charge of surveys was intense. The recent introduction of the Annual Report, which in time became known to surveyors as the 'acreage report' as it gave the square miles surveyed by each ship during the season, established an unofficial competition in which the officers in charge attempted to excel in order to impress the Hydrographer with their suitability for promotion. This unwholesome state of affairs tended to give greater merit to speed than to accuracy and subsequently passed away.

But for a time it undoubtedly had an effect upon surveying Captains who tended to push their assistants and their men, the latter by no means in those days volunteers for the work, to limits beyond their capacity, and in ships, and boats, unsuited in many cases for the work.

The Preface to the *Bogus Surveyor* explains its purpose:

'It is not without some slight diffidence that the Author has finally decided upon producing his present work on Nautical Surveying. So many valuable books have been already written on this interesting subject by even wiser heads than our own, that, were it not for the existence of certain grave omissions in the said works, we should perhaps have been content to remain unknown to fame.

'The well known book *Hydrographical Surveying* by the distinguished officer at the head of the Hydrographic Department, is, doubtless, a most valuable addition to Nautical Literature. It is, perhaps, the best of its kind that has yet been produced (except for the *Bogus Surveyor*), yet the omission that we have noticed in other works is not even here filled to our satisfaction, and, as we suppose, to the satisfaction of others. The expense of the volume, we may add, may unfortunately place it out of reach of many Naval Officers, for the cost is—if we mistake not—fifteen shillings; whereas the *Bogus Surveyor* is, we understand, to be produced at the ridiculously moderate rate of one shilling.

'In these pages we have endeavoured to supply a want which has hitherto remained unnoticed. We have attempted to give some slight insight into the work of Marine Surveying and have, besides, dwelt upon the everyday life of the Surveyor in a manner which, we trust, will prove interesting to those who meditate enrolling themselves as members of this glorious profession.

'To those young aspirants we principally address ourselves. The book may, however, prove of some slight service to those who have actually taken the final step, and if so, the Author will be more than repaid for his labours.

WHITEWASH
(The Surveyor's Friend)'

Extract from Chapter II, *Zeal*:

'Before proceeding further, the author feels the necessity of making a brief comment on the subject of Zeal. These remarks are addressed to the coming race of surveyors, and may be skipped (with advantage) by older hands.

'Zeal is defined as a passionate ardour in the pursuit of an object. Now, some people are of the opinion that, to achieve great success in any undertaking, it should be entered upon with a calm and dispassionate diligence, which is in its nature rather foreign to the "passionate ardour" of our definition.

'But in regard to Marine Surveying this is far from being the case, and we are assured on the highest authority that, without Zeal, our ordinary sense of duty and energy will avail us nothing. In short, Zeal is described as being not only absolutely necessary, but as covering a multitude of shortcomings.

'This qualification, being, it appears, equally expected in

both officers and men alike, it has always seemed to us a queer anomaly that no steps are taken to stimulate it in the crews of surveying ships by some slight addition to their pay.

'The principle upon which surveying is conducted is one of restless energy; even the most unwilling of volunteers finds himself goaded into perpetual activity by the example and precept of his superiors. This at least is the young surveyor's first impression, and he is naturally struck by the businesslike air which the surveyors perpetually wear.

'He sees his companions equipped for a day's work in truly wonderful garbs, of which the most fashionable is as follows: a Baltic shirt (without collar), a pair of flannel knickerbockers, ship's stockings, and a sun-helmet. Round the waist a large cummerbund is usually worn, together with a common jack-knife; whilst suspended from the neck are a variety of articles such as watches, pocket sextants, dog whistles, etc., etc. The equipment is completed by a canvas haversack, bulging with scientific apparatus, or else luncheon.

'To see a man dressed thus, hastily swallowing a few mouthfulls of breakfast at the hour of six a.m. is a most impressive sight and one that is likely to strike the observer with awe and admiration, as it is doubtless intended to do.

'There was once a Captain of a Surveying Ship who ventured to suggest that his officers went away dressed in some description of uniform, however ancient. The proposal was received with so much disapproval that the poor man had to withdraw the suggestion and it is said that he never obtained another command.'

Extract from Chapter IV, *Sounding in Boats*:

'We shall not attempt to bore the reader with any detailed description of the usual method of sounding in ships and boats. We are content to refer them to Captain Belcher's *Surveying*, where orthodox plans are discussed fully. We prefer rather to pass over the bald details of the subject, and endeavour to give the young surveyor a more vivid idea of what is expected of him.

'Having received their instructions overnight, the surveying assistants are usually expected to be ready to sheer off at 7 a.m. by which hour they will have had, of course, breakfast, and possibly even washed and dressed themselves. We strongly advise our young friends not to fall into this very common mistake. The Author's experience enables him to recommend a more comfortable mode of procedure. A really good Marine servant will, if properly trained, soon learn to pack a bag with such necessities in the way of clothes, food and drinks, as may be required during the day. Once establish this routine and the beginner will find himself at liberty to sleep on until the last moment, or at least till 6.55 a.m. The boats all having shoved off and proceeded to work, the ship weighs anchor and commences sounding.

'The novice will usually find about this period that several important necessities, such as instruments, pencils, leads and leadlines, have been left behind. The only possibility of guarding against these omissions is as follows: Before stepping into the boat the experienced surveyor may often be seen to be repeating to himself in a low, almost inaudible tone. Drawing nearer you may be able to distinguish something of this kind: "Spade, shovel, pickaxe, crowbar, theodolite, fieldboard, angle book, tiffin, pencil, leadline, protractor and bottle of beer, etc, etc." At the same time his eagle eye glances into the innermost recesses of the boat and discovers at a glance the absence of the aforesaid necessities.

'Unless this custom is pursued, omissions are almost invariable but there is scarcely time to pursue these investigations when the ship is on the point of weighing and the boats are expected to have shoved off. This is the disadvantage of the 6.55 a.m. principle.'

Extract from Chapter VII, *Between Decks*:

'Meanwhile leaving our friends in the boats to pursue their arduous labours, either on the system advocated in these pages, or on other and still more difficult lines, let us take a peep at the life onboard the vessel.

'The well known and oft-repeated pipe of "Up Anchor" finds comparatively few people left to respond to the call. At least four boats, with their respective crews, have quitted the ship. The working hands are reduced to about a dozen seamen and two or three petty officers, supplemented by a few marines, stokers and carpenters. These poor fellows bring the anchor up to the bows with some difficulty, which is not decreased by the fact that some half dozen of their number are detached to attend the deep-sea line. It is, be it observed, absolutely necessary to begin sounding directly the anchor is off the bottom, though the uninitiated might be inclined to suppose that the loss of a few minutes could make but little difference with so long a day to follow. However up it comes at last, and down go the idlers and marines to growl undisturbed for the rest of the day; having comparatively little to do, they naturally take full advantage of their prerogative.

'And now the day's work begins in real earnest; "Go ahead", "Half speed", "Full speed", "Three quarter speed", "Stop her", "Full speed astern", and so forth. Clang! Clang! goes the engine-room telegraph; Clang! comes the responsive answer from below; and amidst all, the ceaseless rattle of the donkey engine (used for hauling in the sounding line) lends its share to the babel of sounds, which the paymaster curses as he writes up his ledger, and the doctor listens to in despair as he feels the pulses of his patients.

'Ever and again the voice of the Officer of the Watch or the Captain may be heard yelling out "Port two points", or now and then, when the vessel is going off the lines of soundings, "Hard-a-starboard" upon which occasions the quartermasters—who are all deaf—respond promptly enough, "Hard-a-port, Sir" and so the game goes on.

'No matter how bad the weather, through the lumpy ocean plunges the poor ship and her crew, whilst, despite the heavy seas which may be a fathom or two high, the skillful leadsman calls his soundings with painful accuracy which characterises the surveying service. The seamen, who are intelligent fellows in their queer way, soon learn the little tricks of the trade into which they are impressed. Scarcely ever will they call an even sounding; it is always "A quarter eighteen, sir" or a "Half thirty", and so forth. Nor does anybody appear to notice the absurdity of the thing, for long habit has inured the surveyor to these little frauds, which he cherishes even as a first lieutenant does his paintwork.

'We do not allude to surveying First Lieutenants. They, at least, rise superior to the charms of cleanliness, and regard paintwork with fine contempt quite refreshing to witness. It is fortunate that such is the case. The work of the ship puts a stop to all but the most superficial cleaning, and even on Saturdays (the sabbath of No 1) the great work usually continues.

'Even for the dinner hour, the sounding proceeds with undiminished vigour, for no sentimental consideration for station orders can quell the indomitable spirit of the leader, who scorns the notion of a prolonged dinner hour, even in the hottest weather. The same utter want of consideration for man or beast is shown in every detail of the work, and for all this the plea for zeal is, of course, put forward. But, alas! that we should write it, we cannot but say that it is zeal for promotion rather than for the good of the service, which urges—or rather goads—them forward.

'Is this the spirit in which the celebrated Captain Kellett, or the kindly Sir Edward Parry, of Arctic fame gained their laurels? No, gentle reader, be assured that like all other successful men, they studied the comfort of their men no less than the means to ensure success, for, in trust, men cannot be driven to perform great deeds.'

'Whitewash' refers to searching for 'vigias' as the most tedious of all the surveyors' tasks. These are shoals, real or imagined, which spattered the charts of the oceans at this time. They had resulted from reports of seamen, and although a few undoubtedly existed as dangers to shipping far from land, yet many were caused by floating whales, wrecks, pumice or patches of noctilucae or 'red tide' giving the appearance of breaking or discoloured water. The prudent seaman kept well clear and reported the 'shoal' to the Hydrographer.

With the advent of the Lucas machine, which facilitated the rapid taking of deep soundings, Wharton decided that the time was ripe for a number of ocean sounding cruises to investigate the many charted vigias.

The more notable of these cruises in the different oceans were carried out at various times between 1887 and the end of the century. The screw sloops *Egeria, Rambler* and *Penguin* as Commander's commands, and the steam yachts *Waterwitch* and *Dart* and the gunboat *Stork*, as Lieutenant's commands, performed the majority of these voyages during which nearly nine out of every ten charted vigias were eventually disproved.

Typical of this work by the larger vessels were six sounding cruises in the South Pacific between New Zealand and the Tonga (or Friendly) Islands by H.M.S. *Egeria* in the year 1888 under Captain Pelham Aldrich.

The early Lucas sounding machine was considerably more elementary than the model in use today. Although it worked satisfactorily for Nares, Aldrich made many improvements to it in *Egeria*. The machine consisted of a drum carrying 5,000 fathoms of piano wire, and a measuring wheel, secured to a single wooden bed-plate bolted to the deck so that the measuring sheave was towards the ship's side.

Balanced on a strengthened guardrail, and secured so that it could rock, was the sounding spar. To its outer end above the sea was secured a leading wheel, whilst to the inboard end, midships of the wire drum, were secured two or four rubber accumulators held to the deck with a Salter's Spring balance. The sounding wire was rove from the drum, one complete turn around the measuring wheel, and out to the leading wheel whence it was secured by a few fathoms of hempen line to a Baillie Sounder suitably weighted.

As the sounding tube descended towards the sea-bed the wire drum was controlled in its speed of rotation by a cord brake operated by weights, or, in an emergency, by hand. The accumulators absorbed the violent motion of the vessel and the Salter's balance indicated by a reduction in the pull that the sounding tube had reached the sea-bed and released its ring weights. To heave in, a long swifter (endless rope) was brought from a grooved drum on the ship's steam donkey engine amidships to a grooved sheave affixed to the side of the measuring wheel. A second and shorter swifter ran from the measuring wheel to the wire drum to rotate it for reeling in.

The secondary meridian listed for the South Pacific was the flagstaff at the Royal Navy Depot, Auckland, and as Aldrich intended to operate from Tongatabu for his sounding cruises his first task was to run a meridian distance to Nukualofa. He did this by making the double journey, to obtain what surveyors called the 'travelling rate' of his chronometers, being the total gain or loss from the time of leaving Auckland until his return.

The latitude of Nukualofa had also to be determined and this was achieved by observing circum-meridian altitudes of stars with sextant and artificial horizon, as Wharton laid down. Errors were eliminated by taking a number of observations, and therefore the stars had to be near rather than exactly on the meridian, correction tables being available for reducing the observations to the exact time of passage of the star across the meridian. To eliminate refraction errors, both in the atmosphere and passing through the glass roof of the artificial horizon, it was considered best to observe a pair of stars, one to the north and one to the south of the zenith.

For such observations it was necessary to select beforehand pairs of stars of suitable magnitude, altitude and time of passage across the meridian. When observing with the artificial horizon the direct star had to be brought down by sextant to coincide with its own image in the mercury, so that the double angle had to be measured with the sextant, thus limiting the altitudes of the stars to about 60°.

Both Greenwich and Cape Observatory catalogues of stars were carried in surveying ships and a diagram had been prepared by Lieutenant H. B. T. Somerville to facilitate the selection of suitable pairs for circum-meridian altitudes.

With the programme prepared, and the artificial horizon and sextant stand set up before dark, and with a seaman standing by with a lantern in a bucket to show a light when the sextant was to be read, the officer took his seat for the night's observations, hoping that the wind would be strong enough to keep away mosquitoes and sandflies, but that the surf on the nearby shore should not be sufficiently heavy to ruffle the surface of the mercury.

Whilst on the long sounding cruises the deep-sea leadline was kept constantly going, the lead itself being heaved forward at each cast by steam power to the lower boom, suitably topped up and rigged over side so that the lead was released from an endless whip when the boom was reached. A seaman was stationed on the sounding platform aft, 'feeling' the leadline as the lead passed beneath him to gauge whether a sounding or 'no bottom' resulted. This form of sounding could be carried down to about thirty-five fathoms with the ship running at five knots.

Deep soundings, some of them well over 4,000 fathoms, were taken from *Egeria* at regular intervals with the Lucas machine on the forecastle. For this the ship was stopped and held by her engines head to sea with the wire vertical. To ensure this, engine and helm orders were passed aft by a system of hand flag signals by the officer in charge on the forecastle.

The vigias, when they existed, were usually the peaks of submarine mountains, which in suitably warm seas were crowned with coral reefs. A search for a vigia entailed finding the slope of the mountain by sounding and following it in its shoaling direction towards the dangerous summit.

Egeria, cruising for three weeks or so at a time from Nukualofa, where coal and provisions were obtained, searched from May to December for a number of reported vigias. Vibilia Rock, Edith Rock, Somme Reef, Kremhila Rock, La Rance Bank and Seymour Bank, convincing as their names may sound, were all sought in vain, thousands of fathoms and a smoothly undulating oceanbed being found beneath their supposed positions. Despite nine days' search by Aldrich, Wolverine Bank, where 37 fathoms with rocky bottom had been reported in 1877, proved no less than 200 fathoms deep. Pelorus Reef was the only vigia searched for which might have caused a danger to shipping, and, after so many fruitless searches, caused some excitement at last aboard *Egeria*.

The reef had found its way onto the charts as a result of the

Deep-sea sounding with the Lucas machine on board H.M.S. *Egeria*, 1897.

Sounding boat's crew from the hired vessel *Gladiator* in Home Waters, 1898. The leadsman is seen in the bows and the officer with his sextant in the sternsheet.

sighting of discoloured water from the *Pelorus* in 1861. Guided for some days towards the area by gradually reducing soundings, a depth of 95 fathoms was obtained late in the afternoon of 12th July. An '*Egeria* Beacon' consisting of two 30-ft. spars lashed together and secured between a pair of casks was prepared for anchoring on the reef. With a large flag on the upper spar, and compensating weights at the lower end of the other spar, the moored beacon was visible for four miles.

The following morning, having obtained excellent star sights, the men were standing by to slip the beacon when discoloured water was reported from the masthead. Shortly afterwards the beacon was laid in 24 fathoms and the seaboats, each with a small portable Lucas machine, were lowered to sound in the light green water. The ship then anchored to enable the boats to extend their range to three miles or so. Each time a flag was dipped from the peak they obtained their distance from the ship by observing the vertical sextant angle from the main truck to the white line on the hull 90 ft. below, while at the same time an officer onboard took the boats' bearings by the standard compass.

A least depth of 14 fathoms was eventually obtained, with a bottom of loose ashes and cinder denoting a volcanic origin. Pelorus Reef was confidently charted, and six vigias which formerly cluttered the chart were removed to reveal a great area free of dangers to shipping. This was a year's work, but with three or four vessels constantly so employed during Wharton's time, much was done to eliminate many imaginary dangers and to fix with exactitude those which existed.

Many of the coral reefs which formed upon the peaks of submarine mountains were more closely investigated for, led by John Murray, naturalists were questioning Darwin's theories on these strange formations.

In 1888 Commander W. U. Moore was instructed by Wharton to take his ship *Rambler* to examine the Tizard and Macclesfield Banks lying athwart the route through the China Sea from Singapore to Hong Kong. Tizard Bank has a few sand cays above water around its perimeter, whilst the encircling rim of Macclesfield Bank, 300 miles to the north, has no depths less than 10 fathoms.

Both have lagoons within the reefs and their outer walls fall steeply away to great depths.

The ship being anchored at various points on the shallow perimeter formed a base for the steam cutter. Using masthead angles, she ran sounding profiles from the deep water in over the ridge past the ship to the lagoon; meanwhile the second steam cutter made dredgings along this profile. The surgeon, P. W. Basset-Smith, who had an amateur interest in coral, was in the dredging boat collecting and preserving the specimens caught in the dredge and found enmeshed in swabs hauled along the seabed. On Tizard Bank decreasing quantities of live coral were found down to 32 fathoms on the outside slopes, which were thereafter composed of coral debris. In the lagoon sand was mostly to be found with occasional outcrops of coral down to 45 fathoms where, surprisingly, live reef-building coral was discovered. The corals of the submerged Macclesfield Bank were of different kinds from those of Tizard Bank, but grew just as vigorously down to 44 fathoms.

Such data were invaluable to the Coral Reef Committee of the Royal Society of which Wharton was a member. A major expedition made borings in the atoll of Funafuti in the South Pacific during the years 1896 to 1900.

Of the unsuitability of the ships for the work in those days we have ample evidence. Boyle Somerville served in *Penguin* as a lieutenant during sounding cruises in the South Pacific and has said of her:

'The Naval Surveying Service has ever had foisted upon it for its work any old castaway ship that has become useless for other branches of the Navy. No one knows except those who have suffered from them how much more difficult that work—and no more essential work for the safety of the Navy can be conceived—is made for us by the aged hoodlums that are handed out for our use. But of all the old clumbungies with which the Surveying Service has been saddled, the

Penguin would be hard to beat for clumbunginess. She was everything she should *not* have been for her special work, and the sole respect in which she was at all suitable as a surveying vessel was that her hull was of wood sheathed in copper, so that if, as must inevitably happen in an exploring vessel, she should touch on the rock for which she was searching, or come upon it unexpectedly, less damage would be done than if she had only a thin steel plate between her and the chance of sinking.

'At no time, perhaps, did the *Penguin's* limitations become more accentuated than when engaged on Deep Sea Sounding. When this takes place the ship has to be headed up to the wind and sea, and kept in a single position, steadily, for perhaps several hours, while the sounding weight, with its attached wire, is being lowered to the bottom, some thousands of fathoms down, and then wound in again. Consequently the ship required for such a purpose is a handy steam-vessel, with twin screws, steam steering gear, and no top-hamper—a ship with a good hold on the water, that will answer her helm and engines easily and immediately, for it is by these means only that she can be kept in the proper attitude for the sounding. Instead, here was a round-bottomed, three-masted, sailing vessel, with a single (auxiliary) propeller, and a rudder worked by ropes brought to a wheel, slowly moved from hard-a-port to hard-a-starboard by two perspiring, heavily labouring men. Nothing could have been more unlike "business".'

Of the steam yacht *Dart* in which he also served he wrote:

'H.M.S. *Dart* was a schooner yacht of 400 tons which had been bought from a private owner for the Naval Service, and had afterwards been lengthened and fitted with auxiliary steam power. She was a good little ship, and in spite of the alterations to her shape and draught caused by the addition of engines, boiler, and screw-shaft, was still a first-rate sailer. She was intended to be the "Admiral's yacht" for the Australian station; but, by some dark official process, she

became instead a surveying vessel, and thereafter fulfilled a
long and honourable career in those waters in the service of
the chart-makers. She was entirely unfitted for hydrographic
work; but we are accustomed in the Surveying Service, to be
dealt out with "misfits," naval or otherwise, and to make the
best of them. The *Dart* was by no means the worst we have
had in recent years; in fact, she was rather above the average.
We were quite pleased with her. The crew forward on the
mess deck numbered sixty; there were six of us in the
ward-room—three lieutenants of the Hydrographic Branch,
and three "Idlers", as the old Navy, with bludgeon-like
humour, designated the Engineer, Surgeon, and Paymaster.

'Besides, and over all of us, there was the Captain—the
"Skipper", the "Old Man",—a Lieutenant, like ourselves, but
a few years older, having "2½ stripes"; such, in fact, as
nowadays is styled "Lieutenant-Commander". He was separated from our profane society in the ward-room by a pas-
sageway of at least six feet in length, at the end of which was
the door of "The Cabin". Here, in splendid isolation, in
accordance with the law of the Navy, he resided; and if
occasionally he heard from the end of the passage a few home
truths, they were probably welcomed by him as a corrective
to the chorus of approval, and even of affection, which more
often assailed his blushing ears, for he was the best of fellows,
and we didn't mind if he knew it (as well as our opinion of
his mistakes).'

Of the survey ships at work in the 1890s the gunboat *Stork* was
the worst of all, and of her we can read something in the diaries
of Lieutenant Henry Oliver:

'The vertical keel was rusted away in many places and the
iron frames in the bilges were also rusted through. This was
due to the way the Hydrographer drove his wretched little
lug-traps. As soon as they arrived in a port orders were given
to do something else and steam was never down till the end
of the surveying season and the bilges stank.

'Once in Zanzibar we anchored to windward of the flagship and the Commander-in-Chief told us to shift berth as we stank worse than a slave dhow. The Lieutenants in command were all competing at sixteen or seventeen years' seniority for the one annual promotion and dared not cross the Hydrographer.'

Oliver also tells us something of the men who found their way to surveying ships:

'I was sent round the other side of an island with the steam whaler and second whaler for a week to fill in a gap in the survey work.

'The whaler's crew were a bad lot, several out of prison at Bombay sent to us by the flagship. The coxswain had been a warrant officer, tried and dismissed for drink, and allowed to re-enter as a Petty Officer second-class. I always found him a good man. One morning I told two of the whaler's crew to shift two 1 cwt. bags of coal into the steamboat from a dump on shore. They pretended they could not lift them and finally refused and became abusive. I let it go then as I did not want a riot with the rest of the gang. After breakfast I went coastlining and loaded up one of the mutineers more heavily with gear than the other and I carried the pick-axe myself. About one and a half miles from the coast one lagged behind on a bush path. I pretended not to notice. When well away I told the other man to put down his gear and then drew the handle out of the pick-axe and knocked him down and beat him soundly. I left him lying there and went and did the same to the other man.

'On the same trip one of the other gaol birds gave the coxswain a lot of back chat. I took the boat on shore and left the man with the coxswain and took the rest of the crew with me. I went to a hill to put up the theodolite, and watched the boat through the telescope and saw the coxswain giving his man a good thrashing with the tiller.

'When I got back to the ship some days later I told no one about it, but the boatswain said to me later on that he wondered what had happened as since the whaler's crew had been away with me they were changed men.'

Despite the entreaties of Admiral Wharton, Oliver decided after four years in *Stork* to leave surveying and become a navigator, a decision which had far-reaching effects upon the Royal Navy. Oliver realised that the time had passed when the examinations in navigation could be satisfactorily carried out by the Hydrographer and his subordinates, for Fleet work and manoeuvres were assuming a growing importance, and of such things the Hydrographer was, by the nature of his service, ignorant. Oliver wrote a paper on the state of navigational training in the Royal Navy which resulted in his being sent for by Admiral Sir John Fisher, when Second Sea Lord in 1903, and ordered by him to establish a Navigation School. He was promoted immediately to Captain and started the school in H.M.S. *Mercury** at Portsmouth. Since that day navigators and surveyors have gone their own ways, but have retained a mutual admiration. H.M.S. *Dryad*, the shorebased Navigation School, was until recently a monument to Oliver's foresight. A Hydrographic School, first established at Chatham in 1948, was transferred in the 1960s to Devonport where today Surveying Officers and Recorders are trained in the sophisticated electronic and computerised systems which have long since replaced the simple methods described in these pages.

In Wharton's day the survey triangulation was plotted by the long side method. The gnomonic projection was used, whereby the spherical shape of the earth is represented on a flat surface by means of a single imaginary point of contact. Meridians appear as converging straight lines and parallels of latitude are concave towards the poles.

The measured baseline was used to commence a coastal survey only, a means of the true bearings from either end being used as the mercatorial bearing for plotting purposes. The true scale and

---

* Admiral of the Fleet Sir Henry Oliver was in his 101st year when he died in October 1965. On his 100th birthday he discussed with the Hydrographer of the Navy, Rear-Admiral E. G. Irving, fair charts he had drawn in H.M.S. *Stork* seventy-five years before, copies of which Admiral Irving presented to him.

direction of the survey was eventually decided by careful astronomical observations at the two extreme limits of the survey,
where, if the proximity of mountains could be avoided, the surveyors expected an accuracy of position within ± 100 feet.

Plotting, which could begin when a number of lengths of sides
of the triangulation had been computed, entailed the scribing on
linen-backed paper of one of the longest sides, from either end of
which the 'shots' to a third station were plotted by the angles which
had been observed. Chords were used to lay down the angles with
accuracy, a table having been prepared by Tizard giving the
lengths of a chord subtended by a radius of ten inches for any
given angle. From the third station, fixed by the intersection of
the two shots, and from the first two stations, a fourth station was
intersected. Excitedly the tripodal magnifying glass was placed over
the intersection—if all three 'shots' passed through a single point
a gin was called for to celebrate the proving of the plot. The other
stations of the survey were similarly plotted, always working inwards to reduce any accumulating error.

The graduation of the sheet had to await the observing of the
terminal geographical positions, when the related converging meridians and curved parallels were carefully scribed in.

Mr. Malby still had the business of engraving and printing the
charts, and at Middle Yard, Great Queen Street, he conducted
this business. I have been fortunate in getting an eye-witness
account from Mr. H. C. Johnson, who served his apprenticeship
in the nineties under Malby and retired from engraving Admiralty
charts in 1958. Johnson worked with his father on the top floor at
Middle Yard. Discipline was lax and timekeeping poor; the engravers timed their own jobs, each submitting a bill on Friday to
Mr. Malby, who knew well how much work should have been
achieved. The engravers' room swarmed with cockroaches which
came through the walls from the Freemason's Tavern.

On the ground floor were the printers, sweating and swearing
at the huge wheels of their hand presses; they were on piece-work
and earned good money when charts were required in a hurry.
The printers were great drinkers, and boys were kept running to
the 'George' with long poles studded with nails on which were

slung quart pots of beer. Johnson says the heaviest drinkers were the fastest printers, but many died young in consequence.

Wharton's stern and forbidding countenance was often seen at the Middle Yard Factory, shocked as he was by the wooden floors and staircases and the reek of turpentine used in the processes. Although the men never smoked inside the building, Wharton dreaded a fire and feared for the safety of hundreds of his priceless copper plates, which lay around although a safe had been provided for them. The Hydrographer brought great pressure on Malby and before he retired the latter was persuaded to build a modern factory in Grays Inn Road for the Admiralty Charts.

George Forbes, who studied the correspondence between Sir David Gill and Admiral Wharton, has said that, 'it breathes mutual admiration and trust, with wise counsel gratefully acknowledged. It helped on the course of astronomy from 1885 to 1905, and enabled Sir William Wharton effectively to support the greatest of Gill's endeavours in the cause of astronomy. No history of astronomy will be complete that fails to record the debt owed by that science to Admiral Sir William Wharton.' It was the presence in Whitehall of Wharton, responsible for the administration of the Cape Observatory, which enabled many of Gill's projects to weather the financial storms.

Wharton resigned as Hydrographer in July 1904, and in 1905 he travelled with members of the British Association to Cape Town, where he presided over the Geographical Section. He fell ill while returning from a visit to the Victoria Falls and died of enteric fever on 21st October in the home of his dear friends, Sir David and Lady Gill.

A small plaque at the Cape Observatory reads as follows: 'In memory of the Gallant Rear Admiral Sir W. J. L. Wharton who loved Nelson's ship and died at the Cape Observatory in Nelson's Centenary Year.' The plaque is made of copper from H.M.S. *Victory* and was presented by the British & Foreign Sailors' Society.

Captain Wharton published the first edition of his '*Hydrographical Surveying*' in 1882 with a second edition brought out in 1898. In 1909 a new edition, revised and enlarged by the current Hydrographer, Rear Admiral Mostyn Field, was published, with a further issue in 1920. In each edition Wharton's 'Preliminary' has been retained containing encouragement and advice for the young surveyor.

The classic and oft quoted paragraph from Wharton's 'Preliminary' reveals something of the sea surveyors' dedication to their chosen profession during the first hundred years of the British Hydrographic Office.

'Happily, it is a profession of volunteers, and the author's experience is, that in no branch of the public service can the juniors be more anxious to do their duty, not only to the letter, but to the utmost of the spirit, and to such as these no day seems long enough. To them, the interest is constantly kept up. Every day has its incidents. The accuracy of the work of each assistant, when proved, is an infinite gratification to him, and he has also the continual satisfaction of feeling that of all he does a permanent record will remain, in the chart which is to guide hundreds of his fellow-seamen on their way.'

Bibliography

GENERAL

Blewitt, M., *Surveys of the Seas*. Macgibbon and Kee (London, 1957).

Beaglehole, J. C., *The Life of Captain James Cook*. Hakluyt Society (London, 1974).

Campbell, Tony, 'Episodes from the early history of British Admiralty Charting', *The Map Collector*. No. 25. 1983, pp 28–33.

Clowes, W. Laird, *The Royal Navy—a History*. Vols IV and V. Sampson Low, Marston and Co. (London, 1901).

Cook, A. S., *An Author Voluminous and Vast : Alexander Dalrymple (1737–1808), Hydrographer to the East India Company and to the Admiralty, as Publisher : A Catalogue of Books and Charts*. (Ph.D., St. Andrews 1992).

Cook, James, *The Journals of Captain James Cook on his Voyages of Discovery*. Vols I–III. ed. J. C. Beaglehole. Hakluyt Society (Cambridge, 1955–67).

Crone, G. R., and Skelton, R. A., 'English Collections of Voyages and Travels, 1625–1846', E. Lynan (ed.) *Richard Hakluyt and his Successors*. Hakluyt Society (London, 1946), pp. 63–140.

Dodge, Ernest S., *Beyond the Capes—Pacific Exploration from Captain Cook to Challenger, 1776–1877*. Victor Gollanz (London, 1971).

David, Andrew, *A Provisional Catalogue of Logs, Journals, Documents, Letters, Record Copies of Books and Pamphlets published by the Hydrographic Office and held in its Archives*. Hydrographic Office. (Taunton, 1974), Typescript.

——, *A Catalogue of Charts and Coastal Views published by Alexander Dalrymple 1767–1808: privately, as Hyrographer to the East India Company (1779–1808), and as Hydrographer to the Admiralty (1795–1808) and their subsequent history (1767–1959)*. Typescript, 1990. (Copies in various libraries.)

Dawson, Commander L. S., *Memoirs of Hydrography* (Eastbourne, 1855). *Facsimile Reprint*, with Extensive Errata by L. A. Luff, Cornmarket Press (London, 1969).

Deacon, Margaret, *Scientists and the Sea, 1650–1900*. Academic Press (London, 1971).

Edgell, Vice Admiral Sir John, 'The Surveying Service of the Royal Navy.' *Brassey's Naval Annual*, (London, 1939).

Howse, Derek, and Sanderson, Michael, *The Sea Chart; Introduction* Ritchie, G.S. David & Charles (Newton Abbot, 1973).

Fillmore, Stanley and Sandilands, R. W., *The Chartmakers—A History of Nautical Charting in Canada*. N.C. Press Ltd. (Toronto, 1983).

Lord, W. B., 'The Hydrographic Department', *Nautical Magazine, Vol. LXVI*, (London, 1897).

McConnel, Anita, *No Sea Too Deep—The History of Oceanographic Instruments*, Adam Hilger (Bristol, 1982).

Murray, Sir J., and Hjort, Johan, *The Depths of the Ocean*. Macmillan (London, 1912).

May, W. E., *A History of Marine Navigation*. Fowlis (Henley-on-Thames, 1973).

Richards, Vice Admiral Sir George, *A Memoir of the Hydrographic Department of the Admiralty*. Hydrographic Department (London, 1868).

Ritchie, G. S., 'Developments in British Hydrography since the days of Captain Cook', *Royal Society of Arts Journal*, Vol. CXVIII. No. 5165 (London, 1970).

Robinson, A. H. W., 'Early Hydrographic Surveys of the British Isles', *Empire Survey Review*, Vol. XI (1951).

——, *Marine Cartography in Britain*. Leicester University Press (1962).

——, 'Marine Surveying in Britain During the Seventeenth and Eighteenth Centuries', *Geographical Journal*, Vol. CXXIII (1957).

——, 'Some Hydrographic Surveyors of the Early Nineteenth Century', *Empire Survey Review*, Vol. XII (1953).

Skelton, R. A., *see* Crone, G.R.

Spencer Jones, Sir Harold, *The Royal Observatory, Greenwich*. (London, 1943.)

Sulivan, H. N., *Life and Letters of Admiral Sir Bartholomew James Sulivan, K.C.B.* (London, 1896).

Tizard, Captain T. H., *Chronological List of the Officers Conducting British Maritime Discoveries and Surveys*. H.M.S.O. (London, 1900).

INTRODUCTORY ESSAY

Becher, Alexander B., 'Narrative Journal of the Proceedings of H.M.S. *Leven* commanded by D. E. Bartholomew CB Commencing Dec 23rd 1818 Ending . . . (15th Sept 1820)', Hydrographic Office, OD513.

Beechey, F. W., and H. W., *The Proceedings of the Expedition to explore the Northern Coast of Africa from Tripoly eastward in MDCCCXXI and MDCCCXXII.* John Murray (London, 1809).

Dixon, Conrad, 'To Walk the Quarterdeck : The Naval Career of David Ewen Bartholomew', *Mariner's Mirror*, Vol. 79, No. 1, 1993, pp 58–63.

Horsburgh, James, *Directions for Sailing to and from the East Indies* . . . Part First. (London, 1809).

———, 2 vols. 3rd edition. Black, Parry and Kingsbury, Booksellers to the Honorable East India Company (London, 1826).

Hydrographic Office, Taunton. Various correspondence.

Public Record Office. Captain's Letters (Adm 1/1566–8) and the *Leven's* logs (Adm 51/2531 and 3254).

St. John, H. C., *Notes and Sketches from the Wild Coasts of Nipon.* David Douglas (Edinburgh, 1880).

Smyth, W. H., *Memoir descriptive of the Resources, Inhabitants, and Hydrography of Sicily and its Islands, interspersed with Antiquarian and other Notices.* John Murray (London, 1824).

———, *The Mediterranean: A Memoir, Physical, Historical and Nautical.* John W. Parker & Son (London, 1854).

CHAPTER I. DALRYMPLE

Dalrymple, A., *Collection of Voyages in the South Pacific.* 2 Vols. (London, 1770–71).

———, Various papers, 1769–1793, Library, R.G.S. (London).

———, Various papers, 1791–1807, Library, R.G.S. (London).

———, 'Bibliographical Memoir of Alexander Dalrymple, Esq.', *The Naval Chronicle*, xxxv, 1816, pp. 177–204.

Fry, Howard T., *Alexander Dalrymple (1737–1808) and the Expansion of British Trade.* Frank Cass (London, 1970).

Ritchie, G. S., 'Captain Cook's Influence on Hydrographic Surveying', *Pacific Studies*, Vol. 1, No. 2 (Hawaii, 1978).

Skelton, R. A., 'Captain James Cook as a Hydrographer', *Mariner's Mirror*, Vol. 40, No. 2 (London, 1954).

Thrower, Norman J. W., (ed.) *The Three Voyages of Edmond Halley in the Paramore, 1698–1701.* Hakluyt Society (London, 1981).

Woolf, H., *The Transits of Venus*. Oxford University Press (Oxford, 1959).

CHAPTER 2. MEN AND METHODS

Dalrymple, A., *Essay on the most commodious methods of Marine Surveying.* (London, 1771). Re-issued in 1786 with a revised and enlarged edition in 1806.

David, Andrew, 'Alexander Dalrymple and the Emergence of the Admiralty Chart', *Five Hundred Years of Nautical Science.* National Maritime Museum (Greenwich, 1981).

——, (ed.) *The Charts and Coastal Views of Captain Cook's Voyages. The Voyage of the Endeavour, 1768–1771.* Hakluyt Society (London, 1988).

——, ——. *The Voyage of Resolution and Adventure, 1772–1775.* Hakluyt Society (London, 1992).

Des Barres, J. F. W., *The Atlantic Neptune.* Admiralty (London, 1777–1781).

Evans, G. N. D., *Uncommon Obdurate: The Several Public Careers of J. F. W. Des Barres.* Peabody Museum of Salem and University of Toronto Press (Salem and Toronto, 1969).

——, 'Hydrography: A note on eighteenth century methods', *Mariner's Mirror* Vol. 52, No. 3, 1966, pp. 247–50.

Fisher, Susanna, 'The Origins of the Station Pointer', *Int. Hydrographic Review*, LXVIII (2) (Monaco, 1991).

Gould, R. T., *The Marine Chronometer.* (London, 1923.) Reprinted Holland Press (London, 1971).

Howse, Derek, *Greenwich Time and the Discovery of the Longitude.* Oxford University Press (Oxford, 1980).

Kettle, D. W., *History of the Three Ancient Firms of Chart Publishers, Imray, Laurie, Norie and Wilson Ltd.* (London, 1917).

Mackenzie, Murdoch (Snr.), *A Treatise of Maritim Surveying.* E. & C. Dilly (London, 1774).

Multhauf, R. P., 'Early Instruments in the History of Surveying', *Jrnl. American Congress on Surveying and Mapping* (Oct–Dec, 1958).

Robinson, A. H. W., 'The Evolution of the English Nautical Chart', *Jrnl. Institute of Navigation*, Vol. V. (London, 1952).

Taylor, E. W., 'The Evolution of the Dividing Engine', *Empire Survey Review*, Vol. VII, No. 52, (London, 1944).

—— and Wilson, J. S., *At the Sign of the Orrery.* Printed privately by Cooke, Troughton and Sims, (London, undated).

Terrell, Christopher, 'The Magnificent *Atlantic Neptune*', *Geographical Magazine*, Vol. LIII, No. 15 (London, 1981).

Webster, J. C., *Joseph Frederick Des Barres*. Printed privately (Shediac, New Brunswick, 1933).

CHAPTER 3. VANCOUVER IN THE NORTHEAST PACIFIC

Anderson, Bern, *Surveyor of the Sea*. Washington University Press, (Seattle, 1960).

Lamb, W. Kaye (ed.), *The Voyage of George Vancouver, 1791–1795*. 4 Vols., Hakluyt Society (London, 1984).

Watt, Sir James, 'Medical Aspects and Consequences of Cook's Voyages', *Captain Cook and His Times*. Washington University Press (Seattle, 1979).

CHAPTER 4. BROUGHTON IN THE NORTHWEST PACIFIC

Broughton, W. R., *A Voyage of Discovery to the North Pacific Ocean*. T. Cadell and W. Davies (London, 1804).

CHAPTERS 5 AND 6. TERRA AUSTRALIS AND
FLINDERS' CIRCUMNAVIGATION OF AUSTRALIA

Flinders, Captain M., *A Voyage to Terra Australis*. 2 Vols and Atlas (London, 1814). Reprinted in facsimile Libraries Board of South Australia (1974).

Ingleton, Geoffrey C., *Matthew Flinders, Navigator and Chartmaker*. Genesis Publications (Guildford, England, 1986).

Ritchie, G. S., *Matthew Flinders, Hydrographer*. National Maritime Museum Monograph (Greenwich, 1975).

Scott, E., *The Life of Captain Matthew Flinders*. (Sydney, 1914).

CHAPTER 7. HURD : THE FIRST NAVAL OFFICER HYDROGRAPHER

Beaufort, Captain F., *Karamania*. R. Hunter (London, 1817).

——, *Memoir of the survey of the Coast of Karamania*. Hydrographic Office (London, 1820).

——, 'Captain Hurd', Obituary. *Gentleman's Magazine*, Vol. XCIII. (1823).

Fisher, Susanna, 'Captain Thomas Hurd's Survey of the Bay of Brest during the Blockade in the Napoleonic Wars', *Mariner's Mirror*, Vol. 79. (1993).

Robinson, A. H. W., 'The Changing Routes of the Thames Estuary', *Jrnl. Insititue of Navigation*, Vol. IV, No. 4 (1951).

Tavener, L. E., 'George Thomas, Master, Royal Navy', *Mariner's Mirror*, Vol. 36, (1950).

CHAPTERS 8 AND 9. OWEN COMMENCES AFRICAN SURVEY, THE AFRICAN SURVEY COMPLETED

Boteler, Thomas, *Narrative of a Voyage of Discovery to Africa and Arabia*. Richard Bentley (London, 1835).

Burrows, E. H., *Captain Owen of the African Survey, 1774–1857*. Balkema (Rotterdam, 1979).

Lloyd, C., *The Navy and the Slave Trade*. (London, 1849).

Robinson, H. B. (ed.), *Narrative of Voyages to Explore the Shores of Africa, Arabia and Madagascar under the Direction of Captain W. F. W. Owen, R.N.* Richard Bentley (London, 1833).

Theal, G. McC., *Records of South-Eastern Africa*, Vol. 9. (1903).

Wolfe, Lt., R.N., 'Narrative of Voyages to Explore the Shores of Africa, Arabia and Madagascar', *Jrnl. Royal Geographical Society*, Vol. III (1833).

CHAPTER 10. THE NORTHWEST PASSAGE

Barrow, Sir J., *Voyages of Discovery and Research Within the Arctic Regions, 1818–1846*. (London, 1846).

Beechey, Captain F. W., *Narrative of a Voyage to the Pacific and Beering's Strait*. Henry Colburn and Richard Bentley (London, 1831).

Franklin, Captain John, *Narrative of a Journey to the Shores of the Polar Sea in the Years 1819, 20, 21 and 22*. 2 vols. John Murray (London, 1823).

——, *Narrative of a Second Expedition to the Shores of the Polar Sea, 1825,26 and 27*. John Murray (London, 1828).

Gough, Barry M. (ed.), *To the Pacific and Arctic with Beechey—The Journal of Lieutenant George Peard of H.M.S. Blossom, 1825–1828*. Hakluyt Society (Cambridge, 1973).

Lloyd, Christopher, *Mr. Barrow of the Admiralty—A Life of Sir John Barrow*. Collins (London, 1970).

Parry, Captain W. E., *Journal of a Voyage for the Discovery of a North-West Passage from the Atlantic to the Pacific; performed in the years 1819–20*. John Murray (London, 1821).

——, *Journal of a Second Voyage for the Discovery of the North-West Passage from the Atlantic to the Pacific, performed in the years 1821–22–23*. John Murray (London, 1824).

——, *Journal of a Third Voyage for the Discovery of the North-West Passage from the Atlantic to the Pacific, performed in the years 1824–25*. John Murray (London, 1826).

Johnson, Robert E., *Sir John Richardson*. Taylor & Francis Ltd. (London, 1976).

CHAPTER 11. PARRY OF THE ARCTIC AS HYDROGRAPHER

Hall, Captain B., *Fragments of Voyages and Travels*. (Edinburgh, 1833).

——, 'Notice of a Voyage of Research'. *Edinburgh New Philosophical Journal*, No. 2 (1826).

Parry, A., *Parry of the Arctic*. Chatto & Windus (London, 1963).

Parry, Admiral Sir W. E., *Lecture on the Character, Condition and Responsibilities of British Seamen*. (London, 1854).

Webster, W. H. B., *Narrative of a Voyage to the South Atlantic Ocean in the years 1828, 29, 30, performed by H.M. Sloop Chanticleer*. Richard Bentley (London, 1834).

CHAPTER 12. MAGELLAN STRAIT

Basalla, G., 'The *Beagle* Voyage Without Darwin', *Mariner's Mirror*, Vol. 49, pp 42–8 (London, 1963).

King, Captain P. P., *The Voyages of Adventure and Beagle*, Vol. I. Henry Colburn (London, 1839).

CHAPTER 13. HIGH NOON—BEAUFORT AS HYDROGRAPHER

Admiralty Weather Manual. H.M.S.O. (London, 1938).

Collins, Rear Admiral K. St. B., 'Admiral Sir Francis Beaufort', *Jrnl. Institute of Navigation*, Vol. XI, No. 3. (c.1958).

Deacon, Sir George, 'Matthew Fontaine Maury U.S.N.', *Jrnl. Royal Naval Scientific Service*. (1964).

Doodson, A. T., and Warburg, H. D., *Admiralty Manual of Tides*. H.M.S.O. (London, 1941).

Friendly, Alfred, *Beaufort of the Admiralty*. Hutchinson (London, 1977).

Herschel, Sir John F. W. (ed.) *Admiralty Manual of Scientific Enquiry*. 2nd Edition. John Murray (London, 1851). Reprinted with New Introduction by David Knight. Wm. Davidson (Folkestone, 1974).

Hydrographic Department, 'The Development of Admiralty Notices to

Mariners and Radio Navigational Warnings'. *Jrnl. Institute of Navigation*, Vol. VI, No. 4. (1958).

CHAPTER 14. THE VOYAGE OF THE *BEAGLE*

Barlow N., 'Robert Fitzroy and Charles Darwin', *Cornhill Magazine* (1932).
———, (ed.), *The Autobiography of Charles Darwin, 1809–1882*. Collins (London, 1958).
Darwin, Charles, *The Voyage of the* Beagle. Everyman's Library Edition, J. M. Dent (London, 1906).
FitzRoy, Captain R., *Narrative of the Surveying Voyages of His Majesty's Ships* Adventure *and* Beagle, *1826–36*. Vol. II, and Appendix. Henry Colburn (London, 1839).
Stanbury, David (ed.), *A Narrative of the Voyage of H.M.S.* Beagle. Folio Society (London, 1977).

CHAPTER 15. BELCHER

Belcher, Commander E., *A Treatise on Nautical Surveying*. Pelham Richardson (London, 1835).
———, Captain Sir Edward, *Narrative of a Voyage round the World performed in Her Majesty's Ship Sulphur, 1836–1842*. 2 Vols. (London, 1843).
———, *Narrative of the Voyage of H.M.S. Samarang, 1843–46*. 2 Vols. (London, 1843).
Marryat, F. S., *Borneo and the Indian Archipelago*. Longman, Brown, Green, and Longmans (London, 1848).
Wilkes, Charles, *Autobiography of Rear Admiral Charles Wilkes, U.S. Navy 1798–1877*. William James Morgan, David B. Tyler, Joyce L. Leonhart and Mary F. Loughlin (eds.). Naval History Division, Department of the Navy. (Washington, 1978).

CHAPTER 16. HOME WATERS

Denham, Captain H. M., *Sailing Directions from Point Lynas to Liverpool*. (Liverpool, 1840).
Mountfield, A. S., 'Admiral Denham and the Approaches to the Port of Liverpool', *Historic Society of Lancashire and Cheshire*, Vol. 105 (1953).
Robinson, A. H. W., 'The Charting of the Scottish Coasts', *Scottish Geographical Magazine*, Vol. 74, No. 1 (1958).

CHAPTER 17. ARCTIC AND ANTARCTIC

Belcher, Captain Sir Edward, *The Last of the Arctic Voyages*. 2 Vols. (London, 1855).

Bockstoce, John, (ed.) *The Journal of Rochfort Maguire, 1852–1854*. 2 Vols. Hakluyt Society (London, 1988).

Burns, Flora H., 'H.M.S. *Herald* in Search of Franklin', *Beaver* (1963).

Savours, Ann (ed.), 'Two unpublished accounts of the British Antarctic Expedition 1839–43', *Polar Record*, Vol. 10, No. 69, Sept. 1961, pp 587–601.

CHAPTER 18. THE WAR AND WASHINGTON

Clowes, W. Laird, *The Royal Navy—A History*. Vol. VI. Sampson Low, Marston and Co. (London, 1901).

Sulivan, Captain B. J., *Proposal for Organising a Scientific Corps of Naval Officers*. Naval Library, Ministry of Defence, Whitehall Library, Pamphlet 74/14.

Sulivan, H. N., *The Life and Letters of Admiral Sir Bartholomew James Sulivan*. (London, 1896).

CHAPTER 19. THE ANTIPODES

Ashburton, Lord, 'Presidential Address', *Geographical Journal* (1862).

Beete Jukes, J., *Voyage of H.M.S. Fly*. 2 Vols. T. & W. Boone (London, 1847).

Horden, Marsden, *Mariners are Warned!—Lort Stokes and H.M.S. Beagle in Australia, 1837–1843*. Melbourne University Press (1989).

Huxley, Julian (ed.), *T. H. Huxley's Diary of the Voyage of H.M.S. Rattlesnake*. Chatto & Windus (London, 1935).

Huxley, Leonard, *Life and Letters of Thomas Henry Huxley*. 2 Vols. Macmillan (London, 1900).

Ingleton, G. C., *Charting a Continent*. Angus and Robertson (Sydney, 1944).

King, Phillip P., *Narrative of a Survey of the Intertropical and Western Coasts of Australia*. John Murray (London, 1827).

Lubbock, Adelaide, *Owen Stanley R.N. 1811–1850 Captain of H.M.S. Rattlesnake*. Heinemann (Melbourne, 1968).

Natusch, Sheila, *The Cruise of the Acheron*. Whitcoulls (Christchurch, 1978).

New Zealand Evening Star, 'With H.M.S. *Acheron* on her Early Surveys'. (1926).

Pasco, Crawford, *A Roving Commission*. George Robertson (London, 1897).

Ross, J. O'C., *This Stern Coast*. Reed (Wellington, 1969).

Stokes, Captain J. Lort, *Discoveries in Australia*. 2 Vols. T. & W. Boone (London, 1846).

Stubbings, H. G., 'H.M.S. Rattlesnake'. *Jrnl. Royal Naval Scientific Service*, Vol. 19, No. 3. (1964).

CHAPTER 20. RICHARDS AND THE RISE OF OCEANOGRAPHY

Bright, Charles, *The Story of the Atlantic Cable*. (London, 1903).

Hydrographic Department, *A Memoir of the Hydrographic Department of the Admiralty, 1868*. Hydrographic Department Publication, 1868, HD24.

Murray, George, 'The Last of the *Challenger*'. *Natural Science*, Vol. VI, No. 39. (1895).

Murray, John and Hjort, Johan, *The Depths of the Ocean*. Macmillan (London, 1912).

Nares, Vice Admiral Sir George, C.B., F.R.S. 'Obituary Notice', *Nature*, Feb. 1915.

Richards, Vice Admiral Sir George, C.B., F.R.S. 'Obituary Notice', *Proceedings of the Royal Society*, Vol. 60.

Richards, Captain, R.N., F.R.S., and Clarke, Lt-Colonel, C.B., R.E., *Report on the Maritime Canal Connecting the Mediterranean at Port Said with the Red Sea at Suez*. Hydrographic Department Publication, February, 1870, HD31.

Siegfried, André, *Suez and Panama*. (London, 1940).

Thomson, C. Wyville, The Voyage of the *Challenger*—The Atlantic. 2 Vols. Macmillan (London, 1897).

Thomson, Sir C. Wyville and Murray, John (eds.) Report on the Scientific Results of the Voyage of H.M.S. *Challenger*, 1873–1876. Vol. I, Parts 1 and 2, Narrative. (Edinburgh, 1880–1885).

CHAPTER 21. EVANS AND THE IMPORTANCE OF MAGNETISM

Evans, Captain F. J., *Confidential Memorandum on the Supersession of Commander Hull from the Office of Superintendent of Charts, 1879*. Hydrographic Office, Miscellaneous letters and papers No. 70.

Evans, Captain Sir Frederick, K.C.B., F.R.S., R.N., 'Obituary Notice'. *Royal Astronomical Society* (February 1886).

Fanning, A. E., *Steady as She Goes—A History of the Compass Department of the Admiralty*. H.M.S.O. (London, 1986).

Merriman, Daniel and Mary, 'Sir C. Wyville Thomson's Letters to Staff Commander T. H. Tizard, 1877–1881', *Jrnl. of Marine Research*, Vol. 17, Yale University (1958).

Nares, Captain Sir G. J., *Voyage to the Polar Sea*. 2 Vols. (London, 1878).

——, *Results derived from the Arctic Expedition 1875–76*. Report to Parliament. H.M.S.O. (1878).

Tizard, Staff Commander T. H., *Deep-sea Exploration in Faroe Channel by H.M.S. Triton 1882*. Hydrographic Department Publication, 1894, HD141.

Vereker, Commander the Hon. Foley, *Journals, 1870–1885*. Royal Geographic Society, London.

CHAPTER 22. WHARTON AND SCIENTIFIC SURVEYING

Aldrich, Captain Pelham, *Deep Sea Soundings and Serial Temperature Observations obtained in the Indian Ocean by Captain P. Aldrich, H.M. Surveying Ship Egeria, 1887*. Hydrographic Department Publication, 1888, HD96.

——, *Search for Reported Dangers in South Pacific between New Zealand and Tonga Islands made by Captain P. Aldrich, H.M.S. Egeria, 1888*. *Hydrographic Department Publication, 1889, HD108*.

Boyle Somerville, Vice Admiral, *The Chart Makers*. Blackwood (Edinburgh, 1928).

Forbes, George, *David Gill, Man and Astronomer*. (London, 1916).

Gill, Sir David, *History and Description of the Royal Observatory, Cape of Good Hope,* H.M.S.O. (London, 1913).

James, Admiral Sir William, *A Great Seaman—Life of Admiral of the Fleet Sir Henry Oliver*. Witherby (London, 1956).

Moore, W. U. and Basset-Smith, P. W., *China Sea—Reports of the results of an examination by the Officers of H.M.S. Rambler of the slopes and zoological condition of Tizard and Macclesfield Banks, 1888*. Hydrographic Department Publication, 1889, HD106.

Tizard, Staff Commander, T. H., 'Obituary Notice by A.M.F.' *Proceedings of the Royal Society*, A. Vol. 105.

Wharton, Rear Admiral, Sir William J. L., *Hydrographical Surveying*. First Edition 1882, Second and Revised Edition 1898 (London).

Wharton, Captain W. J. L., *Captain Cook's Journal during his First Voyage round the World made in H.M. Bark* 'Endeavour', *1768–71*. Elliott Stock (London, 1893).

Wharton, Sir William, K.C.B., F.R.S., 'Obituary Notice', Harrison and Sons. Printers in Ordinary to His Majesty (London, undated).

'Whitewash' (C. H. A. Gleig), *The Bogus Surveyor*. Published privately in 1887.

Index

Magellan, Ferdinand 21
Magellan Channel (Tierra del Fuego) 201–2
Magellan Strait 32, 39, 376
 and *Beagle*'s voyage 225–6
 charting of
  first survey (1827–1828) 183, 189–99
  second survey (1828–1830) 200–7
  third survey (1860s) 345
Magill Islands (Tierra del Fuego) 202
Magnetic Department of the Navy 341
magnetic deviation 359–60
magnetic observations and research 272
 under Evans 359–60, 362–3, 367
 Great Britain 272
 North-West Passage 157
magnetic poles *see* North magnetic pole; South magnetic pole
magnetic variation, diurnal 363
Magnificent (ship) 109
Magpie (ship) 377–9
Mahe (Seychelles) 138
malaria, in Owen's African survey 132
Malaspina, Alejandro 55
Malby & Sons (printers) 309, 344, 375, 400–1
Malta 292, 348
Manila 22
Mansell, Lieutenant Arthur 293
Maoris 79, 335
Mapoota (Maputo) 132
Maranhão (Brazil, São Luis) 184
Margate 37–8
Markham, Commander Albert 363–4, 367
Marmora, Sea of 381, 383
Marquesas Islands (Pacific Ocean) 248
Marryat, Lieutenant Frank S. 254, 259, 295
Martha Ridgeway (wreck) 327
Martin Vaz (island) 128
Martinez, Don Esteban 51, 55

Masira Island (Arabian coast) 136
Maskelyne, Dr. Nevil 21, 41
Massey Patent log 127–8
Master, rank of, ended 311–2
Mastiff (ship) 259, 292, 314, 343
Matavi Bay (Tahiti) 65–6
Matthews, Richard 221–2, 223–4
Mauritius 100–3, 137, 139, 221
 longitude established 382–3
Maury, Matthew Fontaine 211–12, 213, 310
May, Mr (carpenter, *Beagle*) 206, 225
May, Commander David 351
May, Lieutenant William 364
Mayne, Captain Richard 345
McClintock, Commander, (later Captain) Sir Leopold 360
 deep seabed soundings 311
 search for *Resolute* 283, 287
McClure, Commander Robert
 search for *Resolute* 282, 284–5, 288–91
McLuer, John 43
Meares, Captain John 50–1, 57
Mecham, Lieutenant George T. 285, 288
Medina (ship) 296
Mediterranean Sea 346, 383
 survey of 10, 114, 115, 118, 191, 209, 292
Medusa channel 106
Medusa (ship) 106
Medusae, Anatomy of (Huxley) 334
Mehemet Ali, King of Egypt 191–9
Melbourne (Australia) 93, 315, 319, 338
Melville, Lord Robert (First Lord, Admiralty) 209
Melville, Harden 327, 329
Melville (gig) 126
Melville Island (Canada) 157, 286, 288
Melville Sound (Canada) 285
Memoirs of Hydrography (Dawson) 12
Mendaña, Alvaro de 21
Menzies, Archibald 52